A radical practice in Liverpool: the rise, fall and rise of Princes Park Health Centre

by
Katy Gardner
and Susanna Graham-Jones

Writing on the Wall

Toxteth Library

Windsor Street, Liverpool

L8 1XF

Published by Writing on the Wall, 2021

Cover Design by Maddy Robinson

Layout by Lee Philpotts

www.bodhi-design.co.uk

ISBN: 978-1-910580-56-1

info@writingonthewall.org.uk

www.writingonthewall.org.uk

Stay up to date with our latest books, projects, courses, and events with our newsletter. Sign up on our website: writingonthewall.org.uk

CONTENTS

Chapter 4 - Going the extra mile: teamwork for psychological problems

Chapter 5 - The learning curve continues

Chapter 6 - Battling the Inverse Care Law in the early 1990s

Chapter 7 - The Family Health Project: tackling the needs of homeless people (1993-1996)

Chapter 8 - Medical audit, troubleshooting and research

Chapter 9 - Anti-racism, ethnic monitoring and health (1977-2012)

Chapter 10 - Low pay for patients and their GPs (1990s)

Chapter 11 - Salaried at last (1998)

Chapter 12 - Primary care and public health: a joint agenda

Chapter 13 - Living within a fragmenting NHS (2000-2012)

Preface

This book tells the story of Princes Park Health Centre (PPHC) in Liverpool 8. The practice, founded by Dr Cyril Taylor, gained a reputation for innovation and preventive health care, confronting the challenges of inner-city deprivation, racism and Thatcherism.

By the time Cyril died in 2000, the Princes Park Health Centre general practice partners had opted to become salaried practitioners. The subsequent twists and turns in the practice's story arose from political changes affecting the NHS nationally and Merseyside in particular.

When PPHC turned 40 in 2017, Katy Gardner, who had worked there for 28 years, felt that its story should be told, using the archives accumulated over the years. Susanna Graham-Jones, who was a partner at the practice from 1986 to 1993, agreed. The project became a collaborative effort, with many patients, colleagues and people connected with the health centre and the area contributing their memories. Selecting from these memories has been very rewarding, and we are grateful to all contributors. All selections, and any errors, are of course our responsibility. While we have written this account in the third person, it is inevitably influenced by our own views of events. We have done our best to be fair and objective.

This story has several audiences. Though some of the language may be less familiar to those not working in medicine, and the many NHS institutions described may be confusing (not least to us who worked in them!), we hope the glossary and timeline make things clearer.

Confidentiality: all living patients identified in this book have given their explicit consent. Other references to patients have been anonymised. The encounters described by Katy Gardner when writing as a medical journalist 'Rosa Hudson' are fictional, though based loosely on real experiences.

A note on terminology: Chapter 9 tells the story of Princes Park Health Centre's attempts to promote an anti-racist agenda through an Equal Opportunities policy, pioneering ethnic monitoring in the practice, and other initiatives. Black and ethnic minority people and communities have been referred to in different terms over time. Many locally born black people describe themselves as 'Liverpool born black' or simply 'Black'. Given that ethnic diversity in Toxteth has continued to increase over the last few decades, we have mostly referred to Black, Asian and Minority Ethnic (BAME) people/communities, although we know that no description is without flaws. We have referred specifically to migrants from particular regions.

Throughout the book, we have referred to the area of Liverpool around Princes Park Health Centre interchangeably as Liverpool 8 and Toxteth.

Katy Gardner
Susanna Graham-Jones

Foreword by Roger Phillips

I joined Princes Park Health Centre when I arrived in Liverpool in the early 1970s. I was staying with friends who were patients there and it was close to Grove Park, where I lived at the time. I hardly ever used a GP in those days, but as soon as I did, I realised that this was a practice like no other.

Everyone - from receptionists to cleaners, nurses to doctors - genuinely cared for the patients. It was what I suppose would be called holistic. It catered for the whole person, and not just the medical aspects. There was poetry, music and artwork all over the building, and because it was in Liverpool 8, this came from all over the world. It was an exciting and fun place to be.

Of course, all this didn't happen by accident. It was down to a philosophy expounded by Cyril Taylor, who was so much more than a doctor. His left-wing politics shone through all that he did, not least as an active councillor and chair of the social services committee. But be in no doubt, he was also a brilliant GP. It was he who diagnosed my wife's Bornholm's disease when she was pregnant with our first child, when no one at the Women's Hospital had a clue what her illness was.

I've never forgotten - and have quoted on more than one occasion - Katy Gardner saying that the prescriptions she really needed to write weren't medical, but for new housing, a damp-proof course and better benefits for those who need them, so that they could live and eat healthily.

My dad, who was a single-handed GP, would have hated the way the NHS has changed over the years, but he would have been more than happy with the concept of health centres - as long as they were like the one at Princes Park. It was a place where health and social services genuinely came together, with health fairs, writers' workshops, poetry workshops, embroidery groups and plays, as well as a vast number of health projects. It led the way, and it's such a shame it's taken so long for the idea to be picked up more widely.

This book tells it all, and most importantly - in keeping with the ethos of the health centre - it does so through the eyes of the people who came to know and love the practice as I did.

Roger Phillips, recently retired BBC Radio Merseyside presenter

July 2020

Foreword by Iona Heath

This book is a history of a particular practice in a particular place at a particular time, but much more than that it tells the story of idealism, altruism and commitment laid low by bureaucracy and undermined by meddlesome manipulation of the political context. From the 1980s onwards, health workers had to grapple with the dual impact of rising inequality and increasingly prescriptive government controls. The book shows how they managed nevertheless to be imaginative, caring and clinically competent.

I worked for 35 years at the Caversham Group Practice in London NW5, which has always seemed to me to represent a parallel with Princes Park Health Centre in Liverpool 8. Both Cyril Taylor in Liverpool and Hugh Faulkner in my practice had been members of the Communist Party and both went on to be active within the Socialist Health Association. In the 1950s, shortly after the creation of the National Health Service, both founded innovative practices in deprived inner-city areas, committed to promoting social justice and combatting the devastating health effects of endemic structural violence. Both practices moved into purpose-built health centres in the 1970s.

There is no history of the Caversham Group Practice, which makes me value this book so much. As I read, I find myself reliving my own experience of curiosity and creativity, of innovation, teamwork and mutual support, and most of all, the sense that we were providing a good service to our patients. Like Princes Park, our practice sought to provide health and social care under one roof by seconding a social worker as one of the very first members of the extended primary care team. And I remember the enduring importance of the coffee break as the engine of mutual support.

We took the same pride in providing our own out-of-hours care and knew that we were providing a much better service than those who relied on deputising services of very erratic quality. And we were also proud of never seeing a drug company sales rep. Just like our colleagues in Liverpool, we were well aware of the limited capacity of technical medical interventions to reverse or even impede a lifetime of deprivation, racism, trauma and abuse. We always tried to use drugs and investigations frugally and judiciously. A well-earned sense of self-esteem is a huge sustainer of morale and costs nothing, but tragically no-one in a position of power seems ever to have recognised this. Our sense of doing our best for our patients kept us going when we were fully aware that we were having to work harder for less money than our colleagues in more affluent areas.

I also remember the rapid succession of steep learning curves mandated by the AIDS epidemic, the need to work collaboratively with Drug Dependence Units to care for our increasing population of people addicted to street drugs, and then the whole new challenge of computerisation.

For us, the decline began with the election of the first Thatcher government in 1979. Her ridiculous notion that 'there is no such thing as society' made the work of anyone seeking to maximise the health benefits of social justice that much more difficult. She appeared to have no interest in the predicament of the poor and her rise to power marked the beginning of the epidemic of victim-blaming that continues to this day. Her model for the health service was one of economic transactions within which 'the customer was always right'. Gradually but inevitably, it became almost impossible for practices to sustain their own out-of-hours care. People began to believe that they had a right to such care, whereas previously there was a real sense that patients and professionals were all in this together and needed to support each other.

As hospital doctors began to be gagged and prevented from speaking out, our practice started to see the benefits of the relative autonomy that came with our independent contractor status and we realised that government was not to be trusted. In 1998, we could very easily have followed Princes Park into giving up this precious status and becoming salaried but our increasing distrust, although demoralising in itself, prevented us from doing that. At this point in the history my sense of parallel morphs into a profound sense of 'there but for the grace of god...' Yet for us too, the straitjacket of bureaucracy and surveillance became slowly more suffocating. We too had to cope with health service managers who seemed to have no understanding of what we were trying to achieve or the benefits of teams working from the same space. We too lost district nurses, health visitors and our social worker, and the capacity of the team to make a real difference to our most vulnerable patients' lives was drastically reduced. We too felt we were being asked constantly to level down rather than seeing other practices levelled up.

Much of the story of the Princes Park practice is told in the description of three waiting rooms. The first is the front parlour in Cyril Taylor's home in Sefton Drive, where his receptionist/secretary worked and welcomed all comers. There were comfortable chairs, ready conversation, and the tone was set by the poster of Cyril sweeping away the Tories with a huge brush, the enormous portrait of Lenin, the picture of Paul Robeson in Liverpool and the availability of the *Morning Star*. The second was the relatively spacious but spartan waiting room of the new health centre where the seats were arranged in rows facing the reception desk, but the walls were soon decorated with bright posters and contemporary art. The *Morning Star* was still available to read and, by then, Katy Gardner was writing the regular health column. The new space allowed for Keep Fit and Tai Chi classes, public meetings and arts events, and evening performances of health-related plays. Then finally, in 2012, the waiting room was further 'improved', but all the vibrant, emblematic posters and pictures were removed and never replaced because of the convenient coercion of new health and safety concerns. Per Fugelli, a professor of social medicine in Oslo, used to argue that general practice should always situate itself close to patients and at a distance from the seats of power. The story of the waiting rooms seems to illustrate the gradual reversing of this aspiration.

On the face of it, there is very little in common between rural farming and inner-city general practice and yet the title of George Ewart Evans' masterpiece of rural oral history, published in 1956, is profoundly important: he called it *Ask the Fellows who Cut the Hay*. It seems quite clear that the hay of general practice is cut within the consultation wherever it occurs - at home, in the surgery or even in the street - but the actuality of the interaction between patient and professional is so poorly understood: the courage and endurance that it demands and the uncertainty and unpredictability on which it is built; the extraordinary intimacy and the hidden joys. Deep connections are forged between those on the privileged side of society and those who seem always to be losing, and the truth of these connections has a completely unrealised potential to inform public policy for the better. There remains a pervasive and disturbing lack of knowledge of the daily experience of working at the frontline of general practice, which is why the history of Princes Park Health Centre is so relevant. Primary care professionals see the effects of structural violence and social injustice working themselves out in premature illness and disease, and in blighted and shortened lives, every day. Their hard-earned understanding is as important now as it ever was.

In her remarkable book *The Logic of Care: Health and the Problem of Patient Choice*, Dutch philosopher Annemarie Mol writes, 'Our theoretical frameworks...tend not to explore or build ideals but to undermine them.' I think that all who cut the hay in general practice in Liverpool and London would agree with her and go further to include political and managerial frameworks. This is our predicament; the struggle continues.

Iona Heath, CBE, FRCGP,
President of the Royal College of General Practitioners, 2009-2012.
July 2020

GLOSSARY
list of abbreviations

AGUDA	Association of General Practice in Urban Deprived Areas
AHA	Area Health Authority
AIDS	Acquired Immuno-Deficiency Syndrome
APMS	Alternative Provider of Medical Services
BAME	Black, Asian and Minority Ethnic
Big Pharma	Generic term for large pharmaceutical corporations
BLACK-E	Community arts centre (formerly The Blackie)
BMA	British Medical Association
CAB	Citizens Advice Bureau
CAMHS	Child and Adolescent Mental Health Service
CBT	Cognitive behaviour therapy
CCG	Clinical Commissioning Group - successor organisation to PCT, chaired by a GP
CEO	Chief executive officer
CHC	Community Health Council
CHD	Coronary heart disease
CITA	Council for Information on Tranquillisers and Antidepressants
CND	Campaign for Nuclear Disarmament
COHSE	Confederation of Health Service Employees
CQC	Care Quality Commission - regulator for NHS and social care
CRE	Commission for Racial Equality
DDU	Drug Dependency Unit
DHSS	Department of Health and Social Security
EAL	English as an Additional Language
FACT	Foundation for Art and Creative Technology
FGM	Female genital mutilation
FHP	Family Health Project - health advocacy for homeless people (1993-1996)

FHSA	Family Health Service Authority
FHW	Family Health Worker - health advocate
FPC	Family Practitioner Committee, later FHSA
GMS	General Medical Services (fees for services paid to GPs by the NHS)
GP	General practitioner (family doctor)
GPPS	Annual GP Patient Survey, undertaken in all practices on behalf of NHS England from 2007 onwards
Heal8	Virtual Healthy Living Centre, Liverpool 8
HIV	Human immunodeficiency virus
IAPT	Improving Access to Psychological Therapies programme, started in 2008
IBS	Irritable bowel syndrome
ITU	Intensive therapy unit (also referred to as ICU, intensive care unit)
KONP	Keep Our NHS Public - pro-NHS campaigning organisation
LCHT	Liverpool Community Health Trust
Liverdoc	GP-run out-of-hours co-operative, from 1996
LMC	Local Medical Committee
LMFT	Local multidisciplinary facilitation team
LPSS	Liverpool Personal Service Society
LSTM	Liverpool School of Tropical Medicine
MAAG	Medical Audit Advisory Group
MAAN	Somali mental health project
MPU	Medical Practitioners' Union
NACGP	National Association of Commissioning GPs
NHP	Neighbourhood Health Project
NHS	National Health Service
NICE	National Institute for Health and Care Excellence
NMCT	North Mersey Community Trust (originally North Mersey Community Mental Health Trust)
OPCS	Office of Population Censuses and Surveys
PALS	Patient Advice and Liaison Services
PC24	Out-of-hours organisation, successor to UC24
PCAP	Primary Care Act Pilot

PCDI	Primary Care Deprivation Initiative
PCG	Primary Care Group - successor organisation to FHSA
PCT	Primary Care Trust - successor organisation to PCG
PMS	Personal Medical Services (GP contract)
PPHC	Princes Park Health Centre
QOF	Quality and Outcomes Framework 2004 - performance-related pay for GPs
QoL	Quality of Life - referring to patient outcome measures in research studies
RCGP	Royal College of General Practitioners
REACT	Regeneration Through Environmental Action project
SDI	Service Development Initiative
SHA	Socialist Health Association, previously Socialist Medical Association
SMR	Standardised mortality ratio
SSPH	SSP Health Ltd
THCF	Toxteth Health and Community Care Forum
UC24	Out-of-hours organisation set up as a social enterprise, a successor to Liverdoc
UPA	Underprivileged area score - a score devised by Dr Brian Jarman to rank small geographical areas in the UK in order of deprivation
WHISC	Women's Health Information and Support Centre
WHO	World Health Organization

TIMELINE - the NHS, Liverpool and Princes Park Health Centre

1948   The National Health Service is launched on the so-called 'Appointed Day', 5 July 1948

1950   Dr Cyril Taylor opens his practice at 7 Sefton Drive, Liverpool. Collings report criticises the low standard of urban general practice in England

1952   College of General Practitioners founded

1957   Balint, M., *The doctor, his patient and the illness*

1958   First National Morbidity Study carried out

1965   College of GPs' report - *Special Vocational Training for GPs*

1966   Family Doctors' Charter calls for help with premises and staff for GPs

1967   Royal Charter granted to the College of GPs; now RCGP

1968   Todd Report (Royal Commission on Medical Education)

1971   Julian Tudor Hart formulates the Inverse Care Law (*Lancet* article)

1972   RCGP - *The Future General Practitioner: Learning and Teaching*

1973   Cyril Taylor proposes a health centre on the site of a former church in Toxteth, Liverpool 8

        Pat Taylor and Enid Levy open the first women's refuge in Liverpool

        Medical Research Council sets up the GP Research Framework: Cyril's practice joins

        NHS Reorganisation Act: regional, area and district health authorities established, with 'consensus management'

1974   As part of NHS reorganisation, Area Health Authorities (AHAs) absorb public health function and are coterminous with local authorities

        Family Practitioner Committees and Community Health Councils introduced

1975 Vocational training for GPs made mandatory (Act 1976)

Socialist Medical Association publishes pamphlet *Health Centres: the next steps*

Cyril Taylor accepted as a GP trainer by Royal College of General Practitioners

1976 Byrne and Long, *Doctors talking to Patients*

1977 Princes Park Health Centre (PPHC) opens

Parkside Hostel opens, housing people with disabilities

1978 Dr Katy Gardner joins Cyril Taylor's practice at PPHC

Dr Sheila Abdullah moves her practice from Upper Parliament St to PPHC

Alma-Ata Declaration emphasises primary health care as key to achieving WHO goal of 'Health for All'

1979 Merrison report (Royal Commission on the NHS)

General election won by the Conservative party, led by Margaret Thatcher

1980 *Report of the Working Group on Inequalities in Health,* known as the Black Report

1981 Acheson report on primary health care in inner London stimulates universities to invest in raising standards in primary health care

Toxteth Riots (3-13 and 27-28 July) sparked by a heavy-handed arrest in the Granby area, following excessive use of 'stop and search' powers by police

1982 Liverpool's day care abortion service starts, after a long campaign

Cyril Taylor's and Sheila Abdullah's practices merge - PPHC now houses one group practice

Micros for GPs initiated - pilot scheme of computers in general practice

Katy Gardner and Doreen Vernon start the first Well Woman clinic in the North of England

Griffiths Report recommends introducing general management in the NHS, abolishing consensus management and making managers accountable in return for higher pay

1984 PPHC extension funded by Inner-City Partnership money

Health and Recreation Team (HART) Sports Council project housed in portacabin

1985   University of Liverpool Department of General Practice founded - Prof. Ian Stanley is its first professor

1986   Liverpool Race and Health Project research conducted at PPHC with Pro Torkington

Dr Sheila Abdullah leaves PPHC

Drs Susanna Graham-Jones and Lis Davidson join PPHC as partners

1987   Cyril Taylor retires

First edition of Prinny Post, celebrating 10 years of PPHC

'The Primary Health Care Team - Fact or Friction?' - joint meeting with RCGP Merseyside Faculty and University of Liverpool Department of General Practice

Liverpool Balint group started, facilitated by psychoanalyst Vera Pettit

Liverpool School of Tropical Medicine students survey PPHC patients' views about ethnic monitoring

First race awareness training at PPHC and start of ethnic monitoring

Government white paper *Promoting Better Health* makes proposals for a new GP contract

1988   PPHC Well Man clinic starts

PPHC introduces computerised patient records

1989   *Loosen the Shackles,* Lord Gifford's report on race relations in Liverpool

Government white paper *Working for Patients* proposes a split between the bodies providing care and those purchasing it, creating an internal market in the NHS

1990   NHS and Community Care Act - Family Health Services Authorities have more power over GP remuneration; GP fundholding in sight

New contract imposed on GPs after failed negotiations - GP budgets cash-limited for the first time, with an element of performance-related pay

Sirad Elmi appointed as first link worker for the Somali community, based at PPHC

1991   Fundholding for GPs piloted in some practices
        (practices have their own budgets to purchase services)

1992   PPHC Health Thru Arts Festival

        GP commissioning of health services begins to be discussed

1993   PPHC Family Health Project - health advocacy for homeless
        people temporarily housed in the area

        Susanna Graham-Jones moves to Oxford as University Lecturer

1994   Toxteth Health and Community Care Forum founded

1995   Refurbishment of PPHC

1997   Primary Care Deprivation Initiative follows on from Family
        Health Project

        NHS Primary Care Act introduced by the Tories - facilitates the
        piloting of different ways of providing primary care and employing
        GPs

        General election won by New Labour, led by Tony Blair -
        Frank Dobson becomes Health Secretary

1998   *Independent Inquiry into Inequalities in Health Report,* the
        second Acheson report

        Green paper *A First Class Service: Quality in the new NHS*
        proposes abolition of fundholding and replacing FHSAs with
        Primary Care Groups

        PPHC becomes a Primary Care Act Pilot

        GP partners at PPHC become salaried employees of North Mersey
        Community (Mental Health) Trust

1999   After pilot phase, PPHC becomes a fully-fledged Personal Medical
        Services (PMS) practice

        Government white paper *Saving Lives: Our Healthier Nation* aims
        to address health inequalities

2000   Toxteth is designated a new Health Action Zone in Liverpool

REACT project launched at PPHC

PPHC designated Liverpool's lead practice for refugees and asylum seekers

New Labour launches 10-year NHS Plan - significant new money for the 'modernisation' agenda: hospitals to be built under PFI (private finance initiative) schemes, electronic records in hospitals, increases in staff numbers, improved patient access to 24-hour care

Ethnicity Profiling in Primary Care - The Princes Park Health Centre Model 2000 report

2001   Liverpool's Primary Care Groups become Primary Care Trusts, commissioning primary care, hospital and community health services from NHS or other providers.

Further link workers appointed at PPHC for Somali and Arabic communities, as interpreters and facilitators

2002   Social Inclusion Team replaces the Asylum and Refugee project

Central Liverpool PCT takes over PPHC and other salaried practices under a PCT Medical Services (PCTMS) contract

Somali Mental Health Project launched (MAAN)

2003   Community Health Councils abolished by the Department of Health

2004   APMS contracts introduced, allowing Alternative Providers, other than GPs, to hold practice contracts.

PPHC as a Public Health Organisation report by GP registrar Dr Sarah McNulty

The Quality and Outcomes Framework (QOF) strengthens performance-related pay for GPs

Evaluation of Family Health Project published as two peer-reviewed publications

2005   Dr Katy Gardner leaves PPHC after 28 years

2006   NHS Act establishes commissioning bodies and introduces Alternative Provider of Medical Services (APMS) contracts

Three Liverpool PCTs merge into one whole-of-Liverpool PCT, as envisaged in the NHS Plan of 2000

2007   Dr Mike Ejuoneatse, last of the full-time GPs, leaves PPHC

2008   Dr Martin Smith's departure means that PPHC loses its GP training status

2010   The NHS Transforming Community Services programme removes the 'provider arm' of PCTs, completing the purchaser/provider split

Liverpool salaried GP practices, including PPHC, and district nursing services, are placed under the new Liverpool Community Health Trust (LCHT)

2011   PPHC put out to tender by Liverpool PCT

2012   The very contentious Health and Social Care Act removes state responsibility for NHS provision, allowing widespread marketisation of health services in England

Dr Lis Davidson leaves PPHC

PPHC tender awarded to SSP Health Ltd, a GP owned business

2013   Liverpool Primary Care Trust becomes Liverpool Clinical Commissioning Group, led by GPs, a statutory NHS budget holder

2014   Patient dissatisfaction with management of PPHC by SSP Health - patients call for Care Quality Commission investigation, but no major improvements follow CQC inspection in 2014

Further upgrade and extension of PPHC premises

2015   Repeat CQC visit to PPHC requested by whistle-blowers - patients are consulted by CQC inspectors

2016   SSPH contract not renewed - Liverpool CCG asks Brownlow Health group to manage PPHC temporarily

2017   CCGs begin to take over commissioning of core GP contracts

PPHC, recovering, celebrates 40th birthday

CQC revisits PPHC and finds it greatly improved

2018   Five-year contract awarded to Brownlow Health

Formal establishment of Princes Park@Brownlow

CHAPTER 1

Cyril Taylor's brainchild

Cyril Taylor and his focus on community health services

The birth of the NHS and the context in which Cyril Taylor worked as a GP

Early days at PPHC: the move, the team, the politics (1977)

Liverpool 8: a deprived inner-city area

Health inequalities

Cyril Taylor and his focus on community health services

Cyril Taylor, the founder of Princes Park Health Centre (PPHC), was born on 9th March 1921, in New Brighton on the Wirral. His parents were Orthodox Jews, but his father, a tailor, changed his name from Zadetsky to Taylor. Cyril went to Wallasey Grammar School and joined the Federation of Zionist Youth, but lost his faith in his teens. He told Sylvia Hikins, who became his partner later in life, that when he started university he went to the canteen to eat the most non-kosher food he could find, which was toad in the hole: 'He was so disappointed when he discovered it was a sausage - he expected it to be a toad!' He openly declared himself an atheist and later joined the Communist Party of Great Britain. He trained at Liverpool Medical School during the Second World War and joined the Royal Army Medical Corps, working at Alder Hey Hospital, receiving casualties from Dunkirk. By 1945 he was a major in charge of the British Hospital in Khartoum in the Sudan.

Returning to Liverpool after the war, he took up a post as an orthopaedic registrar at Walton Hospital. He was not reappointed at his six-month review, partly because he was in the Communist Party but also because he was actively trying to get the nurses to join a trade union. In 1949 he was employed as a medical officer for the Liverpool Shipping Federation. Politics soon came to the fore, as he stood for election to the council as a Communist. When asked to leave the federation, again because of his politics, he decided to work as a family doctor. There was no specific training for general practitioners (GPs) at the time. Sick patients queued up to be seen in surgeries, and GPs improvised as best they could with advice and treatment. Two weeks after starting work in a GP surgery, Cyril was again fired for being a Communist. This time he took the option of being his own boss and started up as a single-handed GP.

In 1950 Cyril moved to the Sefton Park area with his wife Pat and began working from their home at 7 Sefton Drive, Liverpool 8. The consulting room was at the back of the house and the front parlour became the waiting room, where his receptionist/secretary worked. This created an informal atmosphere but, as he wrote, did 'little for confidentiality' (1974). Various socialist papers were available for patients to read, including the Communist Party newspaper, *Morning Star,* and *China Today.* Cyril became involved in local government as well as running his practice. He was an active member of the Hospital and Welfare Services Union and later joined the Confederation of Health Service Employees (COHSE). His reputation grew and his 'list' of patients at the Sefton Drive practice gradually increased to 4,000 over the next 27 years.

Lyn Jones became Cyril's (and Liverpool's) first practice nurse in 1969:

> I had the honour of becoming Cyril's first practice nurse. When I went for my interview, a chat over a cup of tea, I was surprised to see a four-foot-high portrait of Lenin on the waiting room wall. A very unusual practice. My post was entirely funded by Cyril in the interests of his practice. Due to his innovative thinking it 'took off' more extensively than most nurses' roles at the time. My duties included seeing housebound patients, to see if they needed any further help or referral, visiting mothers with babies for feeding advice and seeing people with low incomes for advice about diets and shopping. I also held a weekly clinic for electrocardiograms, vaccinations, smears etc. My home visits were fascinating as the practice

area ranged from Karl Gardens tenement blocks, at the time very run down, through Princes Avenue flats to the other side of Sefton Park, which was much more affluent. Cyril was so good to work with. He and his wife, Pat were huge fun, and when my daughter was born, they even babysat her while I did clinics!

Lyn also remembered the parties at Sefton Drive - an essential part of practice life, with 'musicians from the Philharmonic, actors, politicians, artists. It was fascinating, not what I was used to!'

Cyril was a lifelong socialist. He remained a member of the Communist Party until the Hungarian uprising of 1956 and stood for the council in South Scotland ward in 1950. Jack Coward, Communist Party candidate for parliament, urged voters to support him because 'his ceaseless campaign for the elimination of common illnesses caused by bad housing and bad working conditions places him in the ranks of working-class pioneers. By supporting him you will deal a deadly blow to the Tory dominated council.'

An early patient remembered a photo on the waiting room wall showing Cyril with a huge brush, sweeping away the Tories. Another, Gideon Ben-Tovim, later a councillor for Granby Ward and chair of Liverpool Primary Care Trust (PCT), said:

Most medical consultations with Cyril were really political discussions. On one memorable occasion I had been feeling rather exhausted and went to see him. He said, "What do you expect if you've got three children, a full-time job and a busy political life? You've got the TATs - Tired All the Time! Now, what do you think about the political situation?

In his book *Stalin Ate My Homework*, Alexei Sayle (2010) described his Communist parents bringing him all the way from Anfield in North Liverpool to the surgery in Sefton Drive on account of Cyril's politics. These visits would become slightly more problematic when Cyril left the Party in 1956, while the Sayles remained. Liverpool journalist Paul Burnell recalled, 'My dad was a friend and comrade of Cyril's from their Communist Party days. And my cousin Jack, the closest I ever had to a big brother, was a communist shop steward in the docks, and a part-time jazz musician. He and his very radical probation officer wife were Cyril's patients throughout their lives.'

Cyril had joined the Socialist Medical Association (later the Socialist Health

Association) in the 1940s and was a member of a delegation that met with Nye Bevan in 1946 to discuss plans for a new National Health Service, urging him to go ahead with his project despite the resistance of the reactionary medical establishment. He became a Labour Party member in the 1960s and was elected to the city council in 1966. Alex Scott-Samuel joined Cyril's list as a patient when he was a medical student:

> I switched from the very conventional university GP to Cyril Taylor in 1968. My politics then were about the peace movement, so I didn't have a political relationship with him at the time, but I remember waiting in his living room at 7 Sefton Drive, with Sheila Scott behind the desk. By the mid-1970s I was a free-floating libertarian socialist who didn't vote. It was Cyril who pointed out that there was so much more to be gained by compromising my purist political values in order to achieve change through practical politics. He convinced me to join the Labour Party and the Socialist Health Association (SHA), of which he was later president. I am now privileged to hold the position of SHA chair myself.

Alex was inspired to pursue his own career as a public health specialist and went on to work closely with Cyril and his team.

Cyril's approach to the role of GP was strongly influenced by his sense of social justice:

> Both as a medical student and later as a doctor, it has always seemed entirely appropriate for me to be part of the broad struggle to change the unequal society for one in which every citizen would have an equal opportunity for education, the development of their talents and the right to work for their own benefit and the benefit of society. (Taylor, 1986)

Health campaigner Sylvia Hikins commented, 'Well ahead of his time, Cyril recognised that the NHS was a disease service treating the consequences of ill health, not the causes of it. He often said that less than half the patients he had seen actually had clinical problems - their issues were poor housing, unemployment, poverty, racism...' In a 1964 Socialist Health Association pamphlet titled 'Is your GP really necessary?' he referred to the paradox of paying GPs to deal with sick patients, as opposed to incentivising them to practice preventive medicine in order to reduce morbidity and mortality from heart disease and other problems (Taylor, 1964; Morrell, 1998).

Gerry and Geraldine Poole lived across the road from the surgery. Geraldine's family joined the practice in 1950 and Gerry joined in 1967 when he married her. Gerry remembered Cyril's reluctance to prescribe unnecessary medication to his patients. In the days when most GPs doled out 'tonics', Cyril recommended exercise and other relaxing activities for stress-related problems. Geraldine remembered how she was quite anxious when she had her first baby. She rang Cyril in the middle of the night and he came over at once in his dressing gown and slippers: 'The baby was fine, and he told me that she was "having a nice sleep!" But he added that he never minded coming out at night to see a baby.' However, Cyril was also capable of setting firm limits. Lyn Jones wrote:

> He took me on a home visit shortly after I started. I will never forget that he told the patient off severely for calling him up at three am to ask for an aspirin, making him tired the next day. Cyril was a good and caring physician who never hesitated to visit a person in real need, but he was straight-talking, and he kept his patients in order.

Dr Katy Gardner remembered Cyril as a brilliant diagnostician, but he was always straightforward with patients if he didn't know what was wrong. Alex Robinson, another patient, remembered 'more than once being told, "you've got GOK [God Only Knows]". The fact that he was confident about uncertainty was reassuring - I suppose it gently made me take a step back and relax. As a young working mum of two boys under two, he recognised stress was probably the cause.'

Jimmy Rand, then a building worker, and one of Cyril's first patients, remembered Cyril as 'an educator who saw that health was about full employment, good housing and education for all.' Jimmy also remembered how Cyril went the extra mile for his patients:

> I went to university as a mature student, encouraged by my colleagues in the Communist Party, and at mass X-ray - an entry requirement - I was found to have TB [tuberculosis]. Cyril was on the phone to the consultant immediately. He always emphasised the importance of personal communication. He came to my house with medication the same day; completely beyond the call of duty.

Cyril also had a wry sense of humour. Jim and Jean Hamilton joined his list in 1975:

> We belonged to a church in Devonshire Rd, and as increasing numbers of us young folk started getting married, more and more of us were registering with Cyril. Besides being a good doctor, we found him to be

very kind. He was fond of having a bit of banter, and a visit to him was often quite humorous. On one occasion when Jean had an infection, he prescribed antibiotics and told her to take them religiously, adding, 'but that won't be hard for you, will it?'

Cyril began developing his team early on. Cathy Hogan, secretary and later practice manager, reflected:

> Cyril's vision of Princes Park Health Centre had started long before I knew him, but he had the essence of a multidisciplinary team in 1975, when I first met him as a student on a two-week placement from secretarial college. Sheila Scott was the lead administrator/secretary, later to become the practice manager, supported by a part-time receptionist called Coralie. Health visitor Gwyn Lautterberg was based in Hartington Road community clinic. Doreen Vernon as practice nurse worked a couple of days a week doing smears and baby immunisations, all from the front two rooms of 7 Sefton Drive...GPs then did their own on call, and Pat, Cyril's wife, had responsibility for managing calls out of hours. Dr Susie Lewis-Jones and later her husband, Ewan, joined the band of clinical staff and together this team made a vision reality. I joined straight after college in January 1976...I remember Cyril's love of life, helping the underdog, championing social services as chair of the Social Services Committee of the City Council..., hosting Chilean refugees at home and treating patients at the battered wives' hostel, as it was known. He looked after visiting actors, poets, artists from the Playhouse, and the Everyman when that opened, and it gave you a privileged view of life no other practice could possibly have offered. Political friends of Cyril sat with their Liberal opponents in the waiting room.

One innovation at the Sefton Drive practice was an appointments system. A patient remembered being delighted that he could phone or call in and make an appointment instead of queuing for hours, as was common in general practices at the time.

Reflecting on 30 years in general practice in *Socialism and Health*, Cyril wrote, 'To be a community-orientated doctor means involvement in all aspects of the community's health care needs, including health education, screening and prevention. It also means forming an alliance with the community to resist forces - political, social, environmental - which make for ill health' (Taylor, 1980). Between 1935 and 1950, the Peckham Experiment, at the Pioneer Health Centre in south London, had raised its own funding to demonstrate what could be achieved in a deprived inner-city area with a multi-purpose building and 'healthy families' ethos (Pearse and Crocker, 1947). The theory was that healthy families would surely need less, rather than more, health care. Cyril too wanted to practise in a dedicated, multi-purpose health centre, with a multi-disciplinary team. Way back in 1920, Lord Dawson's report on 'the Future Provision of Medical and Allied Services' had proposed primary health centres staffed by GPs. Those health centres never materialised, but during the Second World War the idea of health centres was incorporated into plans for the new National Health Service.

The birth of the NHS and the context in which Cyril Taylor worked as a GP

The National Health Service (NHS) was launched in 1948 as a vital part of the nation's vision of a welfare state. Access to health care, free of charge, in community and hospital settings, was now everyone's right. The old GP 'panels' were abolished, and GP patient lists were opened up to serve the whole population. GPs earned a small sum known as the 'capitation fee' for each patient on their personal list, plus extra 'item-of-service' payments for specific procedures, such as immunisations, specified in a schedule which became known as the Red Book.

As predicted by cautious doctors and the British Medical Association (BMA), the huge increase in workload for GPs proved to be unsustainable. An average GP might expect to do up to 40 five-minute consultations and 16 home visits, six days a week. GPs were also on call for all their patients day and night.

J. S. Collings was an Australian doctor who was funded by the Nuffield Provincial Hospitals Trust in 1948 to explore the state of general practice in England. His study was a qualitative, ethnographic rather than systematic survey. Collings asked informants in Manchester, Newcastle, and Devon and Cornwall to tell him about practices they rated as 'good, fair or bad'. There were no reliable quantitative data to compare across practices or localities. Instead, Collings sat in on consultations and home visits for several days, in each of 55 practices. The report, subtitled 'a reconnaissance', was published in *The Lancet*. It was damning, particularly about 'industrial' practice, which Collings regarded as 'at the best very unsatisfactory...and at the worst a positive source of public danger.' He saw that overworked GPs had little contact with hospital-based colleagues and facilities and were unable to make use of their expensive training (Collings, 1950; Petchey, 1995). The Collings report caused a sensation and alerted a generation of younger doctors to the need for change. The BMA's General Practice Review Committee promptly commissioned a postal survey of almost 13,000 practices in 1951. The survey achieved a response rate of 72%, and a random sample of 188 practices were subsequently visited (Hadfield, 1953). The findings of these more systematic studies satisfied the BMA that many GPs were providing good or at least adequate care. But an inescapable conclusion was that the standard of care in many inner-city practices was inadequate. Single-handed GPs, working long hours from cramped and unattractive premises, were struggling, and many were overwhelmed.

Despite the nationalisation of the hospital sector, GPs had opted to retain their fee-based independent contractor status under the new NHS, rather than becoming salaried employees. But government investment was needed to provide the capital for better surgery premises (Webster, 1998). Following the wartime discussions, Section 21 of the National Health Service Act (1946) had stated explicitly, 'It shall be the duty of every local health authority to provide, equip, and maintain, to the satisfaction of the Ministry, premises, which shall be called "Health Centres".' It was envisaged that GPs, dentists, chemists and local authority children's clinics would be available in each health centre, and that space would be provided for visiting hospital consultants to run outpatient clinics.

While there was support from the incoming Labour government, there also was powerful opposition to the idea of paying for an expensive health centre building programme in the looming post-war economic recession. The Section 21 proposal was shelved and the construction of local authority health centres across the UK was delayed by more than 25 years (Cardew, 1959). In addition to failing to resolve the premises problem, the UK government was slow to acknowledge the intolerable and increasing workload of GPs working in the new NHS. Solutions were hard to find, and disgruntled, overworked GPs were further aggrieved by the accusations of low standards of care. After the publication of the Collings report, a group of young, idealistic and energetic GPs emerged. They made time to meet, in London and elsewhere, to pool their ideas. Despite opposition from hospital specialists suspicious of competition from family doctors who might 'poach' their private patients (Hunt, 1973), these young GPs were determined to make their voices heard, and in 1952 they established a College of General Practitioners. The college set up regional groups (faculties) of like-minded doctors. Social medicine emerged as a new discipline, and members embarked on ground-breaking, practice-based and collaborative research (Pereira Gray, 1992).

In the 1960s, the government was forced to acknowledge the fundamental importance of general practice to the NHS and the need to raise the morale of the overstretched GP workforce. Members of the College of General Practitioners were supported by the Medical Practitioners Union, part of the Association of Scientific and Technical Staff, of which Cyril was a member, and by the Trades Union Congress (Morrell, 1998), in drafting a Family Doctor Charter. This document clarified basic requirements for general practice. It was accepted by the Ministry of Health in 1966, and a new GP contract encouraged the development of group practices by providing financial incentives for employment of nurses and ancillary staff. A practice allowance provided some financial security in the form of baseline funding, though the number of patients (maximum 4,000) on a GP's list was still the principal driver of GP income (Gillam, 2017). Funding was at last made available for surgery premises, in the form of rent reimbursement. Eventually, specific funding for some local authority health centres was found.

Cyril became a member of the Royal College of General Practitioners in 1971 (the Royal Charter was granted in 1967). From his surgery in Sefton Drive, he began to visualise moving his team into a health centre where there would be space for activities including preventive health care, and even a pram park! In 1973 he spotted a possible site within a few streets of Sefton Drive. This was the disused and decaying All Saints Church on Bentley Road in Toxteth, on the edge of Granby Ward in Liverpool 8, one of the most deprived areas in the city.

The 1973 NHS Reorganisation Act changed the landscape of the NHS. Previously, hospitals and primary care services were completely separate. When it was implemented in 1974, they were brought together under regional, area and district health authorities. Area Health Authorities (AHAs) were coterminous with councils and directly responsible for the health of their populations. Responsibility for public health was removed from local authorities and came under the NHS umbrella. Councillors had seats on AHA boards, and Cyril immediately joined Liverpool AHA.

Early days at Princes Park: the move, the team, the politics (1977)

Princes Park Health Centre, the fourth publicly funded health centre to be built in Liverpool, opened on St Patrick's Day, 17th March 1977. Cyril's campaign to create a new health centre had been facilitated by his roles as both a Labour Councillor and a member of the Liverpool Area Health Authority, which funded the centre. His team were involved in the planning of the health centre right from the start. Cathy Hogan recalled:

> My first memories of Princes Park Health Centre are as a plan on a page, displayed in the dining room at Sefton Drive on a large square dining table, with Cyril in his dressing gown poring over the details laid before him on paper whilst I opened the post and he ate his eggs and bacon! As part of the great plan, influenced by the Peckham project in London, Sheila Scott and I were expected to find out all we could about building design. District nurse Maureen Scott-Samuel was charged with taking us all to a newly opened purpose-built health centre in Southport to see what we could find out. What a trip - Maureen had not long passed her test, and we were useless at navigating! We had regular planning meetings with the local health authorities, and Sheila and I played our part in designing the health centre - where the sockets would go, how the reception area would function and how it would be staffed.

Opening the centre, Sir Alec Merrison (see below) said, 'People often say there is a lot wrong with the NHS - but there is a lot that is right, as with the opening of a building like this. The centre will provide more than just medical attention. It is a social experiment which will play an enormous part in the life of the area.' It certainly embodied Cyril's dream: health and social care were to be provided under one roof.

Cyril's team already included Dr Ewan Lewis-Jones, practice manager Sheila Scott, secretary Cathy Hogan and practice nurse Doreen Vernon. Health visitor Gwyn Lautterberg moved in to join the PPHC team, as did Pam Duff, a social worker from Liverpool Personal Social Services. Visiting psychologists, physiotherapists, chiropodists, dietitians and hospital specialists, including geriatrician Dr Playfer, made use of other rooms. The health centre hosted a busy Area Health Authority Well Baby Clinic, doing baby checks and immunisations for families in Liverpool 8. There was space for voluntary projects to hold meetings, and a caretaker employed by the Area Health Authority was housed in the flat upstairs. Cathy Hogan remembered, 'Moving from Sefton Drive to Princes Park was a task in itself, not least because Cyril had just been appointed to the Royal Commission on the NHS, with meeting papers and evidence in abundance, all needing to be transferred!'

Most patients welcomed and understood the need for a pioneering health centre to serve the population of Liverpool 8. Teresa Williamson, a patient and activist, wrote:

> I had my son in late 1977. I was at another surgery but heard about the baby clinic around the corner from where I lived off Granby Street. I used to go weekly to have my son weighed, find information about weaning, get support from nurses and other mothers, which was really helpful being a first-time mother. I was used to a GP surgery in a house, where you gave your name in, saw a doctor on a first come first served basis, and no other services or facilities were offered. PPHC was ground-breaking. I quickly registered myself and my son. I later attended the well women's clinic, accessed physiotherapy at the surgery for a chronic back condition and had counselling with a psychologist...At times I was taken to a room away from the waiting room hubbub, so my anxiety didn't escalate while I waited for a GP, which was very helpful. The surgery was always full and vibrant, but every patient was seen, and emergencies all accommodated.

A few patients were disconcerted. The new waiting room was spartan, with seats in rows facing reception, and some patients missed the comfortable upholstered chairs in Sefton Drive. Jimmy Rand joked to Cyril:

> When we moved it was less cosy than the lovely waiting room in Sefton Drive with its pictures of Paul Robeson in Liverpool on the walls. Conversations were so good there; you were almost disappointed when your name was called. I missed the old waiting room, but PPHC was a huge improvement in health care provision, especially for those in the Granby Triangle. It was a step down in my standard of comfort, but I did get it!

Some practice staff found the move challenging, despite welcoming the opportunities for better patient care. Nurse Doreen Vernon was anxious about the change, but in the 1980 practice report she wrote, 'The great day arrived. It was quite painless. My first impression was a feeling of spaciousness with plenty of room to spread out...The treatment room had almost everything you could want in it; the furnishings, fittings and equipment were all first class.' Sheila Scott shared Cyril's politics and was fully on board with the move. However, she worried about the complexity of the administration in the new centre due to the various clinics and activities, a far cry from Cyril's small surgery. She also criticised the lack of any prior training for the Area Health Authority staff who now joined the staff at the practice. As a receptionist who was employed by the health authority but managed by the practice, Pip Abraham appreciated Sheila's management style: 'She had a knack of keeping everyone together and was very fair in the way she managed us.' Linda Pepper, a women's health campaigner and patient, remembered, 'The practice was patient centred - working with me not at me - I never found the equivalent.' But she also noted:

> In the early days at least, there were certain receptionists who could be very robust gatekeepers. I remember once urgently needing the morning after pill, which you could only get from a doctor. The receptionist absolutely refused to give me an emergency appointment until I told her why. So I shouted out loud to all the waiting room that I had had sex the night before and the condom broke and it was an emergency! She was cross, but I got seen.

The new health centre attracted staff who absorbed Cyril's philosophy, including Katy Gardner, a GP fresh from training. Katy had done a student placement with Cyril at a time when her medical school, the London Hospital, considered students wanting to go into general practice as failures. She joined the practice in 1978. Both Cyril and Katy had been influenced by Dr Julian Tudor Hart, whose ground-breaking community-based work in Glyncorrwg, South Wales, had been the focus of another of Katy's student attachments.

Katy was active in the women's movement and the expanding community health movement. In Liverpool she found a natural ally in Dr Sheila Abdullah, a feminist GP and tireless campaigner for women's reproductive rights, who had met Cyril through the Socialist Medical Association. Sheila had been working in a practice in Aintree and in early 1978 she took over a single-handed general practice in Upper Parliament Street, Liverpool 8, with the express purpose of moving into PPHC. Through Jane Leighton, a feminist friend, Sheila had joined the Central and South Community Health Council (CHC), one of the most political CHCs in the UK, of which Jane was secretary. Marge Bentovim, a patient and campaigner, remembered, 'Sheila Abdullah was a particularly important figure in my life - not just a sympathetic and highly competent GP, but a key sister and friend in the formative years of the women's movement on Merseyside. We worked closely together on many campaigns, mainly focused on women's health issues.' Sheila also worked in the Liverpool Brook Advisory Centre, located at the time in a cold basement of the Family Planning Association building in Gambier Terrace on Hope Street, with no regular funding and a one-bar electric fire. Patient and activist Nina Houghton was a volunteer:

> We carried out free pregnancy testing on Saturday mornings. This was organised by Sheila, using her respectable GP status to access free use of the premises. We were of the generation when, in our teens and even early twenties, you still had to be married to get contraception, though when the Pill arrived, progressive doctors had begun to prescribe it for everyone. But it was still a radical act on Sheila's part to strongly support free contraception, and abortion on demand. She was a little older than us, had a professional job and was married with three kids, so we radical feminists thought of her as a real grown-up, not exactly one of us. However, we all respected her enormously and shared common goals for women's liberation, and so we were able to work together.

Cathy Hogan recalled, 'Her devotion to patients led to her working long hours with morning surgeries often still going at 2pm. A home visit regularly meant Sheila making a cup of tea for the patients whilst she consulted at their home.' Linda Pepper remembered:

> She was not just a doctor but an advocate. I had to have an amniocentesis, and the hospital doctor said I could not be told the sex of the baby, as in their experience the husband could beat up the woman if the sex was not the one they wanted. I said, 'Would you rather I was beaten up when pregnant, or just after the baby was born?!' If they knew the sex of the baby, then I wanted to know. Sheila contacted the hospital, saying that as my GP it was her right to know the full results, including the sex of the baby. She got them and told me.

Nina Houghton also remembered Sheila going out of her way to help:

In 1974 I went into labour unexpectedly in a remote cottage in North Wales and ended up giving birth in St Asaph hospital in the middle of the night, accompanied by a group of women and one child! To the staff we must have appeared like the wildest hippies. I think, because I had a home birth arranged in Liverpool at a time when this was frowned upon, they thought I was lying about this and in fact intended to give birth without medical assistance. It happened incredibly fast and they probably thought we'd put off calling the ambulance. The staff didn't hold back from showing their intense disapproval, and giving birth there was a horrible experience for me as a first-time mother. Fortunately, we thought of contacting Sheila. I don't know what she said, but once she'd intervened, their attitude changed, and they began to treat me with a modicum of respect. She even managed to spring me out of there after a couple of days!

Sheila and Cyril shared a similar vision of primary care. Cyril's innovative approach to primary care had been rewarded early in 1977, when he and Dr Christopher Wells, a Sheffield GP, were invited to join Alec Merrison's Royal Commission on the NHS. Merrison had been Professor of Physics at Liverpool University until 1969 and may have come across Cyril in this context. His commission was set up by the Labour government under Harold Wilson to report on 'the best use and management of the financial and manpower resources of the NHS' (Merrison Report, Royal Commission on the NHS, 1979). GPs from the north of England were at last being given a seat at the table alongside the London-based policy makers. Unfortunately, there was a new Tory government in power by the time the commission reported in 1979, and its recommendations were greatly watered down.

In Liverpool, the health centre movement was sluggish. Despite Merrison's championing of PPHC as a place where GPs would work together with other health care professionals, many Liverpool GPs, 60% of whom were single-handed, feared that health centres would threaten their independence. Three local authority health centres had been built in Liverpool before PPHC opened, including those in Vauxhall and Netherley, but local GPs had not been involved in the plans and lacked any motivation for working together or sharing the building (Merseyside Communist Party, 1982).

PPHC forged ahead to show how a health centre could work, but the members of the influential Local Medical Committee (LMC), a statutory body advising and representing all GPs in the city, remained sceptical for many years. They regarded PPHC as a hotbed of radicalism. District nurse Chas Clegg, whose stepfather was a socialist and knew Cyril, jumped at the chance to join the team in 1983:

> Before I joined Princes Park I worked in Everton and the Scotland Road area of the city, much the same in terms of deprivation and poor health care as Toxteth. Part of my job seemed to be about protecting the patients from the GPs, who had little interest in keeping their knowledge up to date or the standard of care they gave - all were single handed.

Chas also commented, 'The politics of the Princes Park practice were well known but often misunderstood. I was once at an outside meeting where the practice was described as "Reds under the Beds". I took that as a compliment, as at the time Margaret Thatcher was on top of the beds trying to dismantle the health service.'

In fact, the practice was always a broad church. Receptionist and Tory party activist Helen Rigby recalled, 'I was the token Tory. It gave the lie to the rumour that only socialists could be employed at PPHC. I went to an interview with Cyril and got the job straight away.' Ram Poluri, trainee GP in 1987-8, agreed: 'Everybody was on first name terms, and in keeping with this liberal ethos there was the Tory receptionist, Helen - I always remember her in blue - who stuck up pictures of Margaret Thatcher. In contrast, Katy contested on the Communist Party ticket in the 1987 elections and got 801 votes.'

Liverpool 8: a deprived inner-city area

Although Cyril's patients were drawn to him from all over the city because of his reputation and his politics, the majority of those on his practice list lived in Liverpool 8. This was a very diverse but deprived inner-city area with many hostels and small flats mainly owned by private, sometimes exploitative, landlords. Domestic abuse had emerged as a previously hidden problem.

Cyril's wife, Pat Taylor, and Enid ('Ned') Levy, also a GP's wife, opened the first women's refuge in Liverpool in 1973. The practice had strong links with the refuge and the women and children who lived there joined the PPHC list. Katy recalled one of several dramatic episodes when the practice physically rescued women from abusive partners: 'I shepherded a woman out of the back door into the care of a refuge worker, while her husband pounded on the reception desk, demanding to get to her. The receptionists were brilliant at calmly and firmly standing their ground, and the man finally left before we needed to call the police.'

The practice also cared for most of the residents of Parkside Hostel for people with disabilities, on the edge of Sefton Park, which opened in 1977. This innovative project, another brainchild of Cyril's time as a Labour councillor, enabled people with disabilities to live as independently as possible. Katy took on the care of the majority of people at Parkside:

> Residents had their own rooms, but they all ate together and shared living space. Although facilities for people with disabilities have changed for the better, for many at that time it was the first place that they could live with a degree of independence from their families. And living closely together had advantages. The residents came from very different backgrounds; some were in their 80s and some in their teens. They did not always see eye to eye, but they all looked out for each other like an extended family.

Several Parkside residents took advantage of the Greenbank Project (now the Greenbank Charity), set up in 1983 by PPHC patients Anne and Gerry Kinsella. From the outset PPHC had close ties to this project, which provided education, training and sports facilities for people with disabilities at a time when very few opportunities were available. In the late 1990s many Parkside residents were re-housed in individual, warden assisted flats on the same site. Katy reflected, 'While some of the closeness was lost, it was great to see people finally living in their own homes.'

Liverpool 8 also had probation hostels, hostels for homeless men and women, hostels for young people just out of care, and for young single mothers and their babies (in 1984, over a quarter of births in the practice were to single mothers). Liverpool City Council's designation of much accommodation in the area as 'hard to let' led to a further influx of families with multiple social problems. People with mental health issues also gravitated towards the area, often living in isolation in small flats and prone to increasing distress. During the 1970s, housing and green space in Toxteth had deteriorated. Drug use in the area increased, with one newly built street being nicknamed 'heroin alley'.

The diversity of the area made it a vibrant and fascinating place to work, despite the hardship and racism experienced by so many of its residents (see Chapter 9). Liverpool 8 had a long-established Liverpool born black population. Many were descended from seamen who had arrived from West Africa and the Caribbean over generations and often married women from Liverpool 8. Yemenis and Somalis who had also come to Liverpool as sailors continued to be joined by their families in the 1980s. There was also a well-established Chinese community. Granby Street and Lodge Lane were bursting with shops selling produce from all over the world, including vegetables like plantains, which Katy remembered trying for the first time. Different communities were often represented by their social clubs, many sited along Princes Boulevard, such as the Somali Silver Sands and the Yoruba. These were great places to socialise into the early hours.

Thanks to Cyril's politics, the practice looked after most of the Chilean refugees who arrived in Liverpool after the Pinochet coup in 1973. Katy remembered speaking Spanish being a rewarding aspect of her job:

> We looked after several individuals and families who had escaped from the brutal repression in Chile, some with serious medical problems, for whom there were simply no interpreters. One young man developed cancer and I accompanied him to several hospital appointments to explain what was happening. This led me to many friendships, a visit to Chile and a Chilean god daughter in Santiago. This was slightly unusual as I am an atheist, but her adopted family didn't seem to mind! Later, as we took on many more refugees and asylum seekers, I tried to learn Somali, but that wasn't nearly as easy as Spanish.

Health inequalities

The plight of inner-city health care was discussed at a national conference of local medical committees in 1978. One far-sighted proposal acknowledged that some GPs might be unable to attract sufficient funding under the capitation-based scheme. As this scheme awarded funding based on the size of a GP's list, those who had significant numbers of patients with multiple social and medical problems were at a disadvantage. Alas, the proposal for additional direct funding for these GPs was unsuccessful (Downham, 1978). As with the emergence of the College of General Practitioners, however, a resilient minority of doctors continued to highlight the relationship between health needs and health care. Tools for mapping deprivation in the inner cities became a talking point in academic general practice and social medicine. The four Liverpool wards served by PPHC were among the most deprived in Britain, according to Dr Brian Jarman's 'underprivileged area score' or UPA (Jarman, 1983). The 1981 census showed that in Liverpool's Abercromby, Everton, Granby and Vauxhall wards, 40% of adults were unemployed (Merseyside CP, 1985). Granby and Arundel wards also had the highest rates of disability in the city.

Cyril and his team at PPHC were determined to address the very evident health inequalities in the area - for example, a mortality rate for men in social class V (unskilled or casual workers) that was twice as high as the rate in social class I (managers). The Black Report described these inequalities in detail (Department of Health and Social Security, 1980). It was commissioned in 1977 by the Labour government and completed just before the General Election in 1979. Virginia Berridge has pointed out how disagreement amongst the academic authors as to how to formulate their recommendations led to a significant delay in publication, much to the frustration of civil servants ready to adopt its findings for the next round of departmental planning. In the event, with the publication so close to the election which brought in a Tory government, the Labour ministers who had commissioned the report had no chance to act on its findings. Margaret Thatcher's ministers, appalled at the report's implications for increased public spending, were able to 'disappear' it (Berridge, 2003). Only 260 copies were printed when it was finally published, on the August Bank Holiday. A health economist commented:

> The Report showed in great detail the extent to which ill-health and death are unequally distributed among the population of Britain and suggested that these inequalities have been widening rather than diminishing since the establishment of the NHS in 1948...The Report recommended a wide strategy of social policy measures to combat inequalities in health. These findings and recommendations were virtually disowned by the then Secretary of State for Social Services. Very few copies of the Report were printed, and few people had the opportunity to read it. (Gray, 1982)

At Princes Park Health Centre, however, a quote from the Black Report was displayed in the waiting room:

> Achieving a high standard of health among all its people represents one of the highest of society's aspirations. Present social inequalities in health

in a country with substantial resources like Britain are unacceptable and deserve so to be declared by every section of public opinion. Socially and educationally we must encourage a broader understanding of the meaning of health and the means of its achievement. This will include improvement in incomes as well as better housing and environmental and working conditions. Health services represent only a part, though a significant part, of the task. (DHSS, 1980)

Cyril used his role as chair of Liverpool City Council Social Services and as a member of Liverpool Area Health Authority to address heath inequalities through the early 80s. Alex Scott-Samuel remembered:

A group of SHA members and trade unionists met in his kitchen before each meeting to go through the agenda, so that he was optimally informed to challenge proposals coming from the Thatcher government. Although I was a health authority employee, I felt I was doing more to promote health in Cyril's kitchen than I was at work, under the reactionary influence of Thatcher.

Katy supported him though this took its toll on the practice: 'I used to try and catch Cyril in the corridor on his way to meetings and visits. Even then, I mostly received a political lecture before I could get a word in!'

CHAPTER 2

Building and extending the primary health care team

Ground rules for good practice

Social unrest and the aftermath of the 1981 Toxteth riots

The Inverse Care Law

Prevention really is better than cure

Health Through Arts

Community links and patient involvement

Ground rules for good practice

Originally there were three separate GP practices in Princes Park Health Centre, each with approximately 2,000 patients. But Drs Rodgers and Beckett, who owned the third practice, decided to move out to premises in Ullet Road. This was because, as Cathy Hogan recalled, 'the values and behaviours of the practices were really at odds with one another.' Katy Gardner then persuaded Cyril Taylor and Sheila Abdullah to merge their two practices, not without some trepidation given their contrasting practice styles. Cyril was a stickler for time, whereas Sheila listened to people for as long as they needed, including the many young women from the women's movement who registered with her. As it turned out, the combination of styles worked well. There was a range of role models for trainees and new partners, and new ideas could be discussed from several points of view before being put into practice. The two practices became a single primary health care team with shared aspirations and ideals.

Mike Ross heard about PPHC at a Doctors for a Woman's Choice on Abortion meeting and moved from Brixton to become a partner in 1981, just after the riots:

> The mix of people in the area, in respect of social class, ethnicity and education, was dramatically reflected in the practice. PPHC was on the border between the poor working-class areas of the Dingle and Granby and the middle-class areas of Sefton Park and Lark Lane, with a 50/50 split of patients. Cyril referred to this location as 'the Tide Mark'. It was a wonderful immersion experience in applied anthropology and an interesting exposure to Liverpool's 'morose cheerfulness' in all sectors of society.

The practice philosophy was to look at the wider issues which could lie behind the symptom or problem that patients brought to the GP. This was easier said than done, and generally required much more time and effort than writing a prescription. The practice team also developed a reputation for innovative thinking, as Gideon Ben-Tovim remembered: 'Bentley Road for a period was the crucial centre of progressive thinking and action for the local NHS.' Much of Cyril's vision, shared by Sheila and Katy, involved what is now sometimes known as social prescribing: a holistic, problem-solving approach to the difficulties faced by patients, including social and psychological issues. GPs, receptionists and other staff offered advice on benefits and housing, and referral to fitness sessions, swimming or support groups. Patient and activist Steve Munby commented that 'PPHC was accessible, open and welcoming. It's not only what you do, but how you do things that matters. It was a hub for the area throughout the 1980s with arts events, fairs and health meetings.' New partners and trainees were happy to develop skills for this proactive style of primary care. Many chose to live in the area and experience the highs and lows of life in Liverpool 8.

Suzanne Morris joined as a patient in 1984:

> These 'New Wave' GPs knew the issues/problems facing the people from the community, as most of them lived locally. Scary stories were circulating about some of the other local surgeries, where the GPs were

writing out scripts for you before you even sat down. The GPs at PPHC listened to you and looked at other avenues for you to follow, rather than just doling out pill after pill, and never understanding the real underlying reason for a visit.

The growing reputation of PPHC as an excellent training practice was a source of pride for the GPs, and new ideas were welcomed from any member of the team. Dr Barbara Gaze, who did two locum surgeries every week for Katy for several years in the 1980s, remembered, 'Most of the patients were lovely. I eventually became a partner in a suburban practice... This is a generalisation, but over the years I've realised that patients who live in deprived areas are often more appreciative of their GPs and the receptionists than patients in middle class areas.'

Once the PPHC day got going it was hectic, but with many patients being unemployed there was little demand for early appointments, so GPs met together at 8am before their surgeries. They would discuss complex patients, diagnostic dilemmas and problems from the previous night's on-call visits, whilst dealing with the post, looking at hospital letters and checking laboratory results. Writing about teamwork, Cyril stressed that 'the coffee break is more important than the case conference' (Taylor, 1974). Katy agreed:

> It was such a relief, after a night on call, to share worries - could I have missed something? Do I need to check in with the patient later? And when I was perplexed about a diagnosis or felt I was getting nowhere with a patient, my colleagues always gave calm and thoughtful advice. If things went wrong, the breakfast meetings were comforting, but also a time for reflection and learning. Years later, working in a very small practice, this was something I longed for.

These breakfast meetings also saw the beginnings of many new problem-solving initiatives, including partnerships with the universities, the city council, health authorities, community organisations and other practices.

PPHC embraced the mantra 'Health for All' in its broadest sense. This was the slogan adopted by the World Health Organization in 1978 when an international conference in Alma-Ata, Kazakhstan, focused on the key role of primary health care (WHO, 1978). The health centre team worked closely with other groups, including Home Link and the Neighbourhood Health Project (NHP), both based on nearby Lodge Lane. The NHP emerged from an earlier project remembered by Alex Scott-Samuel: 'In the late 70s, Jane Leighton, CHC secretary, and I had been on the steering group of one of the UK's first community health projects. The Foundation for Alternatives and the Health Education Council had placed community health workers in six UK urban settings, including Liverpool.' The new project was funded with Inner-City Partnership money after the 1981 riots. Suzanne Morris was employed by the NHP as a Neighbourhood Health Worker:

> The Management Committee was made up of local women, a public health professional, and GPs Katy Gardner and later Lis Davidson… We worked closely with the PPHC GPs and health visitors and assisted in various initiatives around baby immunisations and smear tests for women. We set up health groups in various venues at times that suited women with small children, in most cases providing a crèche. Our aim was to make a comfortable, safe space for such taboo issues as periods, the menopause, smear tests, bulimia and anorexia, depression and cancer, to name a few, to be discussed, and experiences shared. We invited either a GP or health visitor to talk about health-related topics. With Katy we took women to a nearby swimming facility, teaching some of them to swim, and to enjoy a steam bath, a new experience for many!

Katy remembered 'taking a double decker bus full of women and children to Moel Famau, in the Welsh hills, and struggling up the hill with women in long clothing and babies in pushchairs! Many had not been to Wales before and it was a great day out.'

Health fairs and health promotion days were held in the practice waiting room, its walls decorated with bright posters and contemporary art. As in Sefton Drive, there was much literature on display, including copies of the *Morning Star*, for which Katy had begun to write a regular health column. Health-related plays were performed in the evenings, including a feminist play on body image by Spare Tyre theatre company and the play *Symptoms of Unhealthy Patience* about the politics of the NHS, by North West Spanner, a Manchester-based radical theatre company.

Surgeries often ran until lunchtime, followed by up to four or five visits, with GPs rushing to get back in time for afternoon surgery at 4pm, which often went on into the evening. There was never a lunch hour. Katy remembered:

> Often the morning surgery lasted till well after 1 pm. I usually ran late with appointments and frequently went out into the waiting room to

apologise. I kept special long slots at the end of surgeries to see people with depression and severe stress. Then visits...Cyril told me requests were low compared to 10 years previously, but it was quite enough for me. I didn't have lunch for over 20 years, but there was a bakery in Lodge Lane where the mince pies were especially good, and I remember bumping into Cyril in a wonderful cake shop, Dafna's Cheesecake Factory, when visiting a patient nearby. It would be a good day when I got home before 8 pm, bringing bundles of hospital letters with me. So much for confidentiality, but needs must.

The GPs at PPHC shared an on-call rota with two other practices. Katy remembers feeling that PPHC's idiosyncrasies were tolerated by other practices partly because 'they could get rid of patients they didn't want - we would absorb them all!' Cyril played tennis every Thursday afternoon, come rain or shine, so Thursday was the PPHC half-day. Everything stopped at 1 pm, and a GP from the rota was left on call. The night-visit workload was daunting, but the rota usually worked well. Katy remembered patients' family members coming out in the middle of the night to help her find their flats. However, one GP in the scheme took a dim and punitive view of requests for home visits. If he considered a visit request unnecessary, he would remove the offending patient from his list. Mike Ross expressed the contrasting tolerant attitude of the GPs at PPHC:

> [I remember] a patient ringing me at 2 am to tell me that a tune was going around in her head and she was frustrated that she could not name it. I knew her very well and was able to successfully reassure her not to worry. In fact, I was very relieved not to have to get out of bed and go out!

Receptionist Pip Abraham remembered a misguided visit request: 'When the morning-after pill became available, a patient phoned Lis Davidson at 3 am to ask for it, as they thought they needed to take it straight away.'

Cyril approached health issues from a broad common-sense perspective, educating people to manage their symptoms without prescribed medication when possible. Antibiotics were to be prescribed only when they would really make a difference. Viral infections did not warrant an antibiotic. Cyril's patients got used to his matter-of-fact dictum: 'Your cold/throat infection will get better in seven days with antibiotics. Without antibiotics, it will take a week.' In the 1970s, this evidence-based approach was relatively unusual in deprived inner-city areas, where patients expected 'a pill for every ill'. There were, however, occasional angry confrontations with patients, especially for younger doctors who had not yet acquired Cyril's sense of authority and ability to negotiate and compromise with patients.

As GPs at PPHC gained confidence, their rational and economical prescribing of medication earned praise from funders (the Area Health Authority, and later the Family Health Services Authority) and patients alike. Ingrid Spiegl, a patient since the 1970s, was 'impressed with the holistic approach to peoples' health and the encouragement of exercise and dietary advice, not just the use of medication, to improve overall wellbeing.' However, there is a trade-off between taking the extra time needed for rational prescribing, dealing with psychosocial distress or health promotion, and achieving 'efficiency'. Long consultations meant that appointment times slipped, and patients had to wait longer to be seen. Few GPs could do this kind of behaviour-change work with patients whilst keeping to time, like Cyril.

The use of generic medicines, as opposed to expensive brand-name drugs, was another aspect of rational prescribing. Princes Park was soon a leader among Liverpool practices and remained so for 40 years. This meant closing the practice door to drug reps, the dapper salespeople from the pharmaceutical industry who visited all GPs and hospital doctors as a matter of course, bearing gifts such as pens, pads, diaries and restaurant invitations, and taking every opportunity to 'educate' GPs about the virtues of their latest brand-name drugs. In 1983 some PPHC doctors picketed a pharmaceutical industry-sponsored dinner for doctors in the Liverpool marina, on *My Margarita*, Henry Ford's luxury yacht. The picket was not popular with the doctors on board! Much later, the Department of Health recognised that drug reps were essentially bribing doctors to prescribe their wares, and in 2012 the Human Medicines Regulations were amended in an attempt to ensure that significant gifts from drug companies were declared. Nevertheless, sponsorship of GP events by Big Pharma continues, with advertising and 'freebies', such as free samples, included under the guise of educational materials.

On the other hand, PPHC worked very closely with nearby pharmacies, especially with those on Lodge Lane and Lark Lane, where GPs often dropped in to say hello and share ideas. Ideally the practice would have liked to have an on-site pharmacy. This nearly happened in the late 1990s when adjacent land became available, but it was instead earmarked for housing, despite lobbying from practice GPs.

One particularly toxic result of Big Pharma-led prescribing was the epidemic of addiction to benzodiazepine tranquillisers such as diazepam, enthusiastically and successfully marketed as 'Valium' by Roche. 'Benzos' were deliberately promoted in the 1970s as a so-called safe alternative to barbiturates, which had been very commonly prescribed in the 1950s for sleep problems, or as 'happy pills'. Barbiturate overdoses could be fatal, and GP leaders and trainers worked hard to reduce barbiturate prescribing in the 1970s, only to see them replaced by benzodiazepines, which unfortunately also caused addiction. Cyril wrote, "Psychosocial disorders require a manipulation of the environment, frequently beyond health workers, and it is a pity that so many doctors are willing to medicate social problems with tranquillisers and antidepressants. Vulnerable people slide so readily into dependence and reach a state where "taking the Valium" becomes an integral part of daily life' (Taylor, 1975).

GPs at PPHC followed Cyril's policy of prescribing benzodiazepines very sparingly, if at all, and actively helped to wean patients off these harmful medications, taking a gradual approach over a series of planned consultations. This was time-consuming and difficult, as patients craved the drugs they had become addicted to. Nevertheless, the PPHC team of GPs and social workers persevered and were able to rescue many from addiction, working in collaboration with the Council for Information on Tranquillisers and Antidepressants (CITA), an organisation which aimed to support people dependent on prescribed drugs. PPHC counsellor Ria Hayward ran a 'tranx' group at PPHC for a year:

> There were six women in the group and every one of them got off tranquillisers by the end of the year. We based it on the self-help cassette tapes recorded by CITA. These tapes were excellent and the GPs gave them out to many patients. The biggest fear women had was of falling apart if they stopped the tablets, but there was great trust in the group, and they met outside the group to support and help each other. If someone didn't turn up, one of us would pop round to see if they were OK and encourage them to come. One patient's husband sometimes picked

women up if they were feeling rough and needed support. Everyone really valued that. We always had tea and biscuits. One woman died suddenly midway through the year, and the others were devastated. Her daughter came along to the group to share her grief and hear about her mum. I had to end the group when I went on maternity leave, but the women carried on supporting each other.

When Ria stopped running the group, CITA took over and ran a similar group successfully over the following years.

Among other public health measures agreed by the GPs in the early 1980s was the decision to ban smoking on practice premises, for the health of patients and staff. Cyril Taylor had stopped smoking after the work of Richard Doll definitively linked smoking with lung cancer in a cohort of doctors (Doll and Hill, 1954), and he was enthusiastic about the ban. Jimmy Rand remembered, 'As soon as the information about the dangers of smoking came out, Cyril stopped and encouraged all his patients to stop. He prescribed giving up smoking to treat a sore throat, and advised "keep warm, drink gallons of water" for colds.' However, several staff objected to the smoking ban, and it was difficult to enforce. It took until 1988 for the Area Health Authority, which owned the premises, to implement a city-wide ban in all NHS premises. PPHC, proud to be ahead of the game, celebrated by holding a 'Fit, Not Fumes' day, offering free fruit and vegetables in the waiting room.

In addition to surgeries and home visits, GPs at PPHC could admit patients to the Sir Alfred Jones Community Hospital in Garston, built in 1915 to replace an old smallpox hospital. City GPs did not usually visit community hospitals, but it made sense to Cyril and his team for managing the care of patients who were too ill to stay at home but did not need an acute hospital bed. In this hospital, patients were nursed within easy reach of friends and relatives; one 100-year-old woman stayed there for 8 months. Many such hospitals were built across the UK through local initiatives and made a real difference to a small geographical area. However, they were vulnerable to later calls for a 'level playing field' instead of a 'postcode lottery' and were subject to the vagaries of politically driven NHS reorganisations, local politics and the separation of funding for health and social care. Few survived intact, and in many cases the buildings were sold off. Some, however, were re-purposed. The Sir Alfred Jones Hospital was closed in 2009 and then rebuilt in 2011 as the South Liverpool Treatment Centre, hosting GP surgeries, a walk-in centre, physiotherapy, blood taking and X-ray services.

Cyril and other GPs at PPHC also visited their patients in Liverpool's acute hospitals, to the amazement of ward staff. This was much appreciated by patients. One told Katy, 'It made me feel really cared for.' Suzanne Morris remembered Katy visiting her after her first son was born:

> All the 'girls' on the ward were going on about me getting a visit from my doctor, and being naïve I told them that their doctor would no doubt be in to see them soon (!). Some were on baby two or three and they said, "GPs don't come to visit their patients when they have had a baby, they don't have the time." But that's where our doctors were different.

Although it took time, it was an excellent way of keeping in touch with hospital colleagues and ensured VIP treatment for patients. Those convalescing far beyond the practice area might also receive visits. Katy recalled visiting a disabled patient convalescing in a nursing home near Southport on her day off, while a patient who had cancer surgery in her thirties remembered Sheila Abdullah visiting her in Crosby: 'I date my recovery from that day. I was devastated and she just listened. It made me feel so much better.'

A further example of PPHC staff going 'above and beyond' was care for patients who were terminally ill and dying. The practice had a very hands-on approach from the outset. Much later, a proactive approach to end-of-life care was adopted across the UK, not least due to work done by Liverpool specialists. In the 1970s, however, this was rare. Katy looked after a seven-year-old girl with cancer: 'She came home to die, and I stayed up all night with her and her single parent mum. She died peacefully in the early morning of a beautiful summer's day. The birds were singing as I went home.' She also remembered, 'A young man with cancer I had visited in the Marie Curie hospice came home to die. His partner phoned me in the middle of surgery to say he was very near the end. I dropped everything and went to their house. He died peacefully shortly after I arrived. The surgery patients just had to wait.'

Another GP at PPHC, Paul Thomas, recalled a poignant moment:

> It was the weekend that Maya Angelou was in Liverpool. I did the usual Saturday surgery, then I wanted to go and get my copy of *I Know Why*

the Caged Bird Sings signed. I was looking after a patient who was dying at home. I wasn't on call, but I routinely made private arrangements with my dying patients that included being there for them at all times. I had arranged to get an update from the patient's relatives at the Royal Philharmonic Hall after Maya's presentation, but I couldn't find them. Later, they told me that they were going to tell me that she was fine and there was no reason for me to visit. I then went to the Caribbean Centre which was around the corner from the patient's home. The lack of reassurance played on my mind. I said to the barman, 'Can you look after my rum and coke; I have to pop around the corner to see someone.' I knocked on her door, to be met by the Macmillan nurse who said, 'Thank you for coming so quickly.' Of course, I had no idea that I had been called. The patient was having a terminal haemorrhage. I remember holding her hand in her distress. Time stood still. The nurse and I sat and waited for a while. The room was pregnant with peace. It was beautiful. Then I noticed a book at her side, the bookmark indicating that it was already part read. It was *I Know Why the Caged Bird Sings*, signed by Maya Angelou.

Sadly, not all deaths were so peaceful, especially before the practice began working closely with the Marie Curie hospice in Woolton and the Macmillan nurses. Watching patients die in pain was heartrending; terminal care really is much better nowadays. Chas Clegg remembered that each terminally ill patient at PPHC was allocated two district nurses, so that new nurses could learn from those with more experience. Another district nurse, Maureen Newton, went on to train as a Macmillan nurse in the late 1980s, specialising in caring for cancer patients and those with terminal illness. She founded the organisation later known as the Sunflowers Cancer Centre in Aigburth, Liverpool. As well as an extensive knowledge of palliative care, she had a warm personality, which brought comfort to so many patients.

Excellent doctor-patient relationships often resulted in familiarity. Some patients got used to calling their GPs by their first names, and patients still talk about Cyril, Katy, Martin and Lis on buses and in supermarkets today. Pro Torkington, a researcher and academic who worked with PPHC for many years, remembered, 'The usual gap between doctor and patient was not there. Patients could call doctors by their first names. That is not the case in most surgeries.' Mike Ross too 'noticed immediately at PPHC that both staff and patients spontaneously and amicably addressed everyone including doctors by their first names, which despite requests on my part, I have never managed to replicate anywhere else since. I concluded that this was part of Liverpool charm, or maybe special to PPHC?' On the other hand, Paul Thomas remembered a patient who telephoned at 2 am one night when he was out on a visit, and spoke with his partner, who was taking his calls: 'The next day I saw the patient, who smiled and said, "I spoke with your 'receptionist' last night..."'

Everyday life at Princes Park Health Centre

We had some real characters as patients. We had a patient who came in regularly always needing to be seen at once. He had various stories. One time he said he was a famous painter (whom he named) and was in a rush to get to his exhibition. Another time he said he was an airline pilot and had a plane to fly imminently. Sometimes patients got very angry at reception, but you have to have empathy and see where people are coming from. Awful things happened to people. Maybe it's a gift - you need to weigh up your response. We were all characters at PPHC. I remember once it was 6.30 pm in winter, and it was snowing. A patient was waiting, and I couldn't find Katy. I eventually found her outside the back door just standing in the snow.

Receptionist Pip Abraham

There was a lovely woman with rheumatoid arthritis who I saw a lot of. Her sister, a nun, visited from Trinidad, and from her small suitcase produced the biggest avocado pear I have ever seen, the size of a large melon. No one would have bothered to question a nun in full habit at customs! Another time an elderly patient was very unwell with a urine infection. He was rambling a bit and mentioned goats several times. To my surprise I looked out of the window and saw two goats in his back yard... The patient is almost always right!

Dr Katy Gardner

A typical day for the district nurses began with the allocation of visiting lists, making sure each nurse had a mixed list that allowed them to use their individual skills and learn new ones...All had a mixed gender case load, but patients had the choice to have a same sex nurse if they preferred. I don't remember anyone doing so...We had an opportunity each morning to see the GPs before surgery to discuss patients' care and to pool our knowledge so patients got joined-up care. At 10 am one of the nurses returned to do the drop-in clinic, doing ear syringing, wound care and all manner of things. Oh, the joy of working in a purpose-built building with a treatment room and all kinds of equipment: even an autoclave! The nurse-run clinic was well used, though sometimes inappropriately: 'Nurse, can you give me a couple of plasters for this cut?' It was an opportunity to do some health education, particularly my campaign against Germolene, used on every ailment.

District nurse Chas Clegg

Social unrest and the aftermath of the 1981 Toxteth riots

Princes Park Health Centre was not actually damaged in the Toxteth riots of 1981, as rioting stopped 500 yards up the road. Many practice staff believed local people deliberately protected the practice. However, the area remained physically very bleak. Streets, buildings and shops had been damaged and then neglected due to lack of council resources. Steve Munby remembered that in Lodge Lane 'shops were looted, and in the aftermath, people moved away, leaving large swathes of grassed sites along the side of the road' (2019). Toxteth and Granby residents were badly affected, not just by physical devastation, but also by the ongoing racist attitudes of Liverpool police. GPs at PPHC did home visits on foot amongst the rubble. They also visited patients who had been arrested at the main Liverpool bridewell (a police station with cells). But they were not permitted to see prisoners detained in the cells, much to their annoyance. One of Cyril's patients, Margaret Simey, was a councillor for Granby Ward and chair of the Merseyside Police Committee. She played a major role in calling the police to account for their role in provoking and exacerbating the impact of the riots (Frost and Phillips, 2011). The notorious 'sus' laws permitting intrusive 'stop and search' by the police were repealed later in 1981.

Steve Munby was a member of the Liverpool 8 Defence committee set up after the riots:

Princes Park Health Centre was one of the only functioning institutions in Liverpool 8 when things were falling apart. After the initial response to the riots, locally things were very dire. The riots had created a void in the community. Granby Street, once thriving, was destroyed, and because of very high unemployment many young people turned to crime to make a living. Heroin addiction increased rapidly. Mike Ross from Princes Park took up the challenge, setting up a drugs service that was unique at the time, certainly in Liverpool.

The racism brought into the public eye by the riots galvanised GPs and practice staff, who were active in campaigns and marches (see Chapter 9). The riots, having devastated the area, generated a new sense of purpose. Many Liverpool born black patients continued to campaign against racism long after the riots, running projects and services for people in Toxteth. The practice was closely associated with the Liverpool 8 Law Centre, which was established in 1982 to provide people, including those affected by the riots, with legal advice. PPHC patients were also involved in founding South Liverpool Personnel, a job recruitment centre used by the practice to recruit staff, and the Liverpool Black Sisters, who eventually opened the Kuumba Imani Millennium Centre in 2000, after years of campaigning.

The Inverse Care Law

By the 1980s PPHC was certainly delivering progressive, holistic, bio-psycho-social primary care. This was the model recommended by the Royal College of General Practitioners, based on the work of well-established training practices in relatively affluent areas (RCGP, 1972; Byrne and Long, 1976). However, for Cyril Taylor, as for Dr Julian Tudor Hart, the challenge in deprived neighbourhoods was to go beyond a medical model of good practice and to involve people in a wider political agenda, in which health would be seen not only as the absence of disease, but as enjoyment and creativity. Social and environmental issues could be tackled too. Julian Tudor Hart had visited Cyril several times; Alex Scott-Samuel met him in Cyril's living room in the early 1980s and 'got to learn from his brilliant writings on the politics of the NHS and on how best to provide primary care.' One intractable problem related to the persistence of health and social inequalities was that even in the ideologically egalitarian NHS, the odds seemed to be stacked against the most vulnerable.

Working in poverty-stricken South Wales, Julian had spelt out his 'Inverse Care Law' for the first time in stark terms: 'The availability of good medical care tends to vary inversely with the need for it in the population served' (Hart, 1971). This was certainly true in the inner cities too. In places like Toxteth, the workload for health care teams trying to provide high-quality health care was extremely onerous. Many practices provided very basic, 'reactive' care, and failed to address the public health agenda. The primary health care team at PPHC embraced this challenging work, but health outcomes overall remained stubbornly poor. Preventive health care interventions, such as routine blood pressure measurement, cervical smears and discouragement of smoking, were as yet unfamiliar to patients. Many patients had unrealistic expectations about being referred to hospital; some were truly terrified of going, while others were extremely eager for referral. It took time to understand patients' concerns, discuss the rationale for referral decisions and, if necessary, attempt to get patients on board with a more holistic approach.

The practice was determined to address problems associated with poverty. Toxteth Citizens Advice Bureau (CAB) was invited to run benefits advice sessions at the practice, and the Princes Park Charitable Trust was set up in 1983 to raise funds, including through a ground-breaking newspaper recycling initiative. Patients and staff brought in their old papers to be sold to a recycling company, increasing environmental awareness and raising money at the same time. As well as providing equipment for patients, such as peak flow meters for measuring lung function and toys and books for the waiting room, the charity provided items to help patients at home. These included bed socks and sheepskin rugs for terminally ill patients prone to bed sores. On one occasion a lonely elderly patient was given a canary to keep him company.

After the riots of 1981, 'Toxteth' became a label of stigma and even fear, but PPHC's reputation for provision of patient-centred health care blossomed. More and more patients gravitated to the practice, with 1,000 new patients joining the list every year in the early 1980s. The high patient turnover characteristic of inner-city practices - up to 30% per year - added to the workload for clinicians, receptionists and the back-office staff tasked with sorting out the 'Lloyd George' records (beige envelopes containing handwritten record cards) for newly registered patients. Some of these were huge, chaotic bundles of cards, envelopes and hospital letters. It was dispiriting for the administrative staff who had worked so hard rationalising the medical records to see them taken away again a few months later when the patient left the practice.

Michael Heseltine was chair of the Merseyside Partnership, set up to channel government money into Liverpool to address some of its problems. He became known as the 'Minister for Merseyside' in 1981, after standing up to Margaret Thatcher and challenging Chancellor Geoffrey Howe's 'managed decline' strategy for the city. He brought a party of advisors from different ministries on a fact-finding mission, taking a serious look at the issues faced by people in Liverpool. He visited PPHC, after which Cyril Taylor wrote him a memorandum highlighting the plight of many practice patients. Heseltine came back to the city six months later, and for over a year he returned on a weekly basis, promoting effective partnership between London-based central government departments and Liverpool businesses. With his background in land management, he was keen to ensure that funds were channelled towards the regeneration of the city. The dire effects of the 1980s cuts to council funding were ameliorated to some extent, though Heseltine's methods, bypassing the council with a centralist approach, were not universally popular. After he stepped down in 1983, however, Liverpool's long-term economic decline continued (Parkinson, 1985). Facing huge ongoing funding cuts, the Labour council became locked in a battle with the Thatcher government, culminating in the illegal budget of 1984 and the political crisis which accompanied it. As one of the poorest areas of Liverpool, Toxteth bore the brunt of this.

Inner-City Partnership funding, linked to Heseltine's efforts, paid for an upgrade of the health centre building in 1984, creating more space for clinics, a counselling room and a room for staff and community meetings. This room housed a library, developed with the help of a patient who was a retired librarian. She also worked with the radical bookshop News from Nowhere to set up a patients' library of health-related books. Many of these went missing within a few months, but as a phlegmatic GP commented at the time, 'Well, at least we know people found them useful!' The residential caretaker had recently retired, and the associated funding was withdrawn. This was a disappointment, but it enabled the district nursing team to take over the caretaker's flat. Even so, there was still insufficient space for all the extended team and attached services, including physiotherapy, chiropody and psychology as well as the weekly CAB sessions. PPHC remained a hive of activism. Health visitor Dorothy Zack Williams reflected, 'In my view, the centre's innovations were what I saw as people's responses to the onslaught and challenges faced by the NHS as it impacted on patients in the years of the Thatcher administration.'

In the wake of Heseltine's visit, Cyril wrote to Dr Gerard Vaughan, then health secretary, pointing out that only 10% of Liverpool's GPs were practising from health centres, compared to 20% nationally. A majority (51%) were still single-handed, working from small premises, referred to at the time as lock-up shops, without appointment systems. PPHC provided an altogether different welcome to its patients. As chair of South Central CHC, Sylvia Hikins was involved in the Family Health Service Authority (FHSA) committee which visited and inspected practices:

> At that time single-handed GP practices dominated Merseyside, and the committee drew up a list of the worst 235, many of which I visited. Some did not meet even the basic requirements for good health care, but most importantly, there were no joined-up services, just an appointment with the doctor and a bit of laying on of hands if you were lucky.

Tracy, aged 13 when she became a PPHC patient, described the contrast:

> Our last doctor was single-handed. He never talked to us. I had stomach-ache, and Sheila Abdullah checked me over. She said she was not sure what was wrong, but she didn't think it was just my stomach. She talked to me. In fact, I was having problems at school and I told her everything. It made me feel so much better, as my family were lovely, but they never talked.

Once more, however, Cyril's was a lone voice. The Area Health Authority failed to make progress with opening the recently built Abercromby Health Centre, also situated in Liverpool 8, because local GPs still showed little interest in working under the same roof.

Prevention really is better than cure

The GPs had tried to set up a patients' group when the health centre opened, but it was poorly attended. From 1982 onwards, a series of monthly meetings on health topics, in partnership with the Neighbourhood Health Project, replaced the patients' group meetings, with better attendance. Pro Torkington organised some of these, and remembered one very popular one:

Most people wanted information on arthritis. I contacted Dr Angela Forbes, a rheumatology specialist, to be our guest speaker for an evening meeting in March. It had been snowing for the better part of the week and the ground was covered in hardening snow. The room in the health centre was packed. The class started at 7 pm and was expected to finish at 9 pm. At 10 pm we were pushed out because the caretaker was due to leave. The group decided to continue the discussion in a nearby pub.

The NHP continued to organise Keep Fit and Tai Chi classes in the waiting room for patients and staff. Later, PPHC obtained funding from the Primary Care Development Fund to employ someone for half a day every week to organise posters in the reception area, help with the patients' library and signpost patients to services in the area. Practice staff joined Neighbourhood Health Workers on the streets to take blood pressures and chat with people about their health (see Chapter 9). Dorothy Zack Williams celebrated this outreach work: 'By providing an alternative to the old paradigm of health provision, this empowering model helped to inform people that health delivery systems should not be a chore for patients, preventing them from having to visit surgeries or clinics.'

Occasional cautionary tales arose from well-meaning initiatives intended to benefit patients. Following the building of the extension in 1984, charitable funds were used to create a children's playroom in a room near the reception area. Patients loved it. Suzanne Morris remembered, 'Whenever I took my son to see his GP, Martin Smith, Martin would jump into the soft play area in the waiting room where my son was playing, pick him up and take him into his examination room. Needless to say, my son was never afraid to go to the surgery.' However, a difficult situation arose once when a parent left their children there while they went shopping!

From 1984 PPHC hosted a pioneering Sports Council project, aimed at connecting health centres with local communities (Ashton, 2020). The Health and Recreation Team (HART) organised walking, running, swimming and other activities from a portacabin in the PPHC grounds. There were exercise bikes that staff could use in their lunch breaks. Robin Ireland, the project director, ran exercise courses funded by the Health Education Council in the area, and was later responsible for setting up the Women's 10K run, with support from the Regional Health Authority. Katy remembered pushing wheelchair users from Parkside hostel for people with disabilities: 'The hills were the worst, both pushing uphill and trying not to let the wheelchairs escape on the way down. It was a hair-raising experience going down Upper Parliament Street, but we had a hilarious time and we finished to a big cheer from the crowd.' The Women's 10K became the Liverpool Spring 10K in 2002 and has continued ever since, as a hugely successful national event.

Robin Ireland reflected on his time at PPHC:

> The Toxteth riots had only been three years before I arrived, and the aftermath was still greatly felt. I was shocked, coming from the West Midlands, to see how ghettoised the black population appeared to be. Part of my role was to take referrals from the GPs for patients who needed advice on healthier lifestyles. It was the first time I had worked directly with GPs...Everyone was very open minded about trying new things and I was very much welcomed into the practice. Cyril Taylor took me in hand, but that may have been because I played tennis with him on Thursday afternoons - crucial to work/life balance, as he said! I still see at least two people who I first encouraged to start running over 30 years ago who are still doing it now. I worked with Parent Support Centres, ran Look After Yourself classes at PPHC and other local venues...Although I work at strategic level now, PPHC taught me to keep my feet on the ground. And I had to practice what I preach - something I still try to do. I always remember being criticised by local mums for having sugar in my tea. I stopped at that point!

Health promotion and screening services for women were stepped up in 1982 when Katy Gardner started the Well Woman Clinic (described in Chapter 3). This was followed in 1988 by the Well Man Clinic, run by Chas Clegg, who pointed out that 'until recently, men have only ever had the 'choice' of a female nurse.' Only the second Well Man Clinic to be set up in the UK, it offered health checks to men aged 35-65 years, aiming to detect problems such as high blood pressure, heart disease and diabetes in time to offer effective treatment. The practice initially invited men by letter. Uptake was low, partly due to the high mobility of the practice population, and perhaps also to relatively low literacy. Public health registrar Dr Alwen Parry interviewed non-attenders, finding that half of them did not remember receiving the letter. Once the Well Man Clinic was established, however, posters were put up in the waiting room, and patients could be referred on from GP or nurse appointments. Chas commented:

It was 'slow burn' to start with, it took a little persuading. But after recording blood pressure and weight, there was the opportunity to talk about lifestyle, work, the stress...It was this unquantifiable aspect that helped - that "blokes don't discuss their problems" thing. We had lots of in-house services we could refer them to. We sent all the young men a 21st birthday card, with an invitation to visit the Well Man Clinic, in order to reach all those at risk of testicular cancer.

'Secondary prevention' describes services intended to mitigate the effects of diseases already diagnosed. Dr Paul Thomas described setting up a clinic aiming to do just this for people with diabetes in 1988, one of the first in Liverpool:

This clinic was another illustration of how to go about quality improvements in a practice. I identified a need: poor control of practice patients with diabetes, and perfunctory appointments at hospital diabetes clinics. I had an idea that the practice could realistically run a clinic itself. So, I made a rapid appraisal of the area using literature, observations and interviews, to discover what format other diabetes clinics had followed. I sat in on hospital and GP practice clinics, including a pioneering one run by Dr Robbie Gibbins, a GP with a special interest in diabetes in rural Wales. I also chatted to diabetic patients in the practice, to a community service manager and a hospital consultant. I then piloted the clinic and ran it for a year while training nurses Chas Clegg and Noreen Gilhespy, who then took over.

Chas added:

Diabetes being one of my interests, I was able to help the practice start a diabetic clinic, run by the practice nurses with back up from me. The district nursing team was provided with the first blood glucose meters in the city, enabling us to give much better quality of care to our many insulin-dependent patients, and improve quality of life. At that time we had so many services (now sadly gone) provided by the council and voluntary services, helping to support these patients and their carers.

Health Through Arts

Health Through Arts was an integral part of PPHC activities throughout the 1980s and 1990s. Katy Gardner remembered:

My time working at the BLACK-E (then called the Blackie) community arts centre in the early 1970s, and being a bit of a hippie, gave me a sense of how the arts could enliven people's everyday lives. At Princes Park I was able to join with others to show that health is about enjoyment and pleasure, not simply absence of illness. I hope it made difference to our patients, but I know that over the years it allowed us - as well as the patients! - to let our hair down.

PPHC held several fairs, which included live music, dancing, and activities for children, alongside stalls featuring self-help groups and health promotion, with blood pressure checks and measurements of lung function. In 1983 a UB40 Fair was held at PPHC, named after the unemployment benefit application form, as well as the reggae band. It concluded with a discussion on how to combat the stress of being unemployed. As Cyril told *GP Magazine*, 'Its purpose was to show local people that we are interested in preventing ill health, not just curing it.' The magazine described it as a 'sort of village fair held in a health centre' (Taylor, 1983). Author and former patient Rosie Childs remembered this event:

> At the time I had bought a drawing, which just needed colouring in. It was of people from all around the world in different costumes. I took my time colouring it in, stopping and starting for about a year! It was huge and some of the costumes were very intricate. I wanted to get it right, including every nationality. When I finished, I was amazed at how it represented so many different people. I let Katy borrow it for the Open Day and it was displayed in the entrance, to welcome patients, new and old, to the surgery. Underneath the poster I drew a rainbow and I wrote, 'Whoever you are, wherever you come from, you will always be welcome at Princes Park.' I put a smiley face at the end. Lots of people liked it and someone even wanted to borrow it for their workplace. (Childs, 2007)

At the fair, Sylvia Hikins organised a game called 'The Birth Box':

> People would be born again by pulling a new identity at random out of a hat, just like a lottery draw. From that you would work out your life chances according to class, employment, income, etc....There was a sense of self-confidence and autonomy, that we could create fun happenings - like one Christmas when I turned up in fancy dress as a horse (someone else was in the rear bit of the costume). I trotted up to the reception, asked if I could see a doctor as I was 'feeling a little hoarse', and was asked to take a seat, which I did amidst much laughter. Later we transformed into Rudolf because Father Christmas (Cyril Taylor on a bike) was visiting the

centre! None of this was flippant; it was all about a community actively participating in health-related activities, through which people were more likely to respond and take ownership...Health Through Arts, like patient participation groups, worked on the basis of shared knowledge, and from a patient's point of view was genuinely empowering.

Dave Cornick, a patient and tree surgeon, held an exhibition of his tree sculptures in the waiting room in 1985. Some of these were very big, and Dave remembered being surprised that the practice was so permissive, in view of potential health and safety concerns.

Paul Thomas organised the 'Reminiscence' exhibition in 1986 when he was a trainee working with Cyril. He and Sylvia Hikins encouraged young unemployed people to interview and photograph the 20 oldest patients of the practice about their lives. Cathy Hogan, by that time practice manager, recalled, 'The project involved patients from all walks of life - a publication and exhibition followed, with stories of Jamaican sailors marrying local girls, and an elderly lady who used to be pushed in her pram by her nanny around Sefton Park and Princes Road. Local dockers and Dingle residents all contributed.' The exhibition, a collaboration with the Open Eye Gallery, later toured care homes in Merseyside before returning to Princes Park.

PPHC continued to host occasional exhibitions over many years. After its own Health Thru Arts festival in 1992 (see Chapter 6), the practice took part in Visionfest, a Liverpool arts festival, and later in the Liverpool Biennial, started in 1999. After this, the cost of insurance for exhibitions became prohibitive. However, during Liverpool's Capital of Culture year in 2008, the Foundation for Art and Creative Technology (FACT) and Alder Hey Children's Hospital collaborated on the project 'Wild Song at Dawn'. This involved playing dawn chorus birdsong, recorded by wildlife sound recordist Chris Watson and young hospital patients, in the PPHC waiting room.

Princes Park Health Centre was a trailblazer in making links between the arts, health and health care. It was not until 2017 that the following statement was issued by MPs: 'The time has come to recognise the powerful contribution the arts can make to our health and wellbeing' (All Party Parliamentary Group, 2017).

Community links and patient involvement

A journalist once described Princes Park Health Centre patients as a 'kaleidoscope of human life including doctors, poets, painters, professors' (DOCTOR magazine, 1987). All patients were to be treated with compassion and respect, no matter what their background. As one patient, not a left winger, said, 'I knew Cyril was a Red, but he was scrupulously fair to each and all.' Janice, who joined as a patient in the 1980s, remembered, 'I felt totally at ease with their ethos, which embraced the socio-political views that I held and still hold concerning racial and social equality, and how this was engendered within the fabric of the centre and in the treatment that was meted out to whoever became a patient regardless of race, social class and gender.'

Some celebrities, particularly from the Left and the arts scene, had followed Cyril from Sefton Drive. These included Adrian Henri, Fritz Spiegel, David Knopov (who made a portrait of Cyril on his retirement), Gerry Dawson, founder of Unity Theatre, and folk duo Jacqui and Bridie. As Jacqui (not a communist herself) said, 'You know, in those days, most folk singers were communists!' Singer-songwriter Jennifer John and actress Ebony, who sadly died young from lung cancer, were both patients. Several prominent Liverpool councillors and long-time comrades of Cyril, including Alex Doswell and John Hamilton, were on the list. Some staff at the BLACK-E arts project were also patients, and PPHC continued to look after performers at the Everyman and Playhouse theatres, despite the occasionally excessive demands of distraught actors needing to be urgently cured of their sore throats before going onstage. Africa Oyé, Liverpool's hugely successful international music festival, evolved out of a Toxteth pirate radio station; its founder Kenny Murray was a patient of the practice, as was Roger Phillips, who started his career at the Everyman and later became a beloved broadcaster at Radio Merseyside.

Despite PPHC's inclusive culture, patient participation, in the sense promoted in the 1978 'Health for All' declaration, was patchy (Graham-Jones, 1987). As stated above, this was not for want of trying. Sylvia Hikins pointed out that 'PPHC was a pioneer with its inclusive practice framework, in particular patient participation - there were many support groups run by patients, and the centre was also a base for therapies as alternatives to prescriptions' (1987). Well-documented patient participation groups

(PPGs) tended to be associated with well-organised training practices in traditional market towns and semi-rural areas (Pritchard, 1981). PPGs were rare in most inner-city areas, and when established they were difficult to sustain (Pietroni and Chase, 1993). High mobility and low levels of literacy (in the English language) in much of the patient population hampered the practice's further efforts to set up a formal patient participation group. These included a mailshot to every adult patient on the list on at least one occasion, and newsletters for patients to pick up at reception, which included an invitation to join the PPG. In 1987 Paul Thomas and Katy Gardner launched a newspaper for staff and patients: *Prinny Post*. The first edition celebrated the 10th anniversary of the opening of the health centre.

There were, however, notable occasions when an active PPHC patients' group worked together to address a crisis. A troublesome spate of vandalism in 1994 upset patients as well as staff. Patients responded by organising well-attended meetings and spreading the word in the area. A teenage patient from a very troubled family was identified as the gang leader and arrested. The vandalism promptly stopped. Patients were also involved in redesigning the health centre in the mid-1990s. Much later, some patients came together extremely effectively in response to the 'tendering out' of the practice (see Chapter 14).

PPHC was, in fact, extremely well integrated into its locality through many different channels over the years, as reflected in projects such as the Neighbourhood Health Project, Toxteth Health and Community Care Forum and the Health Through Arts programme. These were not all linked by name to PPHC, nor did they constitute a PPG as such, but there was much effective joint working. This was helped by a decision, after Cyril's retirement, to define a practice boundary, or 'catchment area', in order to concentrate on delivering high-quality care locally. Patients who had moved away to more leafy areas like Allerton and Woolton were encouraged to re-register with nearby GPs. Some articulate and forceful patients resisted. They were loyal to the practice and wanted to stay on the list. The GPs sympathised, but the deliberate decision about boundaries demonstrated the practice's dedication to Liverpool 8 and the surrounding area.

CHAPTER 3

Digging deep to tackle deprivation (1980s)

Research: the early days

A training practice: the world is your oyster

A feminist practice

Learning from 'complex' patients

Continuity of care and complex patients

Research: the early days

With his proactive approach to prevention and treatment, Cyril was keen to promote research in primary care settings, following the example of Julian Tudor Hart. Julian's research topics, aimed at improving the health of his very disadvantaged patients in Glyncorrwg, included the systematic detection of high blood pressure and screening for bowel cancer. Cyril ensured that his Sefton Drive practice, and then PPHC, participated in the multi-centre trial of treatment for mild hypertension (high blood pressure) run by the Medical Research Council's research centre in Manchester, in collaboration with the Royal College of GPs. The research nurses included practice nurse Doreen Vernon, who worked extra hours for the trial. Patients aged 35-64 years had their blood pressure measured, and those with mild hypertension were prescribed medication or placebo tablets. Although it was hoped that patients would benefit from diagnosis and treatment, this trial did not show a reduction in mortality in treated patients (Medical Research Council, 1985). However, many patients became more aware about blood pressure and its impact on health.

The doctors' early morning meetings sometimes functioned as an informal journal club. Susanna Graham-Jones remembered a discussion in 1987, after a couple of partners had read the same research paper about a new medical treatment for gastric and duodenal ulcers. This was exciting, and the discussion triggered a dramatic reduction in practice referrals for gastric surgery within the year. The atmosphere of openness to new ideas meant that innovations were frequently proposed and debated. Some ideas led to formal research projects on topics including ethnic monitoring and patient profiling; angina and barriers to referral to secondary care; cognitive behaviour therapy and depression; effective health care for homeless patients; quality of life and quality of care for patients with epilepsy; and vitamin D deficiency in Somali patients (see Chapters 7, 8, 9 and 12).

A training practice: the world is your oyster

Cyril Taylor had signed up as a GP trainer when compulsory postgraduate GP training was introduced in 1975. His approach to training was 'old school' and informal. Katy was an early trainee in 1978, and Dr Martin Smith was Cyril's last trainee in 1986 before he retired: 'My 'induction' consisted of a brief chat with Cyril, who advised me that as I was already quite experienced, I should simply start seeing patients, and call him if I needed any help. The nearest I had to a tutorial with him was one day when he called me into his room to tell me a patient had complained I had sworn at her. Not strictly true - I had told her slimming tablets were a ---- waste of time. He agreed but suggested a more subtle approach might be better.'

Several GP partners became trainers in turn after Cyril: Drs Alan Forbes and Katy Gardner in the 1980s, and Drs Lis Davidson and Martin Smith in the 1990s. This was a major commitment. Trainers took time out for trainers' courses and meetings. In the practice, they supervised their trainees' surgeries alongside their own, providing debriefing and finding time for tutorials and supervision of trainee projects. Most trainers were men. When Katy became a trainer, her trainers' support group, led by inspirational Merseyside GP Dr Mike Forrest, consisted of 15 men and one woman - Katy. She remembered, 'They always referred to themselves as 'chaps'.' Investment in training, and the partners' subsequent support for these young doctors beyond their time at PPHC, was always viewed as worthwhile.

Dr Karen Kearley remembered having doubts about carrying on with medicine at all when she approached Katy Gardner in 1984:

> It was a last-minute decision to apply to Princes Park Health Centre and abandon my plans to travel to San Francisco. Did I really want to be a doctor? Maybe not. By the end of my hospital pre-registration year, it seemed that the job was making me feel sick - literally. However, it soon emerged that I might have come to the wrong conclusion, both about the cause of the vomiting and the need to change career. During my interview, Katy explained that the part-time GP training post I was applying for had really been designed for a doctor with childcare responsibilities, which was an unusually progressive and supportive arrangement at this time. Somewhat surprisingly, it seemed that pregnancy, the real cause of my vomiting, had made me the perfect candidate! I was to be Katy's first GP trainee, and so I began my long and happy clinical journey as a GP. What was it like to arrive in Princes Park Health Centre in 1984 so early in my career? It was colourful, fun, supportive, friendly, challenging, political, innovative, provocative, multidisciplinary, holistic and a genuinely caring place, not just for patients but also for me. Katy's clinical practice epitomised the biopsychosocial approach and soon I no longer wanted a break from medicine. For the first time, I felt at home, in the right place and on the right path. The horizon had changed.

PPHC continued as a training practice, at times having two trainees in post simultaneously. One of Katy's early trainees was Dr Simon Whitehead, who later moved to Australia, working in Aboriginal health and as a GP specialising in HIV and palliative care. Simon wasn't afraid to push back against authority. Katy recalled, 'A visiting health authority official was shocked that Simon was wearing an earring in a GP surgery. But no patients ever complained, and to me it fitted in fine with the ethos of PPHC.' Simon still wears an ear stud. He enjoyed the diverse experiences of working at PPHC: 'Cyril took me to Socialist Health Association meetings and introduced me to a patient who had been on the Jarrow march against unemployment in

1936. Another vivid memory was of Bolivian band Rumillajta playing in the waiting room.'

The practice was a magnet for young doctors who shared its vision of holistic, community-based primary care. Dr Paul Thomas remembered, 'In 1984/5 I spent a good bit of time trying to identify the kind of practice I would like to work in, having decided to exchange paediatrics for general practice. PPHC and Iona Heath's practice in London [the Caversham Group Practice in Kentish Town] were the only two...' Paul was determined to come to the practice as a trainee. Despite not succeeding in 1985, he tried a second time: 'When I called, the telephone line collapsed and Cathy Hogan said, "Just come", when we had only seconds to communicate... - an unusual introduction.' Another trainee, Dr Ram Poluri, recalled:

> I had been in the UK for 3 years and all my experience till then was in hospitals in India and in the UK. I decided on general practice without having a clue about it, until I came to PPHC. What an introduction it was! Princes Park was way ahead of its time. Feminist, left wing, patient-centred, looking at issues of equality, racism, sexuality and gender. I was dazzled!

GP trainees, later known as GP registrars, brought fresh insight and different perspectives. Dr Galina Artioukh arrived from Russia in 1993 on a scheme arranged by the RCGP. She had trained in paediatric surgery and orthopaedics, and initially worked at Alder Hey Children's hospital. Deciding she would like to do general practice, she became Katy's part time trainee in 1996, running joint injection sessions in the practice. Katy remembered supervising her on a home visit, early in her training: 'A woman had dislocated her shoulder and was screaming in pain. Galina just spoke to her firmly, grasped the arm and put the shoulder back. It was all over in a minute. The patient and I were astonished. Normally this procedure involved going to casualty and having anaesthesia.' When the situation in Russia deteriorated, Katy supported Galina through the complicated process of gaining permission to stay in the UK and finishing her GP training. Galina later worked as a GP in Liverpool and, for many years, at the Brook Advisory Centre. Katy became godmother to her daughter Daria, who, to Katy's delight, followed in her footsteps by going to Cambridge University.

Life as a trainee at PPHC

PPHC was local and set in an area where I lived prior to attending Medical School. I wasn't sure what medical career I wanted so I decided to 'dip a toe' into general practice, applying to PPHC. The approach to training was supportive yet challenging. This experience was validated during conversations with my peers on our half-day release sessions. I felt that in comparison I could not be in a better training environment. The patients and staff were a joy to care for and work with respectively, and despite the challenges of their daily experience they continued to retain significant drive and energy to improve their lot. Late evening practice meetings were made tolerable by fantastic Thai restaurant take away meals. I remember time out at a partner's house spent summarising notes together. It epitomised the sense of collective team endeavour. The PPHC experience instilled in me the importance of looking out for each other and seeking to understand what matters to your patient population in life in general and health in particular; also, the importance of looking beyond your immediate practice team and working collaboratively with the rest of the system. Integrated working was very much in action long before it became such a buzz word in health and social care.

Dr Michael Ejuoneatse

I have never received so much input into my education; supervision in the meeting room, with Katy randomly sampling my previous day's consultations. We talked about so many things medical and personal. It was the first place I felt comfortable to be open about my own sexuality. Other doctors dropped in before their surgeries and started sharing and discussing. I was taking it all in: Balint group [see Chapter 4] on Friday afternoons, joint home visits with Katy and other doctors. A week in a rural general practice in Wales, and another week in a north London General Practice. Supervision at times in the Eureka Café in Myrtle Parade over humous and pitta bread! Boxes of useful papers that came from Katy, books I could borrow from the library in the meeting room. I still have a couple, way past their return date.

Dr Ram Poluri

As the experiences above show, many trainees felt well supported at PPHC. However, for some, like Dr Ed Gaynor, it was a baptism of fire:

By the end of the six months I knew this was the sort of practice I definitely did not want to work in, because it was too stressful and draining. Basically, the practice population was unmanageable due to the demand and unmet need. The funding formulas were such that they would never provide the financial resources that this sort of practice required.

Trainees were certainly thrown in at the deep end. Ram reflected, 'Home visits and nights on call certainly were difficult. The phone ring... it elicited a Pavlovian palpitation!' Trainee Dr Kathrin Thomas echoed Ram's comments:

On call was scary, although I'm more scared looking back than I was at the time. I could be woken in the early hours and then be driving around Toxteth looking for a flat in a dark street with little idea what I was going to walk into. I never had a personally frightening experience, but I had a few that stick vividly in my mind. One woman called because she was bleeding in her 20th week of pregnancy. When I arrived, she had delivered the baby in her bed and was quietly weeping, saying she felt she had killed it because of her alcohol dependence. She just wanted to keep holding it. I recall several times going to see refugee families with many children in one room, who watched silently while I examined the sick baby. In a hostel for refugees from the war in former Yugoslavia, the interpreter was so knowledgeable and helpful - and only admitted on direct questioning that he was actually a doctor himself and had already sorted out most people's problems, just calling us when he thought they needed a prescription! And I will not forget the very elderly gent who convinced me, in the early hours, that the grey parrot in the corner was older than himself.

As in other practices, a good trainee might be invited to join as a partner if there happened to be a vacancy when they became a fully-fledged GP and passed their membership exams for the RCGP. But being a partner was considerably tougher than being a trainee. While it worked out for most, PPHC may occasionally have been too eager to persuade trainees into partnership. Ram Poluri became a partner in May 1989: 'A bad move. I felt overwhelmed by the responsibility and commitment required. It was a difficult time for me, dealing with personal issues and realising general practice was not right for me. I was well supported by everyone, but I left after nine months, the parting amicable...Eventually I found my niche in genitourinary medicine.' Many ex-trainees have gone on to be fearless innovators in primary care in Liverpool, elsewhere in Merseyside and as far away as Australia. Dr Sam Jones, for example, worked with Medecins Sans Frontières in Sudan for two years, and then spent eight years in the Torres Strait Islands, between the northern tip of Australia and Papua New Guinea. Dr Ralph Brussatis was another registrar who went on to work for medical aid organisations overseas.

There were also training placements for nurses, psychologists and social workers. In the 1991 Annual Report, Noreen Gilhespy, the practice nurse who came to work alongside Doreen Vernon, wrote about becoming an unofficial mentor to many new practice nurses in the locality, for whom there was as yet no specific training. Nurse Pat Jones was responsible for training other district nurses, which 'took me away from the hurly burly of the day to day workload, but also exposed me to the academic environment and research that underpinned developing nursing practice. And we learnt a lot from our students.' PPHC also hosted trainee secretaries from the Charles Wootton college on Upper Parliament Street, Liverpool 8. Two of these later came to work at the practice.

Links with the University of Liverpool Medical School were high on Cyril's wish-list, but hard to achieve. Cyril had qualified there in 1943, when teaching hospitals were entirely responsible for the education of medical students. Consultant contracts, especially in teaching hospitals, allowed for teaching and supervisory duties for both undergraduate and postgraduate students. GP remuneration, on the other hand, was based entirely on clinical duties, and effectively discouraged the teaching of medical students. From 1975 onwards, however, GPs could apply for a training allowance for supervision of postgraduate GP trainees.

In the 1950s, Edinburgh and St Mary's Paddington had been the first medical schools to offer optional GP placements to clinical medical students. Other teaching hospitals lagged behind until prodded by the Todd Report, which accepted the RCGP's case that GPs could have an important role in medical education (Royal Commission on Medical Education, 1968). In Liverpool, the majority of hospital consultants continued to regard GPs as failed doctors who had fallen off the specialist ladder and could therefore have no useful role in teaching. The first general practice placements for medical students in Merseyside were organised in 1971 by Dr Tony Hall-Turner, a Runcorn GP who became the first Director of General Practice Studies at Liverpool Medical School. Despite the lack of support from hospital-based academics, he was an innovator, introducing video recording of doctor-patient consultations in the early 1970s, and facilitating extended placements which encouraged students to follow up a particular family, with their consent, over several years.

Dr Hall-Turner appointed Cyril as a part-time honorary (i.e. unpaid) lecturer in general practice. Katy Gardner had originally visited Cyril's practice as a student in 1973 under this scheme. In 1978 Cyril and Katy attempted to contact Dr Hall-Turner again, hoping to link practices in deprived areas to university departments, as had been recommended elsewhere (Downham, 1978). However, lack of funding was such a major stumbling block that Dr Hall-Turner had by then resigned his university post. GPs were overstretched already and were unable to take on the extra work of teaching and related administration without additional resources. The scheme was shelved.

In 1984, Liverpool Medical School was awarded funding for a Department of General Practice. This was thanks to Donald Acheson's 1981 report on primary health care, which 'encouraged the view that university departments might influence the standard of local practice' (London Health Planning Consortium, 1981). An imaginative dean of the Liverpool Medical School, Sir Robert Shields, saw the potential for using university funds to employ academic GPs who might become additional part-time partners in selected practices keen to build links with the university (McGuinness et al, 2011). Drs Peter Campion and Peter Bundred joined Professor Stanley's Department as Senior Lecturers, attached respectively to The Elms Medical Centre, also in Liverpool 8, and to a practice in Maghull, just north of the city.

Dr Susanna Graham-Jones, trained in Oxford and at St Mary's Paddington, arrived in Liverpool in 1985 after working in Nepal for three years with Save The Children Fund. She was appointed to a third GP lecturer post. On the advice of Dr John Ashton, a public health physician at the University of Liverpool, she approached Katy Gardner and Cyril Taylor about joining PPHC. She became a supernumerary part-time partner in 1986, funded by the University, and began to host medical student placements. She also forged lasting links with the Liverpool School of Tropical Medicine. Susanna saw a different kind of deprivation in inner-city Liverpool from the poverty and malnutrition she had observed in Nepal. On her first day in the practice she shadowed Dr Mike Ross. His first home visit at lunchtime that

Monday was to a woman 38 weeks pregnant with her third baby. This baby was going to be taken away at birth by social services and placed in care. Susanna still remembers this harrowing encounter.

PPHC was always aspirational for its patients and local people. One Saturday, Susanna remembered, pupils from primary and secondary schools in Liverpool 8 were invited into the practice. They did hands-on activities, such as taking blood pressures and using peak flow meters to measure lung function. Staff talked to them about careers. The aim was for children living in streets with up to 80% unemployment to realise that they could find jobs in the NHS. PPHC also offered work placements for school students in Toxteth; these had to be discontinued later because of legislation on personal data protection.

After Cyril's death in 2000, a group of staff and community activists set up the Cyril Taylor Trust. Over 15 years, the trust provided funds to support more than 60 school students, mainly from Toxteth and the surrounding area, who were interested in training for the health professions, and many of whom later became doctors, pharmacists and physiotherapists. These included several young patients from PPHC. The trust provided computers, school uniforms and informal support from NHS staff. Pupils were funded to attend open days at universities, giving them an insight into university life. The trust also supported a small number of students during their undergraduate years, later working with a national charity, the Sutton Trust.

A feminist practice

When Katy Gardner joined Cyril as a partner, she was already collaborating with Sheila Abdullah as a campaigner and practitioner in the field of women's reproductive health. Shortly after joining PPHC, Katy wrote *Why Suffer?*, a book about period problems. Many women with premenstrual tension wrote to her and she set up free clinics at PPHC on Saturday mornings for women from all over the North West (Burke and Gardner 1979). Improving women's health in Liverpool 8 became a priority for the whole primary care team at PPHC. Julia South joined the practice as a patient in 1980:

> As a lesbian, I was very concerned to have a GP practice where I would feel welcome and this was definitely the case at Princes Park. I saw several

GPs over the years and I always felt put at my ease and able to be open (not something that was always easy in those days). I also really liked that there was always a wonderful, diverse spectrum of people sitting in the waiting room. You felt valued as a patient and as a person and you could talk about your problems, even if they weren't strictly medical. The practice took a holistic view of health and that was brilliant. I went on to work on health projects in Russia in the 1990s. I realised then that what I understood to be general practice - the commitment to delivering accessible, high-quality care to all in the community - was based on what I had experienced at PPHC.

The Well Woman Clinic which Katy set up with nurse Doreen Vernon in 1982 was the first outside London (Gardner, 1983). Neighbourhood Health Workers came along to provide cups of tea and health promotion advice, and the women who attended got used to discussing their health problems informally, as well as with the GP or nurse. Common but troublesome symptoms were demystified by a series of patient leaflets created in 1985. Sylvia Hikins, with her Community Health Council perspective, recalled, 'I knew how important it was for patients to receive clear information about diseases, both clinical and community resources, written in simple, everyday language. So the CHC worked with Katy to produce a set of leaflets that were freely available. It seems obvious now, but it was pioneering then.' Over 30 leaflets were produced with help from the Neighbourhood Health Workers and illustrated by artist and practice patient Fi Francis (Robinson, 2001). A non-judgemental approach allowed for discussion of sensitive topics, such as heavy bleeding, breast lumps, cystitis, migraine, irritable bowel syndrome, sexually transmitted infections, depression and anxiety, and premenstrual tension and period pains. The series included a leaflet on chlamydia infection, already recognised by specialists as a major risk to sexual health, but relatively unknown to the public until the 2003 national screening programme (see Chapter 12). The leaflets won an award from the GP newspaper *Pulse* (1985).

This patient friendly Well Woman Clinic paid dividends in terms of health literacy. Women who attended were more likely to accept screening checks for early detection of significant problems - blood pressure checks, cervical smears and, later, breast screening and chlamydia screening. This was reflected in an increased uptake of cervical screening. After a successful campaign in the mid-1980s, Well Woman Clinics were rolled out all over

Liverpool by the Area Health Authority. However, under the management of June Phillips, Area Medical Officer at the time, they did not follow the welcoming, informal style of PPHC. Katy worked in one for a few weeks until she got the sack for refusing to wear a white coat! Fortunately, in 1989 a change of personnel enabled the Liverpool Well Woman Clinics to become much more user friendly.

PPHC continued its more informal outreach activities. Practice nurses Doreen Vernon and Noreen Gilhespy visited non-attenders at home to encourage them to have a cervical smear, often doing it there and then. Noreen lived just a few hundred yards from the practice and did not hesitate to chat to women about the importance of having a smear while she was buying groceries in the shops. Katy set up a recall system for women with abnormal cervical smears as early as 1982, using a card index (computers came later). She remembered seeing a sex worker on a street corner, whose smear report suggested a high risk for cervical cancer, picking her up and driving her straight to the Women's Hospital. She was treated in time to prevent cancer developing. Thanks to proactive and sensitive initiatives at PPHC, marginalised individuals such as sex workers felt able to seek the help they needed, and they put the word around to others.

Some GPs at PPHC offered support for home births for practice patients and for patients from other practices whose own GPs did not offer this option. The GPs worked with locally based midwives, notably Ruth Chan, who delivered hundreds of PPHC babies. There were problems when patients did not have telephones, let alone mobile phones. Katy remembered 'a woman having her baby alone, while her husband was in the phone box alerting me and the midwife. I lived nearest and arrived just in in time to deliver the placenta!' Another PPHC midwife, Dorkas Akeju, commented, 'The GPs, especially Katy Gardner and Lis Davidson, were keen on home confinement and supported us. They always listened to our views about our patients; if I was concerned about a patient, they would ensure that she was seen as soon as possible.'

Needless to say, being on call for home births was exhausting. John Kirby treasures this story about his partner Fi Francis, mentioned above as an illustrator:

> Most famously, Katy was asleep in the corner of the bedroom when Simon, our son, was born. Due to a misunderstanding by the ambulance

service, Fi didn't get transferred to hospital just before the final stage of labour, so the midwife decided that it had to be a home birth. The midwife wanted a doctor on hand in case any sewing up was necessary, so I phoned Katy and she came. It was about 11 pm and she had been up much of the previous night for another home delivery. When she arrived, she had a quick word with the midwife before sitting on the floor in the corner and falling asleep. I don't think she woke up until after Simon was born.

A consultant at the Women's Hospital sympathetic to home deliveries gave the PPHC team support and advice. Occasionally, he was a little too enthusiastic. Katy remembered a woman whose baby was very mobile inside the uterus and not always head down, as in most deliveries:

The consultant said it was fine for her to deliver at home, but I remained anxious. She went into labour one night and luckily she lived across the road from me. I rushed over with Ruth Chan only to find the baby lying horizontally, with the danger that the cord might prolapse (come down) and cut off the baby's blood supply. We tipped the woman head down and dialled 999. Ruth and I stayed with her for her emergency caesarean, and the baby was fine. This baby now has children of her own and I have met her with them in the park.

PPHC also hosted a National Childbirth Trust breastfeeding group, and a patient-run post-natal befriending group run by NCT member Sue Halsall. Breastfeeding rates far exceeded those recorded in other inner-city practices.

During the 1980s many of the clinical staff were involved in campaigning for women's health services. Sheila Abdullah and Katy helped to organise meetings. GPs at PPHC took part in the successful campaign to save Duchess Ward at the Women's Hospital. Sylvia Hikins remembered:

PPHC doctors did not need lecturing to about the political aspects of health care. They were themselves pioneers, not seeing the Community Health Council as a threat, but as a critical friend and ally. Some joined the CHC and other activists in direct campaigns that often took to the streets, such as the Women in White demonstration, which made its way from the CHC in Whitechapel to the then Women's Hospital, in an attempt to keep Duchess Ward open.

Patient Linda Pepper remembered this event vividly:

A consultant had said 'there are only 400 women on the waiting list', so 400 women dressed in white to represent the waiting list. My daughter was in her buggy. We also did an impromptu demo of 'bed hopping' on the street near the Women's Hospital. This was to show how, if there were not enough beds, women would have to be discharged early or sit out of their bed, so that someone else could occupy it. At that time Brookside, a Channel 4 TV sitcom, was airing. They came on board because a character in the show had a gynae problem and was on the Women's waiting list. We did a mini play in Williamson Square, where the actress pretended to be taken ill as an emergency. Katy played the doctor, and a vast crowd gathered.

PPHC doctors also supported the development of the Women's Health Information and Support Centre (WHISC), which has offered advice and help to Liverpool women for many years. A huge meeting to support the centre was held one Sunday. Katy was shocked that an off-duty health visitor attending was later disciplined by the Area Health Authority for being 'political'.

Sheila and Katy continued to work voluntarily in the Brook Advisory Centre in their spare time, while lobbying, eventually successfully, for funding for this unique service (Ashton, 2020). They were involved in the campaign to set up a free NHS Day Care Abortion Service in Liverpool, which opened in 1982. Julia South, who worked on the campaign, felt that 'the fact that Princes Park GPs spoke out and lobbied was central to that success.' Alex Scott-Samuel was also involved:

> The then director of public health, Dr Duncan Dalton, and I were enthusiastic supporters of the cause. After I became a public health consultant in 1978 I was given responsibility for planning the day abortion unit, later named the Bedford Clinic. The gynaecologists were mostly unsupportive, and a lot of covert plotting and planning went on to ensure that the unit came to fruition and was adequately staffed when it finally opened in 1981.

Sheila had long campaigned for this service, after having to beg the very few willing consultant gynaecologists to perform abortions for women, who too often experienced unnecessary delays. Linda Pepper summed up the attitude of some consultants: 'I remember one of the consultants who was not supportive of abortion saying women should have their vaginas filled with cement...I nearly organised a cement mixer for outside the hospital as a demo, but this was a step too far for the CHC, which I was a member of at the time.' Nina Houghton reflected, 'There was - and still is - a strong Roman Catholic anti-abortion lobby in Liverpool. It was powerful in the medical profession at the time, and Sheila, supported by colleagues, battled bravely with them throughout her time in Liverpool.' In contrast, despite the new unit having a dedicated counselling service, the practice found the local Catholic priest helpful for women who had abortions, whether they were Catholics or not. Conveniently, he was based just up the road and made a point of seeing women immediately on request, helping them to cope with any feelings of guilt and loss.

The practice itself embraced different views. Dr Barbara Gaze worked as a locum for Katy from 1984:

> My most vivid memory happened shortly after I started. It suddenly hit me that my rather conservative approach to terminations of pregnancy might be a deal-breaker in this progressive practice, so I plucked up courage and went to discuss the situation with Cyril. He was fantastically supportive, and the issue was never a problem...with the other doctors. We devised a system whereby any woman who consulted me wanting a termination of pregnancy (TOP) would be fitted into another GP's session almost immediately.

In 1986 Sheila Abdullah, a beacon of dedication and hard work, left to look after her elderly parents in Sheffield. This was a huge loss to the practice. However, the work done by Sheila and Katy attracted other feminist doctors and trainees to join the team. Dr Mary Belshaw was appointed as a partner to replace Sheila, and former trainee Dr Lis Davidson returned the same year as a partner to job-share with Katy: 'We were the first job-share partners in Liverpool. I'd wanted to work with Sheila, and then she left!'

Learning from complex patients

Doctors today often use the term 'complex patients' to refer to patients with intertwined emotional, psychological and physical health issues. Emotional and psychological trauma may be suppressed or hidden, making it harder for doctors to unravel what is happening, and attempt to help. The process can be distressing to both patient and GP. Time and trust are important. The term 'complex patients', as used here, is not a reflection on patients themselves, but relates to the experiences of doctors and patients dealing with complex health issues.

As PPHC's reputation as a listening practice grew, it attracted patients who had suffered trauma in childhood and were struggling to survive and bring up their own families. Lis Davidson remembered her early days at PPHC:

> Some of my most vivid memories at that time were of the young women at the MIND [mental health] hostel. They started out in a hostel and then moved out to supported living. I remember spending lots of time round at their flats talking. Was it useful? Other women I remember well were in the health centre so very often. I think they had what we would now call post-traumatic stress. I really feel I "cut my teeth" with those women - I learnt a lot.

GPs came to recognise that many of the patients who attended the surgery frequently with chronic pain, depression or multiple symptoms were, in fact, struggling desperately to cope with the consequences of physical, emotional and sexual abuse. Katy recalled keeping 'a log of consultation topics in which 90% involved someone who had been physically or sexually abused.' As Lis noted above, those who were most difficult to help would probably have been diagnosable with post-traumatic stress disorder or borderline personality disorder, a term which at the time carried a lot of stigma, but became acceptable later (Royal College of Psychiatrists, 2020).

Many women eventually trusted their doctors enough to disclose ongoing domestic violence or other forms of abuse, but this took time. 'Battered' women (the term common in those days) were usually and understandably reluctant to go to the police, because they were likely to be treated with scorn, contempt and even brutality; so there were cycles of further hidden abuse which had long term effects across generations. Susanna Graham-Jones remembered her surprise and relief on finding a Home Office leaflet in 1994, which signalled a new approach: 'Domestic Violence - don't stand for it!' Northumbria Police spearheaded a new culture, and gradually police forces across the UK were trained and resourced to support women in violent relationships and their children, rather than ignoring their pleas for help. Not least, domestic rape was eventually recognised as a criminal offence.

It was deeply satisfying to help patients disclose underlying problems for the first time and to learn by experience that, given time and continuity of care, traumatised patients could sometimes recover their health and self-esteem. Janice first became a patient at the health centre in the early eighties, 'at a very dark time in my life, suffering from severe depression and attendant mental health problems. Without the knowledgeable care of Katy Gardner and the very patient and caring counsellor that I was assigned to, I doubt if I'd be able to work today and lead anything like a 'normal' life.'

As rewarding as this work was, it had an emotional and physical impact, as Katy described:

> I still get a fantastic buzz seeing patients whom I have helped through very difficult times going about their lives out and about in town - or occasionally in in the media, doing exceptional things. But it took its toll. My friend Pete Betts, artist and cartoonist, put it so well when he drew a picture of me with my hair wildly standing on end, stethoscope round my neck, sitting in the surgery, while the patient, swathed in bandages, leans across the desk and asks me: 'So how are you today doc?'

SO HOW ARE YOU TODAY DOCTOR ?

Writing as 'Rosa Hudson' in *Health Matters* magazine, Katy gave a fictionalised account of one such experience, entitled 'From Heartsink to Hope':

Louise stopped in the doorway. 'These are for you.' She handed me a bundle of reprints from medical journals on 'deliberate self-harm', papers that attempt to explain why Louises everywhere burn and cut themselves. Ten years ago, when she was coming into the surgery every day, we did not know about any of this. Together we have been on a rocky journey. We have not arrived yet, because Louise still often binges and vomits and cuts herself when crises arise, but she now chairs the user group of a community mental health centre and runs a self-help group for women who self-harm. I met Louise in my first week in the practice. She was already a source of desperation for doctors in the early hours and at the end of a busy surgery. Today she is a mentor and champion for many with mental health problems. It took a long time to find any key to her problems, partly because she lived in a fantasy world, divorced from the truth, including her horrific past. The answers came slowly, or sometimes in sudden leaps. Often I got angry, as did all the doctors, and felt hope was in very short supply. But over time we worked together to move her from heart-sink to hope. I had to build my own defences against the waves of distress, but with enough openings to let her in. Five years ago, when her despair was controlled enough to make it possible, she told me about her long-term abuse by family members, physical, sexual and emotional. This produced a deluge of cutting and burning, but we patched up her wounds and hung on. As a practice team our role is sometimes to provide a stable and caring substitute family, with enough distance to keep ourselves sane in the process. The key GP, health worker or therapist has the main role, but the team is the steady background of care. Looking back, I feel that what seemed like attention-seeking behaviour was in fact total self-absorption brought about by emotional pain. Over time, by just being there, we allowed her to try new safe relationships, allowing her to begin to heal. (Hudson, 1992)

GPs supported each other and their GP trainees in helping complex patients, and looked around for other resources. In 1980 Katy, a fan of psychotherapist Susie Orbach's book *Fat is a Feminist Issue* (1978), attended Orbach's monthly group in London for members of the caring professions. The group offered a safe space to talk about complex patients and their impact on the professionals supporting them.

John Howie's research in Edinburgh on patient enablement had provided good evidence for 'what works for patients' in general practice: time in the consultation, shared language and a feeling of 'knowing my doctor'

(Howie at al, 1999; Freeman et al, 2002). At practices such as PPHC, trust and empathy became indispensable tools of the trade.

The close doctor-patient relationships which ensued could, of course, be risky. Occasionally, important professional/personal boundaries became blurred, leaving GPs and/or patients bruised. Some GPs came close to getting burnt by the unrealistic expectations of patients to whom they had become very close. As Michael Ejuoneatse explained, 'boundaries of acceptable behaviour were sometimes stretched to just about tolerable limits, and this I believe took its toll on staff.' Katy remembered a patient who was a drug user and lived nearby:

> Once, he came to my house in the middle of the night saying he was going to kill a dog which had got loose in the hallway of his flats and had been howling all night. I called the police, who took the dog to the RSPCA, and told the patient off for disturbing me. I was quite fond of him though. His heart and his politics were in the right places and his story has a happy ending. Despite becoming homeless when his wife eventually threw him out, he managed to get off all his drugs a few years later.

She also recalled at times becoming too close to patients despite all the warning signs:

> On one occasion I knew had to withdraw and hand over to another GP. I had become entangled with a patient and we were not finding a way forward. It was hard not to see this as 'failure', although talking this over with my PPHC GP comrades really helped. Years later I met this patient in the park. Although our parting had been extremely stressful - I had finally persuaded him that I was not the right doctor to help him - he came up and gave me a big hug.

Working with complex patients could of course be risky in other ways. Katy recalled trying to help a young woman who had both drug and mental health issues:

> I felt I was getting somewhere with her, but she was very challenging. One Saturday morning (we did an emergency surgery in those days) she came in very agitated and angry, demanding Diazepam. I said no and was probably more abrupt with her because it was a Saturday. She walked out and jumped off a nearby tower block. I have never forgotten her.

Long consultations with complex patients caused difficulties for receptionists. GP appointment systems are always under pressure. These consultations took much longer than the five to ten minutes that were then the norm in general practice. Soon after PPHC opened, Cyril Taylor had implemented a revolutionary change to a 10-minute appointment system from the usual five. This was a step in the right direction, but even so, running late was common and a source of frustration. GPs knew that they would need to bring complex patients back for further long appointments before seeing any light at the end of the tunnel, but they still ran late. PPHC used the practice newspaper, *Prinny Post*, to explain to patients why this was sometimes inevitable. Counsellor Ria Hayward said, 'My view, which I told the GPs and patients at the time, was that running late saved people's lives.'

Other patients with complex issues included several transgender patients, who turned to PPHC at a time when no specialist services were available locally, and their own GPs were often reluctant to help. The PPHC team had to learn how to support them, battling for help from the few available UK services. Receptionist Pip Abraham remembered, 'These patients came to see Sheila Abdullah, who had an excellent rapport with them. We just saw it as part of normal life.' Likewise, PPHC, which had already attracted many gay and lesbian patients, now took on several patients diagnosed with HIV, some of whom had received poor care from their previous practices. Martin Smith remembered how, in the late 1980s and 1990s, 'we looked after a number of men dying from AIDS and developed good links with Sahir House, a local HIV support group, who awarded us a medal for good care.' Martin remembered going 'above and beyond' for some of these patients:

> An HIV positive woman developed pneumonia but refused hospital admission. I organised morphine and oxygen, fully expecting her to die over a weekend when I was on call. I bought food for her carers so they could stay with her. Remarkably, she recovered from the pneumonia and lived long enough afterwards to make arrangements for the care of her four-year-old daughter.

Dr Judith Hindley, who joined the practice in 1988, wrote, 'I only learnt about this new illness after qualifying, and we were learning on the job. This period is inexorably linked in my mind to the death of Freddie Mercury.' One patient with HIV, who was very lively, but at times challenging, flew to Greece when he was terminally ill. He sent the GPs a beautiful postcard from the beach to say 'Thank you and goodbye.'

Continuity of care and complex patients

There was always debate in the practice about continuity of care for patients. This can become a difficult issue when the number of part-time GPs increases, as it did at PPHC over the years. In *A Fortunate Man*, John Berger describes the 'sharing of pain' as a key aspect of the doctor-patient relationship in which continuity of care is important (1967). GPs at PPHC recognised that, while for some patients, often the young and well, it was not important to see the same doctor at every appointment, for others it was crucial. Many PPHC doctors and patients valued personal continuity of care highly and managed to maintain it; patients could and did choose to wait for an appointment until 'their' part-time GP was on duty. But elsewhere, there were predictions that primary care would adopt a team approach, relinquishing the focus on the individual doctor-patient relationship. In a paper on 'The new general practice', Anna Livingstone and David Widgery wrote that the future 'depends on transforming the 'attachment' model into a more democratic primary health care team in which the doctor is not always the key worker' (1990). Katy agreed with this view. And, as structured care for people with chronic health conditions developed over the years, practice nurses began to take on this key worker role.

Communication within the team was vital in caring for complex patients. Lis Davidson reflected:

> We had become quite good at getting supervision for ourselves, and with each other in the team. The problem was that some vulnerable patients suck you in. You think you are the only person, and you don't communicate with the others. As a group we were good at communicating, but every now and again people would split us. People who have been severely damaged in the past, and are angry, are risky in therapeutic situations. And I guess the time when doctors get more vulnerable is when you are not functioning so well as a team. There were times our team functioned better and times when it didn't. I remember talking with a non-GP friend. At the time we might have been not getting on so well as a team, and my focus became more on the patients. She reflected, 'When you get cosy with your work colleagues, do the patients lose out? And vice versa?' How do you keep a balance? You can collude with colleagues against patients.

After a couple of episodes of the type described by Lis, PPHC developed a 'usual doctor' sticker system for vulnerable or complex patients. As a GP built up a relationship with a particular patient and felt they would benefit from continuity, a coloured sticker would be put on the patient's notes. Later, this was flagged up on the computer. Katy and Lis, who job-shared for many years, used purple stickers, and made huge efforts to hand over their most vulnerable patients to each other every week. Lis remembered 'seeing one woman once a week, to try and control the amount of times she came to the health centre.' If she was ever away, she briefed Katy, to 'reduce the risk that she would revert to frequent and fruitless attendances, attempting to see every available doctor.'

The 'usual doctor' sticker system was soon adopted by all the partners and worked relatively well for many years. In the 1991 PPHC Annual Report, Dr Alan Forbes wrote, 'When someone has been a patient of the practice for some time and usually sees one of the 'older' GPs, that patient should see that doctor unless there are very special circumstances. Often a consultation with a different doctor will result in wasted time and effort for both patient and doctor.' Practice nurses similarly adopted patients with multiple chronic conditions, attempting to ensure they saw the same nurse regularly. Continuity was also helpful for others with whom it took time to develop a relationship, perhaps because of language and cultural barriers. The 'usual doctor' system needed GPs and nurses to stick around long enough to provide continuity. In the mid-2000s, as established GPs left, the system started to fall apart. Fewer of the new salaried GPs were really dedicated to maintaining personal continuity of care, and the increasing turnover of GPs undermined it.

CHAPTER 4

Going the extra mile: teamwork for psychological problems

Supervision for GPs: the Balint group and beyond

The wider team: practice-based social work, counselling and psychological medicine

Health care for drug users, another group of complex patients

Supervision for GPs: the Balint group and beyond

Michael Balint was a Hungarian psychoanalyst who had arrived in Manchester as a refugee in 1939. He moved to London in 1945 and worked at the Tavistock Institute of Human Relations with an interdisciplinary group looking at marital problems. British psychiatrists were generally hostile to psychotherapy and insights from psychoanalysis, but from 1950 Michael and Enid Balint helped to challenge this view. They inspired and trained groups of GPs to attend to the psychological distress behind the 'presenting symptoms' of patients whose symptoms did not appear to have a physical cause or respond to conventional treatments, and for whom hospital investigations often seemed fruitless. Julian Tudor Hart commented that the Balints 'showed GPs that far from being inferior to hospital specialists, for this large group of patients they might be more effective and less dangerous' (1988). Michael Balint encouraged a deeper than usual connection between doctors and patients, resulting in new insights which could be used to resolve 'stuck' consultations, at a time when counselling in primary care was non-existent, and GPs had to rely on their own initiative with 'difficult', 'heart-sink', or 'hard to reach' patients (1957). He emphasised the immense therapeutic power of the doctor-patient relationship.

In Balint groups, GPs were encouraged to talk about patients who puzzled them in a peer-to-peer confidential setting. Reflecting on their own feelings was a new technique and threw up surprises and challenges. An early example of what was later termed reflective practice, Balint groups encouraged the development of patient-centred medicine. Julian Tudor Hart again: 'For the next 25 years Balintry was the principal innovating ideological force in British general practice, and was particularly influential among the younger GPs forming the second generation of leaders for the College of General Practitioners' (1988). This approach became central to GP training in the 1970s and 1980s, and differentiated it from the more traditional 'do as I do and you'll be all right' training offered to junior doctors by hospital consultants. A generation of GPs was inspired by Balint to deal with complex bio-psycho-social issues. Doctors who listened well, without the detachment and apprehension which often prevented patients from disclosing their underlying problems, could and did make a real difference.

Dr Len Ratoff from The Elms Medical Centre, an old friend of Cyril Taylor, had been a member of an early Balint group in London. Susanna Graham-Jones, who had trained in psychiatry and counselling/psychotherapy, approached Len in 1987 to ask about setting up a Balint-like group in Liverpool. He contacted Dr Vera Pettit, a psychoanalyst who ran groups in London and Manchester, and she agreed to supervise the group, which ran successfully for two years, funded by the RCGP.

The Balint group experience helped Katy to engage with some of her complex patients. Joe (not his real name) was one. She wrote about him as Rosa Hudson:

> Joe had been a sailor until his ship sank and several of his mates were drowned. He is convinced the CIA and MI5 are after him because of his lifelong socialist views. They visit in the night, interfering with the treatment I give him for his chronic chest condition. When I had gently suggested he try taking tablets to help these unpleasant thoughts he was

very cross. In many ways he lives a 'normal' life, very much the loner and rarely revealing his thoughts to others as 'they wouldn't understand'...I'd never dream of forcing him to take medication or admitting him to hospital unless something drastic happened, as he lives fairly peacefully with his delusions. We have talked long and often about his experiences at sea and in politics, but I feel a little helpless as I know he is suffering. Being part of the Balint group has helped me to understand that his experiences have a basis in reality, and to empathise with him. However, I will not accept them as real and he knows this. Many of our patients tread the line between 'sanity' and 'madness', and as a practice we probably accept this more than most because of the support mechanisms we have. (Hudson, 1988b)

The Liverpool Balint group ended in 1989 on Vera's retirement. Princes Park GP Judith Hindley then got in touch with Linda Gask, a professor of psychiatry, who was using a different approach to help GPs in Manchester to review and reflect on their consultations (Gask,1992). Linda agreed to visit PPHC once a month. Lis Davidson described these sessions:

Our work with Linda was about reviewing videos of consultations, finding the right questions to ask - trying to look at consultations in a new way. Anyone in the group could stop the tape, rephrase the questions and suggest looking at things in a different way. Alan Forbes was keen on this approach. GPs looked at some consultations with Linda, and then we did some on our own later. It was in the early days of using videos with GP trainees, and it also helped us with that. I remember specifically, when HIV was still new, a patient came back from Egypt with symptoms that were difficult and confusing. I rang the infectious diseases consultant and he said, 'Have you asked him about HIV?' I said 'no', as I knew he was married. I asked the patient to come back in the afternoon, with the video running. I psyched myself up to ask the question. The guy was really cool and said he wasn't at risk and he was in a stable relationship. I remember it was clear on the video that I was anxious, partly because HIV was quite new and we hadn't had practice at asking patients about it. It needed a new way of thinking things through and asking the question. Looking at videos in this way was really helpful, but sadly we lost momentum with it when Alan Forbes left, as we were short of permanent GPs and felt rushed and busy.

Linda Gask's abiding memory of this time was the meeting in 1991 when Katy Gardner's waters broke and she went into labour!

The wider team: practice-based social work, counselling and psychological medicine

Even before the move to PPHC, Cyril had built up a multidisciplinary team. Pam Duff, a social worker with the Liverpool Personal Service Society (LPSS), a charity founded in 1919 by Eleanor Rathbone, was one of the first non-medics to join him in Sefton Drive. In the 1980 practice report she wrote, 'The DHSS working party in 1974 had seen the development of social work for general practice as a priority for the future.' Despite this, she continued:

> Social workers widely regard GPs as middle class, middle minded individuals who are accountable to no one and eager to see the problem presented as purely 'medical'...GPs on the other hand see social workers as under qualified, irrelevant and ineffective...PPHC has tried to bridge this gulf...A wide range of problems I encounter are because of the Centre's location, in which financial problems, difficulties in dealing with the DHSS and poor housing are rife, and unemployment is twice the national average. Much of my caseload is one-parent families claiming benefits and elderly people, often alone and infirm. Finding time to discuss patients/clients with the GPs can be difficult, because I am part-time and they are busy. All of us need to give this more priority in future, but having a social worker on site is a great advantage over the distant duty officer in the Social Services team with no immediate knowledge of the problems, and I enjoy being here so much more.

Appointments in the familiar setting of PPHC were certainly convenient and discreet for patients who might have felt stigmatised elsewhere. Nevertheless, liaising appropriately with busy GPs continued to be problematic. In a 1987 practice report another social worker, Carolyn Saxton, expressed disappointment that there was insufficient time for discussions with GPs. That year 53 clients were referred to her, of whom 40 attended. Issues included financial problems, housing, depression, emotional difficulties, childcare, drug use, care for elderly patients and disabilities.

Gradually the number of professionals running clinics at PPHC increased. Mark Fisher, who started working as a psychotherapist at PPHC in 1989, remembered, 'There were health visitors, social workers, advice clinics to deal with housing, benefits, legal rights. The local psychiatrist had a clinic too, supported by a variety of counsellors, psychotherapists and psychologists, an incredible achievement' (2019). These were much needed: 'Why can't just one patient have an ordinary cough or cold?' asked Katy's trainee at the time.

Bill Barnes, clinical psychologist and psychotherapist working in the mental health service, was attached to the practice to run weekly clinics in the early 1980s. Like most of the PPHC counsellors he was always open to an informal chat about difficult dilemmas concerning patients. He later became clinical director of the Liverpool Psychotherapy Service, but sadly died prematurely in his 40s, soon after leaving PPHC.

The practice was an early adopter of cognitive behaviour therapy (CBT), thanks to the enthusiasm of Mike Scott who joined as a social worker in 1981, when he was also training in clinical psychology.

Cognitive behavioural therapy at PPHC

Mike Scott told me about a treatment for depression called Cognitive Therapy. I had never heard of it, and to be honest the rationale did not sound all that convincing. However, I was also aware of the huge waiting list and apparently negligible positive outcomes from the two - yes, two - psychologists who worked in the practice. He described Cognitive Therapy as being similar to a learning experience. He provided written material both for the patients and for their carers, who to this day are usually excluded from the therapeutic process. I knew how to construct a clinical trial from my experience doing a Master's in Community Medicine, so together we designed, then implemented, a randomised prospective clinical trial of Cognitive Therapy for depressed patients in PPHC.

Mike Ross

Bill Barnes, a clinical psychologist, had been offering psychodynamic therapy, but I was keen to offer cognitive behaviour therapy (CBT), a psychoeducational approach that had been positively evaluated in the United States by Aaron Beck. I felt that the social conditions contributing to depression needed to be addressed, a view shared by Dr Mike Ross. We agreed that I would not only provide psychological help in the form of CBT but also address social issues by, for example, writing to a

Housing Association about a patient's difficulties and liaising with the then Department of Social Security. Mike secured funding from the Health Authority and the Mental Health Foundation to compare the effectiveness of individual and group CBT to patients on the waiting list.

Mike Scott

The CBT trial

Dr Roger Chitty from Liverpool University's Department of Psychiatry did the independent ('blind') evaluations of patients. We found that group CBT was as effective as individual CBT in improving people's mood, and superior to the waiting list. We had to modify our protocol because the offer of group CBT went down like a lead balloon, but when we offered potential group patients up to three individual sessions in addition to the group, it was much more acceptable. In fact, few people took up the three sessions. Strangely, neither Mike nor I anticipated that running a group programme from one practice might be problematic until on two occasions attendees turned up who knew each other! Fortunately, they were quite accepting of one another. One benefit of the group was that some people made friends and met up afterwards, lessening social isolation, often a driving force for depression.

Mike Scott

After the trial had been running for a couple of months it was obvious to me that the treatment that Mike was delivering was being hugely effective. Sometimes even psychologically related symptoms, such as migraine, seemed to evaporate. It was particularly interesting to me... because Mike was treating working class patients, who previously had not been referred to the psychologists...The effect of [the group treatment scheme] was a rapid reduction in the cost...- £25 to treat a depressed patient effectively, with the patient still not depressed one year later. (Ross and Scott, 1985)

Mike Ross

Both Mikes came to feel that, for ethical reasons, patients on the waiting list who had not received CBT also needed treatment. These patients therefore received CBT at the end of the trial.

Counsellors and social workers were trained to engage with vulnerable patients. They could offer long appointments, helping GPs to manage these patients, many of whom had longstanding emotional problems. Ria Hayward started working as a counsellor at PPHC in 1990 and only left when funding was withdrawn in 1999, due to changes in the NHS approach to mental health care (see below). Counsellor Liz Muir joined the practice in 1993.

Counsellors at PPHC

The thing I remember when I joined the practice was the incredibly welcoming atmosphere, to all people of all backgrounds and all nationalities. People would find a way to get on the practice books by hook or by crook. Different GPs were engaged in different health issues, but they all listened. I could ask any GP to squeeze in a patient if they had raised a medical issue during counselling. The GPs never judged people medically because of their mental health. If they needed to be seen they were never turned away. People would be heard. Each week I had an emergency slot so a patient could skip the waiting list if there was an immediate problem e.g. bereavement. I could see them for an hour and address the issue head on, hopefully avoiding them bottling things up - part of the GPs' strategy to keep people off medication if possible. We had a team approach to patients with complex psychological or emotional problems, those referred to in the past by some health professionals as 'heart-sink'. We would hold a team meeting (with the patient's permission) of GPs, counsellors and nurses to exchange thoughts about how we could further help the patient. GPs were really committed to holding these complex patients and I sometimes took them on just to help the GPs out. It was a philosophy of 'leave no-one behind'. One time a patient who used to be in the health centre several days a week was sitting on the floor in the GP corridor. I had seen her often in the waiting room, so I sat next to her and chatted. I checked with the GPs she saw regularly whether I could take her on. They were a bit apprehensive as she was very stuck in her behaviour and they thought it would be lots of work, but they agreed to let me, and I saw her for an hour every fortnight. Between us we managed to keep her going, knowing, sadly, that there was not likely to be a miracle cure.

Ria Hayward

I had always wanted to work as a counsellor in a health setting because of my belief that counselling can complement medicine in a holistic way. It was clear the PPHC doctors also had a holistic approach to the care of their patients, understanding that listening and attending to emotions were important ingredients to their progress and wellbeing. This was borne out in practice. In 1993 the counselling rooms were in a portacabin, so there was a bit of a feeling of isolation from the rest of the practice. On the other hand, it was suitably private. Later we moved into new rooms within the health centre. This was preferable for all sorts of reasons, most importantly we became centrally heated! I valued the respect of the staff and their trust in my judgment. This enabled me to grow as a counsellor and learn from the experiences I had and challenges I faced. I valued the passionate commitment to caring for their patients as well as they possibly could and their openness to continued learning.

Liz Muir

Terms and conditions for mental health workers changed over time. Liz could see the writing on the wall:

Changes were on the horizon in the world of counselling in primary care, most of which I did not welcome. It was clear that if I had stayed my work would have become more constrained by the need to measure outcomes, use questionnaires and offer fewer sessions to patients. These changes would not have suited my style of therapy, so I was glad to retire when I did in 2004.

Mark Fisher reflected:

Cyril Taylor's trailblazing health centre was a very local undertaking. It was not just a place for dispensing treatments, but a socio-political hub fully integrated into the hopes, fears, longings and anger of its community. A historical paradox for me is that it was a socialist government that began relentless attacks on localism - though under the auspices of noble sounding economic and social programmes. National minimum standards are indeed important and necessary, but not when they impose a boring managerial minimalism.

Mark and others were infuriated by the UK government's approach in the late 1990s, which attempted to replace admittedly patchy practice-based counselling and psychology services with standardised interventions. Mark complained, 'A new objective was dictated by central government. It was enforced by health bureaucrats and apparatchiks insisting on minimal care.' This standardised approach started by restricting primary care counselling 'courses' to 6 sessions. Later, explicit objectives promoted by UK government adviser Lord Layard in the 2009 Improving Access to Psychological Therapies (IAPT) initiative, included 'happiness', and getting people off sick pay and back into work. The economic arguments advanced by Layard to the Labour government resulted in a large injection of funds (£300 million) for chronically underfunded mental health services. The new 'stepped care' IAPT model, however, provided only 'low-intensity' treatment for most patients, monitoring their progress with repetitive telephone calls and questionnaires. Face-to-face appointments for CBT and access to computer-based CBT were reserved for patients with more severe symptoms. IAPT funds were ring-fenced to train a large cadre of psychological wellbeing practitioners (PWPs) in listening skills and other basic techniques, and a smaller number of CBT therapists. This scheme did extend very basic psychological help to more people in a fairly equitable way, but Mark Fisher felt the whole formula was wrong:

> No longer was it possible for counsellors to help, ease and give voice to distress...Now they had to promote 'happiness'...This was a sinister manipulation geared to masking real distress...Cognitive Behaviour Therapy does not make happy workers or happy, grateful patients. To threaten distressed people, already living on basic benefits with the mantra 'employment and compulsory therapy, or cessation of benefits' is a cruel manipulation...Equally abhorrent to me is the suggestion that depression, anxiety or strain in workplaces can easily be remedied by a few cognitive techniques.

As Mark's comments illustrate, the IAPT approach proved controversial (Marzillier, 2009). Training in other therapies, including counselling and problem-solving therapy, was eventually included. However, Mike Scott, who had successfully trialled individual and group CBT for depressed patients at PPHC (see above) was scathing about the later direction of psychological therapies, and the lack of evaluation of services (Scott, personal communication, 2019).

PPHC continued to build strong links with mental health services. GP

Judith Hindley commented confidently:

> The practice embraced and cared about all the issues prevalent in a deprived inner-city population. We felt we had an experienced voice that was listened to. We had excellent relations with the psychiatry department. I recall being in a lift in a block of flats with community psychiatrist Dr Ian Davidson, discussing whether there was any value in dream interpretation!

Despite these links, GPs at PPHC occasionally had dangerous encounters with severely mentally ill patients. Paul Thomas remembered an incident soon after he became a partner in 1987:

> [I was] trapped for an hour in my room by a psychotic patient who wanted to harm me. When I got him calmed down, eight policemen bundled him to the floor and took him away. But when they found out that he was a policeman himself, they let him go home. He happened to live two doors away from me, so I had his wife banging on the door in the middle of the night.

From 1988 to 2004, another community psychiatrist, Dr Rob Poole, ran a weekly clinic at PPHC. He also established the Criminal Justice Liaison Team and the Homeless Outreach Team, and worked with mental health projects in BAME communities, including the Somali mental health project, MAAN (see Chapter 9). Dr Julia Nelki, meanwhile, came to Liverpool in 1989 as a psychiatrist with the Child and Adolescent Mental Health Service (CAMHS).

Psychiatrists working with PPHC

I arrived in Liverpool in 1988 to be consultant psychiatrist covering an area that included Liverpool 8. I had clear (although often misguided) ideas about developing community mental health services. I'd taken the job because of the diversity and deprivation within the area and because I felt that there was a job to be done. My catchphrase was 'there is nothing more radical than providing good quality basic psychiatric services to an inner-city area'. As a South-East Londoner, everything was a bit strange. People struggled to understand my accent. However, I quickly came to feel that the PPHC GPs were kindred spirits, although as I remember it, it took a while to gain the necessary credibility. Alan Forbes had a healthy scepticism about secondary care which I shared, but, of course, I was part of secondary care and needed to show that I did things in a different way. There was an early lesson about relying on deeds, not words, if you expect colleagues to trust you. There was something about PPHC: actually doing it was the point...Years later, when I was a clinical director, Alan Forbes accused me of having become a Tory apparatchik. He wasn't joking. 'Saying it as it is' was always part of the PPHC culture. I remember frank exchanges with Martin Smith, Lis Davidson and Susanna Graham-Jones. That suited me. It made life more straightforward and I rarely felt that relationships were strained...I've stayed in touch with Martin Smith. We've both stopped smoking, but we still argue about the merits of the Grateful Dead. I still see Clare Wilkinson. She was on the appointments committee for my first academic job, which has taken me far from Toxteth.

As we moved mental health services to align more closely with primary care, I stopped holding clinics in hospitals and for many years held a weekly clinic in PPHC. Cyril was still doing occasional sessions and his strength of personality was evident; I regarded some of his ideas about managing mental health problems as archaic. Spending time in PPHC created the opportunity to develop really different ways of working. We often saw patients jointly, sometimes in their homes. Many people in the area had complex problems, and joint working was a huge step forward in finding constructive solutions for all concerned. The period 1988 to 2000 was a time of great creativity for me. There is little doubt that the mental health service provided to people in Toxteth improved substantially during that time. Learning to work closely with primary care was a major part of that. I developed a similar close working relationship with other practices: Vauxhall Health Centre and, later, Brownlow Group Practice, to name but two. But PPHC was the starting point, in this as in so much else.

Dr Rob Poole

My newly created post was to develop a community mental health service based in Myrtle Street Children's Hospital. It seemed an exciting possibility and links with GP practices, as well as community groups, were crucial. As with many good ideas, and especially in the NHS, it did not materialise as planned. Almost immediately the Myrtle St Hospital and our project were under threat, and I joined the fight to save them. We did develop important links, one of which was with PPHC, a welcoming place with interested GPs, health visitors and counsellors. I ran a series of 'Think Family' seminars there. The possibility in general practice of knowing families over generations, and having sustained contacts over years, gives many opportunities for understanding why an individual might present at a certain time, and for knowing what support systems might be available. Helping families create genograms [graphic representations of a family tree] and testing this by doing it ourselves first, around certain themes or beliefs that may be transmitted down generations, was a useful driver of change. I also sat in sessions with GPs where there were particular issues that a systemic focus might help with, or with patients who had medically unexplained symptoms and returned to the practice often but did not seem to benefit. With Dr Alan Forbes, we arranged a clinic where there was extended time to see families together, to see if we could move things along. Sadly, Myrtle Street closed, and the children's centre never happened, but for a few years a community child mental health service offered weekly clinics in a few health centres such as Princes Park and The Elms...This increased understanding of the way child mental health practitioners work. It also helped GPs feel they could continue working with some families that they might otherwise have referred.

Dr Julia Nelki

Health care for drug users, another group of complex patients

Patients with substance abuse problems required careful management as well as long consultations. Many Liverpool practices were wary of drug users, to the extent that they refused to register new patients who disclosed substance abuse. They found reasons to remove registered patients from their lists when drug problems came to light. Scare stories circulated about addicts behaving unpredictably and violently or making unreasonable demands on staff and doctors. In fact, this was rare.

When clinical need remains undisclosed, the risk of complications from drug misuse is likely to rise. The PPHC ethos was to treat patients with respect rather than fear, and to encourage them to disclose drug dependency. This meant that they could be given proper health care. Quite apart from managing drug misuse itself, these patients could be offered health checks, immunisations and screening, all of which might have been missed because of stigma and neglect. Although most GPs at PPHC looked after one or more drug users at any given time, two partners took a special interest in these patients: Dr Mike Ross from 1981 to 1988, and Dr Martin Smith from 1988 to 2008.

Mike Ross realised that drug users were not getting the help they needed:

> I became aware of the problem of heroin addiction amongst the patients. A friend of mine from medical school days, Ashley Grossman, now a professor of neuroendocrinology, told me about his work in Barts Hospital, using clonidine to detox people off heroin. I obtained his protocol and tried it out. The results were pretty good. Mainly, patients were incredibly grateful to be listened to. A much overlooked fact, even now, is that most doctors (and other drug dependency treatment professionals) fail to realise that there are significant numbers of dependent patients, probably the vast majority, who hate being drug addicts! The very act of listening to these pleas for help, not rejecting the patient by signposting him/her to someone else who would tell them that they were unable to help, but instead offering significant direct assistance, was a huge surprise to these patients and provided the basis of a really good therapeutic relationship...I started to work with Merseyside Drugs Council and our cooperation was, I think, much more effective than working separately.

Mike Ross also encouraged psychologist/social worker Mike Scott to work with drug users, with varied results. Mike Scott remembered, 'He encouraged me to see some patients to whom he was prescribing the heroin substitute methadone, and I tried providing CBT. To say it was hard going is to put it mildly. For example, I discovered that one of the patients I considered to have had a great success from CBT had been supplying drugs to another patient!'

Martin Smith, who had been a trainee at The Elms practice and was Cyril's last trainee in 1986, joined the practice in 1988:

> When a partnership became available, I applied, more in hope than expectation, and was quite shocked to be offered a job. I started in May and worked at PPHC until April 2008 - 20 years minus 1 month. My initial feeling was one of tremendous excitement...a 'permanent' job with stimulating colleagues who shared a similar broad ethos. My predecessor, Mike Ross, had done a lot of work with heroin addicts. I had not had any training in this area, so I went on a steep learning curve. I had a couple of friends who had overcome addiction, who were very helpful in the early days. Over the coming months I sought help from the Drug Dependency Unit and its consultant, Dr Sue Ruben. In addition to advice, she loaned us one of her specialist nurses to help with management. This was the beginning of 'shared care', which is now the norm. At the time there was a lot of opposition from the Local Medical Committee (LMC)...However, I ended up being co-author of the first Liverpool Shared Care Guidelines. Later, I spent a year at John Moores University doing the Postgraduate Diploma in Addiction Studies.

This effective collaboration with the Liverpool Drug Dependency Unit (DDU) took place at a time when UK government policy on drug misuse was confusing patients, professionals and the public by swinging from one extreme, namely refusal of funding for treatment, to its opposite, the 'harm limitation' approach, which involved maintenance treatments and needle-exchange schemes. Thanks to collaboration with the DDU and the Merseyside Drugs Council, the practice was able to care for an increasing number of drug users effectively and safely. Martin Smith, Susanna Graham-Jones and Ria Hayward were involved in educational initiatives for GPs and medical students, attempting to demystify the topic of drug dependence and enable young doctors to engage with drug users. Ria remembered, 'Sometimes we would get outsiders to come in and work with us on complex problems. We hosted a meeting of Liverpool practices dealing with addiction problems. We had small groups and exchanged ideas about how to help our patients.' From 2000, Martin Smith and Sue Ruben taught on a course for GP registrars called 'Managing addiction in primary care'.

Mike Ross passed on some advice to Martin Smith about strategies for managing drug-dependent patients. Neither GP favoured the written contracts used by the DDU when prescribing methadone as a legal substitute for heroin, but Martin drew up some ground rules for a leaflet: 'These were shared understandings - nothing personal - same rules for everyone.'

METHADONE, YOU AND US

As a result of some recent misunderstandings which have caused upset to both patients and doctors we feel it would be helpful to reiterate certain "shared understandings" which are necessary to enable us to provide you with a good service.

1/ Your prescription will only be provided for you by your "own" doctor, except in the following circumstances:-

a) Your doctor is absent for a prolonged period of time. In this situation he/she will make arrangements for you to see an agreed alternative doctor.

b) Your doctor is otherwise unavailable. In this situation another doctor will prescribe for you. However, they will only prescribe sufficient to see you through until your "own" doctor is available. Of course, if your next prescription is not yet due, none of this applies... see below (it's not much fun just writing out a script for someone you don't know).

2/ Sorry... but we do not give early prescriptions. Stories about dropped bottles, lost prescriptions etc. etc. will fall on deaf ears. Even bringing in your stoned cat as proof that she/he drank it will not produce an early script......

3/ Appointments - whenever possible please make your next appointment when you leave the surgery. Where this is not possible please ask the receptionist to discuss this with your doctor. If, like some of us, you have difficulty getting up in the morning, please don't make early appointments. It's a real pain having to fit someone into an already busy evening surgery because they haven't managed to get out of the pit!

4/ Requests for prescriptions out of normal surgery hours and at weekends will always be refused.

5/ Random urine tests. One of the least savoury aspects of our relationship... Unfortunately, they have to be supervised, i.e. you have to have a member of staff with you while you do your pee !

- compulsory i.e. no pee/no script

- beware other medicines you may be taking!

6/ The only medication we prescribe for the relief of primary symptoms of opiate withdrawal (i.e. to stop you turkeying) is Methadone. We do not also prescribe benzodiazepines i.e. temazepam, diazepam (valium) lorazepam (ativan). If in doubt please discuss this with your doctor.

7/ We often work in close liaison with staff from Liverpool DDU. Your co-operation with them is appreciated.

... uh, that's about it. Sorry if it appears Draconian. Any comments you wish to make, preferably constructive, on how we can make things run smoothly would be appreciated. Please write your comments overleaf and return to your doctor.

Ta!   THE PRINCES PARK DOCTORS

Consistency and firmness were key. Martin remembered:

> [There were] a few screaming matches with patients in the early days. Fortunately, my patented 'Automatic Bullshit Detector' kicked in. Part of my ritual for introducing myself to someone seeking help for their addiction was to get them to look down my ear to see if they could see the latest Japanese technology I had installed - the ABD! Not sure I could get away with that now.

Not all GPs at PPHC had Mike and Martin's skills and experience. Those new to the practice sometimes got their fingers burnt when responding to drug users with a hard-luck story seeking an off-the-cuff prescription for opiates (diamorphine, codeine or oxycodone) or tranquillisers. Having succumbed and issued the prescription, they then felt hurt and humiliated to find they had been conned by the patient. For some doctors it felt like a betrayal of the sacrosanct doctor-patient relationship. Katy remembered some tactics used by new patients asking for opiates: 'They would use the familiar 'Katy', even if you had only just met them, to make you feel you were their friend. As such you might be more likely to bend the rules and prescribe them opiates.' It made sense for all GPs consulting with drug users to stick to strict guidelines.

Writing in *Health Matters* magazine as Rosa Hudson, Katy described one such situation:

> John was squeezed into my fully booked evening surgery. A locum GP had seen him that morning when he had just registered. He said he was using heroin and wanted Temazepam capsules and dihydrocodeine to help him cut down. The locum knew our policy and told him he would have to check with his previous GP and the Home Office before we would do anything. John had given his address as his girlfriend's, who was already registered with us, and as far as we knew not a drug user. The practice had been unable to contact John's previous GP by the time I saw him, but their receptionist had told us he had been prescribed Temazepam and dihydrocodeine - something we never did, because of their street value. I told him we wanted to help but suggested that he provide a urine sample, that we checked further with his GP and the Home Office. If his story held water, we would start prescribing methadone and refer him to the DDU. He got angry. I said: 'This is the deal - take it or leave it'. Part of me wanted him just to go away, because my surgery was busy and I was running late, but part of me wanted to be there on the day he decided he

really did want help. He left after a further aggressive 10 minutes saying 'What am I going to do tonight? You don't care!' But he did provide a urine sample. He is due to be back in two days. Fingers crossed. (Hudson, 1988a)

GPs needed to recognise what was going on in the consultation, learning by experience to respond to Dr Sue Ruben's succinct plea to GPs, as remembered by Martin: 'There are 3 types of GPs: will touch [addicts]; won't touch; soft touch. Fine if you're a 'will touch'. Fine if you don't want anything to do with addicts. Just don't be a ----- soft touch.' One of Martin's teaching exercises about 'how not to be a softie' was a true story:

A bloke comes in and tells me his son had died of meningitis at Alder Hey. As a result of the shock he had drunk all his week's supply of methadone and been admitted to Fazakerley hospital after an 'overdose' - could he have some more? 'Oh', says I. 'I'm sorry to hear about that. That's awful. Which ward was he on?' 'Er...', says he, 'I can't remember.' 'Oh', says I. 'He must have been on the Intensive Care Unit. Hang on, I'll just give them a ring.' Ring, ring... 'Hello', says I to the ITU nurse. I hear you had a little boy called xxx on the ICU.' 'Never heard of him', says she. I shrugged and smiled at the bloke. I waved 'bye'. He went - quietly, with a sheepish look on his face. A few years later I used this as a teaching exercise for GP colleagues. Nearly everyone in the room would have given him a prescription for methadone.

Opiate misuse remained hidden in some areas of the country. Mike Ross remembered:

In 1988 I decided to move to Bradford and took over a single-handed practice. For the first three months I did not see a single heroin addict. I thought: how interesting - I wonder why this is? Then I saw one, and then another. After five years, with the support of the Liverpool Family Practitioner Committee (FPC), I had a primary care based drug dependency clinic with 800 patients.

He obtained funding for Mike Scott to spend a day per week in Bradford working with addicts until 1993, providing clinical psychological diagnoses: 'The vast majority were on daily pick-up scripts comprising the opiate replacements, methadone or dihydrocodeine together in addition to symptomatic prescriptions, which included antidepressants and hypnotics. From his previous work Mike [Scott] adapted an addiction-related, problem-orientated version of CBT. A statistical assessment of urine test results before and after Mike Scott's brief interventions demonstrated mild benefit.'

Back at PPHC, Martin Smith was notifying the Home Office about 40 new opiate addicts in a single year, a heavy and time-consuming case load for a single practice:

> We had established links with the DDU and the counselling service at Merseyside Drugs Council. In 1990 I corresponded with Julie Bradley at Liverpool FPC about available funding for various clinics through the new NHS Health Promotion Clinic scheme. Eventually she recognised the time-consuming needs of attenders at our Drug Clinic; letting us record only six attendances rather than the normal 10 to claim for the extra payments.

Hallelujah - a concession from on high, a recognition of the graft put in by the practice team! A tiny victory, for once, in the battle against the inexorable truths enshrined in Julian Tudor Hart's Inverse Care Law.

Time for health promotion was important. Martin Smith recalled caring for patients with hepatitis C and HIV, despite the low prevalence amongst Liverpool drug users: 'In 1985 the Advisory Council on Misuse of Drugs had recommended that GPs become more involved in helping heroin addicts because of the increasing prevalence of HIV/AIDS. In fact, there were remarkably few addicts in Liverpool with HIV/AIDS, although it was ravaging the gay community.' He continued, 'In 2002 I spent time working at the liver diseases outpatient department at the Royal Liverpool Hospital. This was the early days of developing treatment for hepatitis C, an increasing problem for current and ex drug users. The plan was to develop community treatment, which is now becoming increasingly common.'

Martin also recalled the evolution of multidisciplinary teamwork:

> For a couple of years we had a registrar from the DDU, Dr Ruth McCutcheon, doing a weekly clinic along with a community nurse. By 2008, most face to face appointments were between client and a specialist nurse. Over the years there has been a gradual change in addiction care from being almost entirely managed by psychiatrists, to a much more multidisciplinary affair with nurses, psychologists and social workers often managing prescriptions, with medical input much more intermittent.

Summing up his work with patients suffering from addiction problems at

PPHC, Martin concluded:

> It certainly wasn't all doom and gloom and rules and regulations. I had a wide range of patients with addiction problems. As is to be expected, a fair number were struggling with their lives. For them it was a case of trying to keep them as healthy as possible with the long view. I met many interesting people - musicians, artists, academics. I even got a credit on a musician's CD.

CHAPTER 5

The learning curve continues

Cyril Taylor's retirement

Practice management: links with the University of Liverpool Department of General Practice

The Inverse Care Law, workload and strain

The Association of General Practice in Urban Deprived Areas (AGUDA)

Medical records and computerisation: a great leap forward

Cyril Taylor's retirement

Cyril Taylor had set the bar high with his prodigious energy, combining full-time general practice with being a city councillor and more. He had been made a Fellow of the Royal College of General Practitioners in 1981 and was invited to give the Albert Wander lecture at the Royal Society of Medicine in 1985. Cyril retired in 1987. By this time, the practice had 5 partners and 9,000 patients. Looking back, he was a hard act to follow. He was still around for several years as a much-valued part-time locum GP, but he had handed over the reins and the huge burden of his large list and patients' expectations to Paul Thomas, his trainee (and tennis partner). Paul worked alongside Cyril for a six-month handover period after completing his trainee year. But he was taken aback when he learnt that '4,000 patients had just got a letter saying that I was now their doctor.' His surgeries were already fully booked, while the patients inherited from Cyril included 'some of the oldest and sickest - as well as all the drug addicts that Mike Ross had shared with me - and some very senior people, medical specialists and Liverpool grandees.' 'In those days', Paul added, 'I attended a funeral every month.'

In retirement, Cyril followed in Sheila Abdullah's footsteps and became a member of the Central and South Community Health Council, whose chair, Sylvia Hikins, was Cyril's partner for the last 13 years of his life. She recalled Jenny Murray on Woman's Hour describing it as 'the most radical in the country.' The CHC continued campaigning alongside health workers and local organisations to maintain and improve services that were under threat. An example was the Children's Walk-In Centre set up after difficulties with staffing forced the closure of Myrtle St Children's Hospital in 1990. The health authority and the CHC both recognised the level of need in Liverpool 8 and the surrounding area. A primary care-based clinical team was employed to run the Walk-In Centre when Alder Hey Children's Hospital declined to be involved. The centre now houses the Smithdown Walk-In Service on Smithdown Rd, within easy reach of people in L8 and L15. Cyril was also involved in the campaigns to save Duchess Ward at the Women's Hospital and to create the Windsor Day Hospital, a community mental health unit in Liverpool 8. His professional and political achievements were recognised by public health professionals as well as GPs, and in 1990 he was awarded the Duncan Medal by the Institute of Population Health at Liverpool University. As president of the Socialist Health Association, he continued campaigning locally and nationally until his death in 2000 (SHA 2000).

Game, Set and Match

Seamos Amables Con Los Pacientes
smiles the blue-faced, smiling Cuban nurse
from the blue poster on the wall.
We wait in the hall. Litany of familiar names,
familiar rooms. We wait to hear ours.

First you played singles, then
mixed doubles, then trained a squad,
playing on new courts

Hard-fought games against pain, disease, ignorance.
Sometimes a win in straight sets,
sometimes a struggle to hold the service.
The grim finals against the unbeatable opponent.

Now you will retire,
play the desperate game only for pleasure,
watching the young players
in the Autumn park.

This poem from the loyal fans
who have cheered you over the years
as you leap the net to a new beginning.

Game, Set and Match was drawn by artist David Knopov and written by
poet Adrian Henri

VOICES newspaper, February 2001

Practice management, and links with the University of Liverpool Department of General Practice

As more GPs were taken on and the primary care team expanded, PPHC became an increasingly complicated organisation. Medical schools provided no training in management, nor did GP vocational training schemes. Nevertheless, all GP partners were *de facto* managing small businesses. This was something many GPs, and perhaps the idealists at PPHC especially, found hard to prioritise. Dr Kit Oi Chung commented, 'Often GPs who are interested in community activities and other innovative ideas are not that careful when looking at the financial side of the business.' Dr Mike Ejuoneatse, appointed as a partner in 1994, agreed: 'Given that general practice is a small business, there was not enough focus on this aspect of the job.' Lis Davidson, one of the more business-minded partners, commented, 'The expectation of what is to be delivered in such a complex system is bordering on impossible.'

Nevertheless, some things worked very well. Susanna Graham-Jones was pleased that the partnership ran on a 'one partner, one vote' basis, so that part-timers were fully involved. Also, she felt that individual GPs were able to work to their strengths and be more effective because they each had backup from a particular secretary who knew their referral patterns and could work proactively. Like other GPs, she valued the morning meetings at which problems and solutions could be batted around:

> It was the absolute opposite of what you'd find elsewhere, the moaning and groaning and slumping into learned helplessness and demoralisation in the face of pressure. GPs at PPHC mostly trusted each other, listened to new ideas, and acted with the courage of their convictions - to me this explains the astonishing flow of innovations which I witnessed between 1986 and 1993.

Karen Hewitt, receptionist and later practice manager, agreed:

> It was always busy if not chaotic, but it was organised chaos. I have had to deal with everything from someone threatening to burn the place to the ground to providing shelter for a patient in his shirt/underpants and socks who was locked out of his house! But when you have clinicians who have their finger on the pulse it reflects in your management of a practice. PPHC shaped me as a manager, I experienced some of the best years of my working life there.

As in other larger practices, the new role of practice manager was taken on by experienced administrative staff, but there was no bespoke training. Sheila Scott had worked with Cyril in Sefton Drive and did her very best as practice manager at PPHC to keep the show on the road, meeting weekly with the GP partner responsible for administration. Fortnightly management meetings on Wednesday evenings rotated between the partners' homes, depending on family circumstances. Issues discussed over a bottle of wine ranged from old chestnuts like the unmet demand for appointments to exciting proposals for research, teaching initiatives or community-based events. Minutes were circulated and decisions recorded. Susanna looked forward to these meetings, alternately exhilarated and engloomed. However, Judith Hindley recalled, 'I enjoyed our practice meetings because I liked the company of my partners. But I distinctly remember one meeting when we got at least an hour through the agenda before realising that it was actually the agenda of a previous meeting...I am still not sure if we reached the same decisions or not.'

Professor Ian Stanley, appointed as the first Professor of General Practice at the Liverpool Medical School in 1985, had made links with the Merseyside RCGP Faculty, which ran the GP vocational training scheme and with the Local Medical Committee, which represented all GPs in the city. He became a partner in a practice based in Old Swan. Ian Stanley's was the first academic department of general practice in the UK to be funded independently of NHS GP income. This meant that as well as funding GP lecturers, non-clinical lecturer posts could be created in his department. Dr Chris Atkinson was a lecturer in management science interested in 'complexity mapping' in primary care settings. Dr Maggie Pearson was a social scientist and Dr Alan McWilliams specialised in information technology. Over time, all these academics worked with PPHC. Chris Atkinson attempted a project on 'effective use of staff time' and 'team-building' exercises. These did not always go down well. Pip Abraham remembered, 'The facilitator told us we had allowed patients to run a coach and horses through the appointment system, and at the end of the day Lis Davidson said she would probably ignore it all!'

At the time of Cyril's retirement in 1987, he was Provost of the Merseyside and North Wales Faculty of the RCGP. That year PPHC hosted a joint meeting of the RCGP Faculty and the University of Liverpool Department of General Practice, with a string quartet from the university playing during the lunch break. Katy Gardner, Sheila Scott, Chris Atkinson and Susanna Graham-Jones had worked on the agenda. This centred on the existential difficulties of a team in which GPs were independent contractors, while some team members were their employees, and other administrative staff, health visitors, district nurses and social workers were employed by other organisations. Hence the theme of the meeting: 'The Primary Health Care Team - Fact or Friction?'. There were discussions about power, conflict of interest and - in a foretaste of bitter things to come - lack of control. The practice GPs told a cautionary tale about the perils of investing in teamwork involving other agencies. This concerned the fate of a social worker whose attachment to the practice had been a real success. Funding for her job was summarily abolished when Liverpool City Council reconfigured its social services provision, and the practice was powerless to keep the post.

The Inverse Care Law, workload and strain

In 1989, a quality-of-life survey indicated that over 44% of Liverpool households were living in poverty (Liverpool City Council, 1989). Trainee GP Kathrin Thomas described her impressions on arriving in Liverpool that year:

> [I arrived] a week after Hillsborough. This, and the Derek Hatton/Militant legacy, were powerful influences on the culture and political discourse, which I never really got to understand as an outsider. Liverpool felt like an island; jokes about the 'Republic of Liverpool' felt attractive to me. I really liked the anger that the city had, even if I didn't get every cause for it; and that so much of this was turned into something productive.

Many consultations were about social issues; just being there reliably in the surgery seemed to meet a need. Paul Thomas remembered:

> [There was] a boy who liked to come and see me to say hello. He had no father in evidence, and I had once helped him get out of trouble with the police. One day he came and said 'Dr Thomas, I've got a sore throat.' I said 'How nice to see you, how's your mum? School?' Then: 'Well I'd better look at your throat.' 'Oh,' he said, withdrawing into the chair, 'it's better now.'

Paul commented, 'Here's a message - GPs can be the most accessible, educated, caring people that disadvantaged people can routinely get to see.'

The first phase of the World Health Organisation's Healthy Cities programme began in 1988, encouraging cities to identify problems and set out their priorities for change. Dedicated public health physicians such as Dr John Ashton led Liverpool's early involvement in the programme (Ashton, 1994). Professor Peter Townsend, who had written extensively on poverty and social exclusion and had visited Liverpool as part of the Healthy Cities programme, came to PPHC to take part in a Channel 4 documentary about poverty (Delamothe, 1988). Katy took Peter Townsend and the TV crew to visit some patients; but several declined to take part in the programme, perhaps because of shame, low self-esteem, or fear. One of these was a single parent who had got into debt after being made redundant and had been threatened by loan sharks on her doorstep. Another had no cooker after hers had blown up a few months previously; her child was eating baby dinners heated on a neighbour's stove. A patient whose daughter had cerebral palsy only had two sets of clothes and wore sandals all year round. She had recently got into further debt as her mum had died and she had to feed the mourners at the funeral.

The TV programme ended up featuring more run-down streets and buildings than people. In the Communist Party newspaper 7 Days, Katy wrote:

> Channel 4 photographed empty buildings, when in fact people had been keen to move out, leaving them empty, because of the run-down condition of the area. They were less interested in the stories of patients who were doing their best to keep afloat with dignity, despite having their benefits cut and no job prospects. I have patients who have killed themselves because they could not tolerate unemployment, and felt worthless. (Hudson, 1989)

Peter Townsend, however, understood what Katy saw every day: that the worst effects of poverty might be felt as social exclusion. This may not have been as visible as derelict buildings, but it was there, and it mattered.

At PPHC, the ethos of proactive health care and the large number of patients with complex needs meant that the number of patients who could be registered with each GP, and properly looked after, remained well below the national average. Full-time GPs' patient lists at PPHC generally ran at around 1,600, compared with the RCGP's recommendation of 1,800. Because of the capitation-based GP payment system, the small list sizes generated below average income for the practice. Lengthy surgeries to accommodate long appointments and emergencies meant that, even with a low GP consultation rate of three per patient per year (data from 1990-1992 annual reports) and an excellent primary health care team, GPs felt overstretched. Christine Wall, FHSA manager in 1990, was aware of the significant differences between practices:

> There were many good practices in Liverpool working hard to provide a service to a deprived inner-city population. There were also a number of single-handed practices which, despite having a high list size and high income based on capitation, were unable to provide the service required...There were patients who loved their GP because they were always referred to hospital. There were premises that were quite frankly not fit for purpose, and there was an overwhelming need to attract more general practitioners to the area.

Choices could be hard when practice finances were tight. Practice nurse Clare Corless recalled. 'Many patients could not fill in forms and felt intimidated by social security, so the nurses and GPs helped them to get the benefits they needed to survive, thus improving their health.' Doctors sometimes attended benefit tribunals, as they could often help to secure positive results for patients, but their time cost the practice money. GPs in other practices were less likely to 'go the extra mile' for their patients in this way. The GP's contribution could improve the outcome, but the indignity of the whole process could be deeply damaging to the patient. Katy remembered telling the tribunal for a depressed diabetic patient that if they took away her benefits the patient would die, either by suicide or neglect, due to poverty and being unable to manage her illness: 'It was heart rending - both the patient and I were in tears, but we won.'

Frontline staff and secretaries bore the brunt of patients' frustration when things took a long time or did not go according to plan, and the GPs felt it was appropriate to recognise this. The partnership's decision to pay their receptionists and other staff above the going rate in the 1980s further reduced the GP partners' earnings from so-called 'practice profits'. Some partners would have liked to run the practice as a co-operative and profoundly reduce inequality of income, as was the case at the Darnall

Practice equal pay collective in Sheffield, where Lis Davidson had previously worked. However, the PPHC partners never reached a consensus, and the idea was dropped. In fact, the Darnall practice eventually had to abandon this model due to their inability to attract new GPs to relatively low-paid posts. Retired Darnall GP Jack Czauderna reflected, 'The 1970s were the most equal decade in recent times and it was possible to attract doctors mostly because of their political passion, commitment to patients and public health ethos. As Thatcherism got going it became increasingly difficult to sustain.'

In preparation for advertising for a new partner, a 'Belbin team-role self-perception role inventory' exercise was undertaken once or twice by the existing partners (Belbin, 1981). This is a management tool intended to highlight any unfilled but necessary roles in the team. Gaps were identified, but filling them was difficult. Susanna remembered, 'As with other practices I have known, the missing role was always the 'completer-finisher' - we had most of the other roles covered. Katy was always the 'plant', or seeker-out of new resources, adept at making contacts outside the practice and bringing in new ideas. Alan Forbes scored high as a chairperson. I was always betwixt and between.'

Despite offering relatively low GP pay, the practice continued to attract highly motivated young doctors throughout the 1980s, including Mike Ross, Lis Davidson, Alan Forbes, Martin Smith, Judith Hindley and Paul Thomas. Being on call continued to be stressful. Paul remembered the adrenaline rush: 'Once I was so tired that I couldn't eat supper and my head was falling into my plate at home. The phone went, and immediately I became clear-headed and fully awake; for me, a stark illustration of the power of the mind to overcome difficulties when the motivation is there.' Judith described a weekend on call:

> The Motorola mobile phone (or brick!) we used was huge and very awkward. You had to divert to your home number and we each had our own code. This divert involved a fraught period of saying STOP as clearly as you could, as the automated programme counted down. It could take ages! Another issue was battery life - 3 hours, I think. You had to carry a spare battery and ensure you could get home regularly to charge it. This was difficult with a busy on-call and added to the pressure. There was no filter on calls received, so a patient came straight through to you,

whatever state they or you were in. The night on call which stays with me was when I was woken by a young man who'd had too much to drink and had chest pain at 2.30 am. This was fairly clearly not an emergency, but necessitated a visit, essentially to reassure both him and me. Then at 6.30 am I had a call from an elderly lady with chest pain all night. She had waited till the morning to call rather than disturb anyone. She died in the ambulance on the way to hospital. I always remembered this illustration of how difficult it is to inform people of how to use the health service effectively.

Given the high workload and the stress of working in a deprived area, turnover of GPs tended to be high, and strongly driven and motivated GPs did not always take good enough care of each other. Some GPs escaped, making career moves or going off to travel or study elsewhere. Lis Davidson and Katy Gardner combatted burnout by both working part-time and job-sharing for many years. This was unusual at the time, but they saw it as essential for work-life balance. Accepted by the other GPs, it worked well in that continuity was assured for their shared patient list. For others, there was more risk of burnout, an increasing hazard of inner-city general practice which can affect the whole team. The decision of a valued but stressed colleague to leave takes a toll on everyone, especially the full-timers.

A few decades on, it is rare for GPs to offer 10 or even 11 surgeries per week, as was the norm in the 1980s. Today there is more scope for GPs to work part-time and deliberately develop portfolio careers with different interests. But the advantages of reduced time commitment to their practices in terms of job satisfaction, emotional health and quality of life may compromise continuity of care and satisfaction for patients. Smaller lists, buddying pairs of GPs, and job-sharing are strategies still used to mitigate this problem.

GPs at PPHC did strive to address work-related stress. There were 'time out' team-building events for GPs and staff, including one which began with a South African Wellington Boot dance led by Lis Davidson. Lis also remembered, 'Alan Forbes organised an away-day when Alder Hey Hospital set up a bereavement service. We sat and talked with each other about things. It was about dealing with loss. There was another one when a psychologist came up from London - we had been struggling with each other a bit and she came to help us sort things out.' PPHC parties were also legendary. Chas Clegg: 'Our parties were lots of fun, mainly in-house catering by the Clegg team, Christmas gifts for all the children of staff, and later a visit to the panto with sweets and ice cream, all paid for by the GPs.' Karen Hewitt also enjoyed these events: 'I fondly remember the Christmas parties, usually held in Jan/Feb, dancing at Susanna's house, or sometimes at the health centre.' Administrator Ann Cunningham remembered a party at PPHC where 'someone left the back door open and a couple of our patients walked in and joined the party. We didn't have the heart to tell them it was a private party, so they stayed and helped themselves to the buffet and drinks.' Health visitor Isla Cameron commented, 'There was always a lighter side to PPHC and great socials, including legendary nights out to let off steam at the Everyman 3rd Room.'

The Association of General Practice in Urban Deprived Areas (AGUDA)

AGUDA was founded in 1988 when a group of inner-city GPs in Bristol decided that they had had enough of being isolated and desperate. By whistleblowing about the risk of burnout, they wanted 'to inform, support, nurture and enthuse each other, and to speak out about their plight and their patients' plight.' At the first two-day workshop in Bristol there were 35 attenders, including Katy Gardner and Paul Thomas. Discussion focused on the constant tensions between wanting to work proactively with communities to address the causes of ill health, while struggling to cope reactively with the deluge of unhappiness coming through the surgery door.

The first AGUDA workshop

I don't ever recall feeling like this after going to a meeting of doctors. Usually I am 'playing the game', being the 'post-feminist woman' with my best dress and my best behaviour, in an attempt to see my GP colleagues as allies, even if it means some uncomfortable compromises. This weekend was different. The meeting was called by a practice in Bristol very like ours, in the inner city with a large proportion of black people, high patient turnover, high unemployment, racism and so called 'care in the community' - the sort which consists of dumping people out of mental hospitals and prisons into bed-sits and leaving them to get on with it. We decided to set up an association of GPs working in areas of urban deprivation.

Those who know Kirkby in Merseyside can be in no doubt that people there suffer just as much as people in inner Liverpool. In Toxteth we have a vibrant diverse neighbourhood with two parks and cinemas nearby, while they live in a concrete jungle. This suffering affects not only those we care for but the social workers, teachers and health workers on the patch. Who listens to us? I am thinking of getting a parakeet. I could train it to say soothing things to me when I walk in at 4 am after a night visit, and to shout at burglars. We GPs want to do wonderful things like having Well Man Clinics, diabetic clinics, welfare benefit sessions in the waiting room; but we are deluged by waves of distressed people pouring through the door. At our practice we are even deluged by those who are not our patients, because of our reputation. Last Friday a social worker rang in the middle of surgery with a 15-year-old victim of incest in her car. 'She won't go to her own GP; she can't talk to a man. She's got a terrible discharge, she's not eating. You've got to see her today PLEASE.' We are the practice that likes to say 'yes' - but at the AGUDA weekend a GP quoted Graham Greene - well, he thought it was him: 'Graveyards are full of indispensable people.' The walls of that Bristol health centre were covered with good ideas. The one I liked best was 'Politics with a large or small p'. This was the first time I had been to a meeting of 'ordinary' doctors, not active in the British Medical Association or in trade unions, who wanted to lobby for a better deal, not just for ourselves, but for our patients. Thatcherism is definitely affecting the doctor in the street. (Hudson, 1988)

Katy Gardner, writing as Rosa Hudson

AGUDA acted as a support group for GPs working in areas of urban deprivation in and around cities across the UK, including Liverpool (Livingstone and Widgery, 1990). It attracted left-wingers from the start. It had a short life as an organisation (1988-1994) but helped to ignite activism elsewhere. GP academics in the group shared links with the Association of University Departments of General Practice at local and national meetings. Paul Thomas continued networking through AGUDA when he worked for the Liverpool Primary Health Care Facilitation Project (1989-1994). The Royal College of General Practitioners had previously published substantial papers describing the problems of inner-city practice in London (Jarman, 1981; Bolden, 1981), and in 1991 it set up an Inner-City Taskforce, which consulted GPs nationwide. Its recommendations were published in an

RCGP Occasional Paper (Lorentzon et al, 1994). This highlighted the conflict between treating illness and meeting health promotion targets. The recommendations included improving access to deprivation payments, allowing smaller list sizes for GPs in deprived areas without loss of income, increasing GP input into commissioning decisions for hospital services in their areas and encouraging multi-agency support for team building in primary care.

Twenty years later, the Scottish initiative 'GPs at the Deep End', formed in 2009 under the auspices of Professor Graham Watt in Glasgow, revived the principles and aspirations of AGUDA (Watt, 2019b). Welcomed by both the Scottish government and the Royal College of General Practitioners, GPs at the Deep End brought together GPs from the 100 most deprived urban and rural areas in Scotland. Brainstorming sessions in protected time enabled these overstretched GPs to articulate their priorities and needs. Crucially, they were encouraged to do so without outside guidance or protocols, though these were available if needed. By 2009, Deep End practitioners had the benefit of a substantial evidence base for clinical decision-making, which was not available in 1988. But their core priority from the outset was this: patients with complex needs living in deprived areas often need long consultations, and their GPs need time to think.

Writing recently about GPs at the Deep End, Watt added that GPs needed to stay 'long enough in one place to make a difference' (2019a). He also commented, 'Developing long-term productive relationships [with patients] continues to be the cornerstone of generalist clinical practice, but increasingly the focus is on building similar relationships with professional colleagues, other services and local communities' (2019b). The Deep End movement regards the Inverse Care Law as 'the difference between what practices can do to help patients, especially those with complex multimorbidity, and what they could do if better resourced and better connected' - though Watt was keen to emphasise that this distinction was not about categorising 'good' versus 'bad' medical care by individual doctors (pers. comm., 2020). While AGUDA was a short-lived grassroots organisation with no funding, Professor Watt's success in leveraging the resources of an academic department to obtain government funding has enabled GPs at the Deep End to flourish and persevere.

Medical records and computerisation: a great leap forward (1986 onwards)

PPHC was an early adopter of computerised GP records. Mike Ross, who became a partner in 1981, looked forward to having computers in general practice. Receptionist Helen Rigby remembered, 'Mike started to type his patient records and stick them on the Lloyd George record cards. This meant they could be read more easily, but he drove us mad with his requests for Pritt sticks!' A call for information from GPs using computers on Merseyside went out via the Merseyside Faculty of the RCGP (Hudson, 1982). Susanna Graham-Jones took up the challenge on arrival at PPHC and catapulted the practice into the digital era. In her presentation at a 1987 Merseyside RCGP research symposium, she stated, 'Ever since I first set eyes on a Lloyd George envelope, that tatty but invaluable cradle-to-grave account of a specimen of humanity, I have been concerned about record-keeping in general practice. It seemed such folly to watch receptionists collecting armfuls of notes and stashing away the day's hard-earned information back in filing cabinets where it is almost totally unusable.'

Exasperated by labour-intensive manual systems for keeping track of immunisations, cervical smears, blood pressures and repeat prescribing, as well as time wasted writing patients' names and addresses over and over again, Susanna had invested in a small computer and printer. She devised her own structured consultation records to demonstrate the value of entering information onto a computer where it could be organised and searched. At the 1987 symposium, she continued:

> The extent to which we waffle along with unanswered questions in general practice could be cut back by routine recording of morbidity and prescribing. For example, we could monitor side-effects of drugs, we could map illnesses and symptoms in families, in postal districts, in age, occupational and ethnic groups. Our manual records deter us from asking questions like 'What is the incidence of stress-related symptoms amongst unemployed school leavers after one, two or three years of unemployment?', or 'How many patients default from treatment with antidepressants after the first prescription?' We could be advancing the frontiers of epidemiology and therapeutics.

The potential value to pharmaceutical companies of the information in GP medical records had already been identified. A Department of

Industry 'Micros for GPs' pilot project in 1982 ran out of funding without producing much impact, but by 1987 several improved computer systems were available for GPs to buy. The vision was that every GP might want a desktop computer. However, Susanna's view was that 'the computer packages on offer are best equipped to deal with a rather uninspiring set of procedures from a GP's point of view: age-sex register, call-and-recall systems, repeat prescribing. The catch is that they do not yet have user-friendly consultation recording software, and coding systems for diagnostic information are clumsy.' In 1987 two companies offered systems free to practices in exchange for anonymised prescribing data. This incentive certainly increased uptake, and Mike Ross had been keen for PPHC to opt for a free VAMP (Value Added Medical Products) system. But Susanna was doubtful about handing over information to Big Pharma. She saw her own system as 'an intermediate step between no computer and a tailored GP software and hardware solution.'

Such solutions were not far off. Dr James Read, a university colleague of Susanna's, was already at work on a comprehensive coding system for diagnostic, occupational, social, demographic and therapeutics data, along with codes for medical and surgical procedures. These 'Read Codes' were soon adopted by the NHS. This was a transformational step, as Susanna had predicted, and computer uptake spread rapidly. Lis Davidson devised a questionnaire to consult patients about the free offer mentioned above, as practice GPs were extremely wary. In the end, however, the offer closed, so the practice had to pay for its computer in 1988. PPHC chose the AAH Meditel system and Susanna joined its national GP advisory group. By 1990 about half of UK practices were using computers, and a systematic approach to many aspects of health care became feasible.

As in most practices, individual GPs at PPHC varied in their attitude to and use of the computer. Cyril, returning as a regular locum after his retirement in 1987, never took to it. Administrative and reception staff faced a steep learning curve. Receptionist Helen Rigby said, 'None of us knew what we were doing, but we knew if we pressed F3 we would get the patient's records!' They were assisted by Pat Aglimanye, employed as a computer facilitator after her computer skills training at Blackburne House Women's Technology Centre. This centre was founded by a group of women including Clare Dove, a patient at PPHC. Pat worked closely with Susanna, and alongside Val Ravenscroft and Ann Cunningham on the administrative staff. Ann, who joined the practice in early 1990, became an expert:

> I started my duties collating information on childhood immunisations and cervical cytology and running a well woman clinic and well-baby clinic with a really lovely nurse named Doreen Vernon. In the beginning everything was recorded manually on paper, but I fathomed out the computer system and got all of the information recorded electronically, setting up a call-and-recall system for both immunisations and cytology.

GP record-keeping gradually shifted onto the computer. The printable problem-oriented patient summary was soon recognised as a key resource, and GPs got used to entering consultation records on the computer. Eligibility for GP training practices from 1990 onwards depended on familiarity with computer use and maintenance of high-quality patient summaries. Even the appointment system was computerised. Karen Hewitt looked back in amazement at life before computerisation: '9 years in reception, before good IT - I am surprised I am here to tell the tale!' Across the rest of the UK too, the ideal of going paperless was now on the horizon, and central funding was at last provided for NHS general practice computers.

CHAPTER 6

Battling the Inverse Care Law in the early 1990s

The 1990 Act: a different kind of NHS?

The new GP contract

Campaigning and advocacy as a way of life

Toxteth Health and Community Care Forum

The Health Thru Arts festival (1992)

The 1990 Act: a different kind of NHS?

The NHS and Community Care Act 1990 was preceded by four white papers, rushed out without much consultation. Cyril Taylor, still working as a locum at PPHC, noted the hasty launch of the white paper *Working for Patients* (Department of Health, 1989). He contrasted this with the methodical gathering of evidence and wide consultation undertaken for the 1979 Merrison Report. A major factor behind the 1990 Act was government concern about the increasing costs of health care, although the proportion of UK gross domestic product spent on health care was consistently lower than that in most developed countries, at around 8%, compared to 11-12% in most of Europe. The USA was always more extravagant, with its free-market system (Office of Health Economics, 1995).

The 1990 Act brought sweeping changes to the NHS and presaged a shift in the balance of power between primary and secondary care. Christine Wall worked at the Liverpool Family Health Services Authority (FHSA). Her memories give an insider's perspective on these changes:

> FHSAs were NHS organisations involved in the planning and delivery of primary care...replacing family practitioner committees (FPCs). FPCs had often been dismissed as bodies with limited functions other than to provide 'pay and rations' for general practitioners under contract to them. FHSAs on the other hand had general managers with much greater powers than their predecessors to plan services and hold contractors to account...I was one of the first general managers to be appointed and was a strong believer in primary health care and in the need to work with GPs and the local community...My overriding memory of PPHC is recognising that it was a practice which against all odds had been striving to deliver this agenda for some time.

The Griffiths Report (DHSS, 1983) had introduced an emphasis on management in the NHS. Efficiency and 'increased consumer choice' were to be the new watchwords. This had already led to changes in primary care services. District nurses continued to be managed by health authorities, but as Chas Clegg described:

> In the late 1980s district nurse management began to change; lots of new people and new ideas, not always for the better. They wanted to move people round to different practices and I was not prepared to do that. For me it was PPHC or go! Luckily for me, a post became vacant as a primary care diabetes specialist and I continued to work with PPHC in that role, and in the Well Man clinic.

District nurse Pat Jones also found the changes disruptive:

> The early 1990s were a challenging time in district nursing, as the Community Care Act meant the transfer of some responsibilities to our social service colleagues. It was a struggle to rationalise this to patients and families, when we felt that it fragmented care and confused everybody. This division of responsibilities, still not properly clarified, is a major inhibiting factor in care pathways, almost thirty years later.

Provider and purchaser functions were eventually to be separated (see Chapter 10). 'Fundholding' by GPs was piloted from 1991, allowing participating practices to manage elements of their own budgets and purchase some patient services. PPHC, along with most Liverpool practices, vigorously opposed the idea of competing with other practices for resources. It seemed outrageous that government was allowing a two-tier health service to develop, with the prospect of worsening of inequalities in health provision, abandoning any notion of a level playing field. Kathrin Thomas reflected, 'I think people were really fed up with the wider context, as the Conservative government policies in the 1990s were so antithetical to the PPHC ethos. General practice was under huge pressure, and morale in general across primary and community care was very low.' When the policy was reversed and fundholding was abolished by the new Labour government in 1997, Chris Smith, Labour's former Shadow Health Secretary, commented, "I grieve at the damage that has been done over recent years by the imposition of the internal market in the NHS" (1997).

The new GP contract

A new contract for GPs had been under discussion since 1987. In 1990, after several rounds of negotiations had failed, the government imposed it on the profession (Drury, 1998). Christine Wall discussed the implications of the new contract:

> The introduction of a new GP contract in 1990 gave weight to the general manager's powers. General Medical Services (GMS) payments to GPs became more related to performance in meeting targets...More importantly, however, this era heralded a major turning point regarding not only the issue of 'prevention' but also the function of primary health care within the NHS. The challenge was to shift the emphasis from an illness service to a health service, offering help to prevent disease and disability...The new GP contract reflected this by specifically including health promotion and disease prevention..., making funding available for health promotion clinics, training in health promotion, and the employment of a much wider range of ancillary staff.

Writing as Rosa Hudson, Katy Gardner described the reality of life on a typical GP day in early 1990 just after the publication of the 1989 white paper.

Stunningly irrelevant

Our recent advert for a new partner began: 'Want a challenge? Come and work in an inner-city practice where the White Paper is stunningly irrelevant'...My day: I arrived at the health centre at 7.45 on Monday morning after a weekend on call and found that our long-awaited new prescription cards which should have arrived from the printers have been lost. The printers were apologetic, and I was apoplectic. After sorting through letters and results, buoyed up by strong coffee and chat with the GPs about our forthcoming Health Fair, I was just about ready for the day. By the time it got to 11 am I was ready for bed, having seen several people with colds and flu. But I was woken up by the next patient who had recently had an abortion and experienced the full force of anti-abortionists outside the clinic, to the extent that she had to walk past a police cordon. As a practising Catholic, who had agonised about her decision to have an abortion, she was devastated. 'What sort of Christians are these?' she asked. After talking with her at some length I referred her to our local priest for support.

The next two patients had Irritable Bowel Syndrome (IBS), both greatly helped by our patient leaflet on IBS. I started to cheer up. Another half hour passed at an even temperature and then a patient I know well told me she had 'feelings'. She smiled rather strangely and told me that the 'feelings' followed her about. The 'feelings' were a sense of the presence of her best friend who died two months previously. She was from Barbados where, her nephew told me, feeling the presence of spirits is not uncommon. However, her family were worried that this did not seem to be the normal type of visitation, and she was very frightened. She insisted there was nothing I could do, but her nephew promised to take her to have some blood tests. I decided that after surgery I would ring our excellent psychiatric consultant, Rob Poole, and arrange to visit her at home very soon, where we might get a much better idea of what's going on.

A social worker then phoned from the home of a patient with three young children who was extremely drunk, asking what I could do. Over the years I had tried everything to help and support this woman, and I had no answers. 'Nothing,' I replied - and certainly not in the middle of a busy surgery. 'You do what you have to do.' This seemed blunt, but I couldn't help feeling angry and that this might be the end of the line for me, in terms of trying to keep this patient's children with her. The next patient was pregnant. After trying for three years her pregnancy test is finally positive. Jubilation all round - I felt fantastic! Finally, a woman was brought in by a friend after being mugged in the night. She hadn't been to the police as she was too upset, and she looked as if she had a facial fracture. I did a letter for Casualty, encouraged her to go to the police, and arranged to see her again in a couple of days. She was very overdue for a repeat cervical smear as her last one was abnormal, but now was not the time. Suddenly it was 2 pm; the calm after the storm, followed by eating burnt toast and getting marge on the prescriptions. Just think - soon, with the new GP contract, I will be able to make more money for doing some nice check-ups on my patients. I can't wait. (Hudson, 1990)

Katy Gardner, writing as Rosa Hudson

As Katy's description illustrates, practices in the inner cities, with their transient and chaotic populations, had to work ever harder to address patients' needs and meet government targets. Christine Wall recognised this and tried to help: 'Targets for health promotion, admirable in themselves, were difficult for inner-city practices, including Princes Park, to achieve.' Amongst other initiatives she arranged funding for a Somali link worker to act as an advocate for recently arrived Somali refugees (see Chapters 7 and 9). But this was a drop in the ocean. Investment in healthy lifestyles is a luxury item for those living on the edge. Stressed patients, struggling to make ends meet and bringing up their children in poverty, were unlikely to attend appointments for screening tests and routine checks which did not address their immediate worries. A shift to a more target-focused culture in health care could even be perceived as a form of victim-blaming by health professionals, focusing on individual lifestyle choices and ignoring the wider determinants of ill health, precisely those highlighted in the 1980 Black Report (see Chapter 2).

Worse still, the introduction of financial targets threatened vital doctor-patient relationships based on genuine trust. The need for on-the-spot recording of data as evidence for achievement of targets meant that the computer, useful though it was, became the 'third person in the room' and could distract the doctor from the patient's own agenda. Given the nature of the psychological problems experienced by many PPHC patients, this could be very counterproductive. GP Julian Pratt highlighted the exacerbation of role-conflict for GPs under the new contract: were they to see themselves mainly as practitioners of public health, as first-line providers of health services, or as advocates for their patients? (Pratt, 1995). David Widgery, a radical inner-city GP and member of AGUDA, remarked, 'The new work generated, and the new financial regime which went with it, were simply distracting workers from the attempt to reverse the Inverse Care Law and provide better quality primary care in the city' (Hutt, 2015).

Nevertheless, the encouragement of health promotion in the new GP contract validated what PPHC was already doing, and the emphasis on deployment of a more diverse primary health care team was welcomed. At last there was some funding for the nurse-run secondary prevention clinics for people diagnosed with heart and lung problems and diabetes, for whom good health care could prevent or delay serious problems.

Health visitor Isla Cameron, who joined the team in 1991, described this as a 'golden time':

> I was happy to move from a geographically based patch to be attached to a primary care practice…It was great working with GPs who understood the health visitor's role in preventative public health, and with pioneers in well women clinics, primary care innovations, IT. I had known Cyril and Pat Taylor, as Cyril had helped my mum and her friend Maggie Williams form a nursing trade union at Walton Hospital in the 1950s. It was good to have that continuity…I had the freedom to set up post-natal support groups, including a Muslim Womens' post-natal support group, baby massage groups and antenatal yoga groups, before such things started in the nearby Granby Children's Centre. I also worked closely with the staff of the Amadudu Centre, a women's refuge, to support families experiencing the double stress of domestic abuse and cultural and language barriers. When it all fell apart later, I knew I had been so lucky to have had this time at PPHC. I will always cherish what it meant and the ripples it sent out to the world. And all the gorgeous babies and mothers I had the opportunity to help!

Campaigning and advocacy as a way of life

Following Cyril Taylor's example, PPHC had always extended its advocacy and campaigning work beyond the boundaries of the practice. A patient reminded Katy Gardner of the time when a train of campaigners on the way to a CND demonstration in London hit the electric pylons, breaking several windows and showering people with glass. Katy recalled, 'Luckily there was a plentiful supply of vodka, which we used to clean up cuts and as a medicinal drink for shocked and upset people.' The train eventually limped on to Euston just in time for the end of the demonstration.

As a part-time GP, Katy was able to devote time to activism (Gardner, 1998). She stood as a Communist Party candidate in the 1987 General Election. She was involved with the Toxteth Health and Community Care Forum from its early days (see below), and in the 1990s, after fighting tooth and nail to resist fundholding, she became involved with commissioning (see Chapter 10): 'The heavy burden of people's lives drove me, every minute of my spare time, to try and improve things. With hindsight, there was a cost, both to me and those around me.'

From its inception, PPHC attracted visitors and media attention. In 1982, the television programme *Mission of Mersey* featured the work of the health centre team (BBC, 1982). Cathy Hogan wrote, 'TV and film crews were regular visitors, and sometimes politicians pitched up. Michael Meacher MP is one I remember. The deputy editor of TASS, a newspaper from Russia, was given a tour.' As Shadow Health Minister, David Blunkett MP visited PPHC in the early 1990s with Labour councillor Gideon Ben-Tovim and members of the L8 community. Chas Clegg remembered:

> In 1984 we had a visit from a reporter from a socialist paper in Holland... On my morning round, we visited a couple with their permission: the man was a double amputee with type one diabetes. Although they lived in a council house, only downstairs was accessible to him. Social services were very limited. Nowadays he might have an adapted bungalow - or would he?

Steve Munby also recalled taking several international visitors to visit PPHC, including 'a Nicaraguan doctor, as well as several anti-apartheid campaigners.' In the late 1980s the practice hosted the Corinto Health Campaign, which supported a hospital in Corinto, a Nicaraguan port twinned with Liverpool. Katy travelled to Corinto during her annual leave in 1989, as a doctor with the Liverpool Building Brigade.

GPs and practice staff often took part in actions in support of the NHS, including one in which an epidemic of 'Thatcher's disease' was staged in the city centre, complete with an ambulance for its victims. One advantage of the independent contractor status was that the practice had a certain autonomy in deploying its staff. Cathy Hogan remembered, 'We had a love-hate relationship with the then Community Health Services, who owned and managed the building, and the managers...We often played cat and mouse. During the miners' strike in 1984/5 we collected money from patients, hiding the buckets if we knew we had a visit.' PPHC also collected money to support the anti-apartheid campaign. Katy remembered visiting an elderly patient who was a brilliant seamstress and roping her into making hats for participants in a 5K run to raise funds for the African National Congress.

On one day of action on the NHS in 1988, Katy recalled that 'practice staff positively stampeded to get to the demonstration.' During the 1992 General Election, the practice was able to maintain a skeleton service for a day while many staff went to campaign in a marginal seat on the Wirral. GP trainee Kathrin Thomas, who was there, reflected, 'The Tories won the 1992 election (unexpectedly) after dumping Margaret Thatcher. That was one of the worst days of my life, after campaigning for Labour with great enthusiasm. We had to wait until 1997 for the horrible political climate to change.'

The Health Thru Arts festival (1992)

After the *Reminiscence* exhibition (see Chapter 2), receptionist Marion Barr, working with a group of enthusiastic patients and staff including counsellor Ria Hayward and GPs Lis Davidson and Katy Gardner, set up the Health Through Arts charity. The team obtained funding to run a festival of arts-related activities throughout August 1992. They worked for 12 months with a dedicated group of patients to organise the festival. Katy wrote at the time, 'It was hard work, but the meetings were fun and enthusiasm was plentiful. Many local people advised us, sometimes in opposite directions!' Poet and patient Levi Tafari sent a poem to inspire the team and participating artists. Ria remembered, '[Practice nurse] Doreen was great at drawing in lots of people though her work in the baby clinics immunising children. She would chat to the parents and tell them about the Health Through Arts stuff.' The festival motto was 'Anyone can do it: everyone is welcome'. Liverpool Primary Care News noted that the aim was 'to facilitate the artistic creativity of health centre users and other residents of the area, for the better health of everyone in the area and to be a forum to celebrate the area's talents and vitality' (Liverpool FHSA, 1992).

The Health Promotion team at Alder Hey Children's Hospital was involved in the day-long fair that launched the festival, as were the FHSA and local organisations and artists. Team member Clare Mahoney remembered:

> PPHC was famous for being a radical and creative practice…I was working in health promotion and Katy asked me to help plan the Health Thru Arts Festival. Lis Davidson, Isla Cameron, Robin Ireland and Dorcas Akeju were involved…The Festival took place one sunny Saturday. It was beautifully organised chaos. The community turned out in force and I remember there was music, singing, lots of play activities, babies and children everywhere. And a jumble sale. I noticed a jacket on the stall that looked just like mine… until I realised it was mine. It was a good cause, but it was my favourite jacket, so I retrieved it and hid it behind a filing cabinet, so it didn't happen again!

Over 400 people came to enjoy the free healthy food and entertainment, including music, dance, circus skills and poetry. Levi Tafari performed in the waiting room along with fellow poet Eugene Lange. Katy recalled, 'Some of Eugene's poetry was quite loud, and we had to ensure the sickest patients were seated in a quiet area!' Lis Davidson remembered, 'We had fireworks, firebrands and juggling. We even had animal petting! For me that was a high point. I loved doing it and it was fun.' A massage and relaxation session run by patient Fiona McDavid was so oversubscribed it had to be held in two separate rooms. Fiona later continued the sessions in a nearby alternative health centre, as there was no room at PPHC. Twice-weekly workshops were held during the festival, on themes ranging from kite-making to anxiety management.

A series of poetry workshops produced *A Picture of Health*, a poetry collection written by patients and staff in collaboration with The Windows Project, a local charity. Sylvia Hikins obtained funding from Liverpool Community College to run a weekly writers' workshop, which continued for two years: 'Referred patients could discuss and write about their emotions, hates, loves, hopes and fears, which was a therapeutic activity.'

Another event showcased the paintings of a 90-year-old patient who had never exhibited his work before. Katy wrote about him as Rosa Hudson in *Health Matters*:

Jack (not his real name) had severe agoraphobia all his life, helped only by his wife who enabled him to go out. After she died, he became very depressed, but his social worker found him a residential home with a bright garden. There he started to draw and paint, encouraged by other residents. Had he not been from a working-class background he might well have had therapy for his condition when he was younger and gone to art college. As it is, he has been celebrated at 90 for the brave and talented man that he is. (Hudson, 1992)

Some of the festival workshops were funded as health promotion clinics by the FHSA. Its chair, Rosemary Hawley, wrote to Katy, 'Congratulations on such an imaginative and successful month-long event. I know you have had a long-term interest in a very broad view of health. It seems that many others are at last realizing this is the right view of health.' Taher Qassim, who later set up and chaired the Liverpool Arab Arts Festival, remembered:

I asked: what does a cultural event have to do with health? Only now do I understand that important vision: health is more than clinical health. But I do remember once telling a PPHC GP with excitement about a public health event, including a cultural event, coming up shortly. I asked him if he would attend, and his immediate response was, 'this kind of stuff is for Katy.' It stuck in my head then that not all the PPHC GPs had similar views.

Shape your own destiny

The meditation of the heart
Motivates the mind
seek deep within yourself
explore and find
Your purpose in life
With all its meanings
opportunities will come
can you feel the feeling
You can move mountains at will
but you have to have that intention
from the tree of life
pluck the fruit of inspiration
have faith in yourself
is what I believe
stand firm, speak up
and you will achieve.

OPPORTUNITIES EXIST, WHAT'S YOUR VOCATION
INSPIRATION..MOTIVATION..AND A LITTLE DEDICATION.
OPPORTUNITIES EXIST, WHAT'S YOUR VOCATION
INSPIRATION..MOTIVATION..AND A LITTLE DEDICATION.

People have ideas
on how life should be
when you travel life's road
move carefully
Fulfil your ambitions
what ever they are
with the right attitude
you can go far
Believe you can achieve
as time passes by
find your space on earth
and then rise high
The right state of mind

can obtain your goal
express yourself
mind, body and soul.

OPPORTUNITIES EXIST, WHAT'S YOUR VOCATION
INSPIRATION..MOTIVATION..AND A LITTLE DEDICATION.
OPPORTUNITIES EXIST, WHAT'S YOUR VOCATION
INSPIRATION..MOTIVATION..AND A LITTLE DEDICATION.

Flowing through your mind
embedded in your head
are pictures that are painted
when words ae being said
Translate the images
then make your decision
put them into perspective
and make a contribution
this life is to be cherished
if but for one day
because where there is a will
there is always a way
Take the tools of life
to shape your own destiny
one life, one aim, one opportunity.

OPPORTUNITIES EXIST, WHAT'S YOUR VOCATION
INSPIRATION..MOTIVATION..AND A LITTLE DEDICATION.
OPPORTUNITIES EXIST, WHAT'S YOUR VOCATION
INSPIRATION..MOTIVATION..AND A LITTLE DEDICATION.

Levi Tafari, June 1991

The Toxteth Health and Community Care Forum

The Toxteth Health and Community Care Forum was a Lottery-funded charity providing health information and advocacy services. It was formed in 1994 when a group of people recognised the need for an organisation within Liverpool 8 to campaign for better services and greater involvement in health care. Sam Semoff, a PPHC patient and health campaigner, was instrumental in founding the forum, along with Carmel Dersch, who had previously worked at Alder Hey Children's Hospital. Another PPHC patient, Geraldine Poole, became its administrator. The forum had premises in Lodge Lane, just up the road from PPHC, and worked closely with the practice. Staff contributed to the forum newspaper, *VOICES*, edited by Sam and distributed door to door in the neighbourhood. Links were made with Black, Asian and Minority Ethnic (BAME) groups including the Chinese community.

The forum organised health days on topics such as diabetes, women's health and older people's health, events promoting opportunities for Toxteth residents to work in the NHS, and health fairs in the park. Following in the footsteps of the 1980s Neighbourhood Health Project, the forum arranged outings to the seaside and helped Somali women to learn to swim in women-only sessions at a nearby pool. Carmel remembered taking a group of Somali women for a day out to Formby beach: 'The sun shone and everyone was so excited to see the sea. Shoes came off. Women ran down the beach, lifted their dresses to their knees and paddled in the water.' Later, funding was obtained for a drop-in health information service on Lodge Lane. One of the forum's notable achievements was to put Asperger's syndrome on the map in the 1990s, not only in Liverpool 8, but throughout the city. A day on Asperger's and autism was so oversubscribed that a larger meeting room had to be found.

In 2000 the forum organised a conference with Central and South Primary Care Group (PCG), attended by more than 60 people, to encourage more effective working with local communities. Forum chair Carmel Dersch memorably asserted, 'It is no longer enough to start pilot projects and then, just as they are proving their worth, allowing them to come to an end because the funding has run out.' But in 2004, after 10 years and two tranches of Lottery funding, the money for the forum did run out; Central Liverpool Primary Care Trust, though supportive, was unable to pick up the tab. As an article in *Radical Community Medicine* had pointed out years before, 'NHS and other funders are always wary of organisations which challenge medical hegemony' (Watt, 1987). The forum had certainly done that. Katy reflected, 'Challenging the NHS to respond to local voices has been important to me. Although this has never been plain sailing, the Toxteth Health and Community Care Forum succeeded in being this voice. Lip service is often paid to such community organisations, but long-term funding is always an issue, even if the organisation has been successful in achieving its objectives.' Activists had to bide their time, but did not give up. Eventually, a virtual healthy living centre, Heal8, stepped into the forum's shoes (see Chapter 12).

CHAPTER 7

The Family Health Project: tackling the needs of homeless people (1993-1996)

Dangerously near breaking point

Building the Family Health Project team (1993)

Health advocacy: the research project

Project evaluation

What happened next?

In the late 1980s the practice list size had increased, with a new wave of temporary residents. Due to housing need, more hostels for homeless people, single people and families had opened in the area. Some housed newly arrived refugee families fleeing from the conflict in Somalia. The practice used the city interpreting service to deal with the language barriers, but post-traumatic stress is difficult to deal with in any language. The increased workload associated with the new arrivals was undeniable and began to feel burdensome. Practice finances were tight, and it was disappointing that the new 'deprivation' allowances for practices, based on underprivileged area scores (UPAs, see Chapter 1), did not apply to temporary residents.

GPs had to care for temporary residents without the benefit of any medical records, and often without the help of interpreters. Initial encounters often followed night calls from hostel staff requesting visits for symptoms such as coughs, sore throats and earache. Anxious hostel residents were often not aware that GPs, on call night and day, would expect patients to take over-the-counter remedies for minor illnesses, waiting until the next morning to make an appointment. Sirad Elmi, recently appointed as a Somali link worker based at PPHC, pointed out that most newly arrived Somalis were given no information about how to use the health service: 'People coming over from Somalia had no idea of the UK NHS. Back home they just went to the doctor if they were sick, and usually got medicine. They also had to pay. There was no appointment system' (See Chapter 9).

Dangerously near breaking point

A run of night calls in early 1992 was the straw that threatened to break the camel's back. At a breakfast meeting, one of the full-time GPs exploded with frustration about the previous night's repeated calls from a hostel housing Somali refugees, saying that patients were abusing the system. Alarm bells rang loudly for Susanna Graham-Jones - it was clear that attitudes to 'demanding' patients were hardening. Only a handful of patients had ever been taken off the PPHC list by GPs, following rude, abusive or racist behaviour. PPHC doctors prided themselves on empathy and had a high tolerance of patient demand, including requests for night visits which would have been regarded as inappropriate by many GPs. Generally, they preferred to negotiate and educate. Now, however, some GPs started muttering about using a locum GP agency for on call services for the first time. Previously this option had been shunned because it was regarded as providing a second-class service for patients.

Susanna recognised the symptoms of burnout in the practice. She herself hugely enjoyed her two days a week in PPHC. She was on call for the practice every Thursday afternoon and night, covering the half-day closure, but she did not work at weekends. She spent the other 3 days of her working week at the university. She worked full-time as a doctor with small children, but had a manageable workload; she also felt bolstered by her earlier psychiatry training, which she regarded as a definite bonus for a GP working in the inner city. But for the stressed full-timers, the selfless image of GPs at PPHC was breaking down. Being victims of stress themselves, they were beginning to blame their most vulnerable patients. This vicious circle - the Inverse Care Law at work yet again - seemed to centre, at this point, on the 'temps', as temporary residents placed in hostels were known. Susanna reflected on this and voiced her thoughts at a practice meeting. She pointed out that doctor-based care for temporary patients with overwhelming social distress, housing and benefit problems, was unrealistic as well as expensive. The practice could not afford to build doctor-patient relationships of the 'cradle-to-grave' variety for patients who would only stay in the area for a few weeks or months. An alternative to the traditional GP model was needed.

Susanna took her research proposal for streamlining the care of homeless temporary residents to the FHSA and the University of Liverpool Department of General Practice. Christine Wall at the FHSA picked up on the proposal's emphasis on increasing skill-mix to address the complex needs of temporary residents, whilst protecting GPs from burnout. She recognised 'the ethos that has driven the practice to provide services tailored to the needs of their patients and to come up with innovative ways of tackling health inequalities. The practice was indeed ahead of the game in many ways. As an FHSA it was our duty to support, encourage and wherever possible fund these innovations.' With support from the Regional Health Authority, an application for ring-fenced funding for services for homeless people was made under Section 56 of the NHS Act 1977. Funding was agreed for a three-year trial of health advocacy for homeless temporary residents at PPHC, starting in 1993. Patients would have their housing, social, medical and psychological problems identified, and GPs' involvement would be limited, as far as possible, to medical problems.

Building the Family Health Project team (1993)

Two new posts were created for the project. The first was for a Family Health Worker (FHW) with clinical qualifications, to work with new temporary residents. This role involved listening to their stories, identifying medical needs and following up other problems with health advocacy, signposting and support. Liz Gaulton, who was both a general and mental health nurse, got the job and stayed for five years (1992-1997): 'I saw an advert in the Liverpool Echo and it looked interesting and different. I was commuting to Ormskirk and wanted something nearer home. Once I came for the interview I was hooked. I loved the feel of the place, the people who interviewed me and the idea of working with the Toxteth community.' Liz's previous experience in mental health day centres turned out to be invaluable. She was unfazed by complicated stories and was a sensitive listener. Her job amounted to needs assessment, followed by helping patients to navigate health and social services and systems. She was able to help distressed patients identify what they needed to do and support them through their stay in the area, whilst taking care not to allow them to become dependent on her.

The second post was for a team member to help with record keeping and project evaluation. Siobhan Reilly took on this role:

> I applied for a support worker/researcher role and when I read the job description I felt it was written for me. I was so excited to be offered the role and to have a job in Toxteth, Liverpool. It was exactly what I was looking for, having recently graduated with a Business Studies degree in Bradford. The vibe I got from the interview was an indication of the culture of PPHC. There was always a buzz and I loved working with the staff who were incredibly committed, hardworking and enthusiastic...I was welcomed and accepted even though, as a researcher, I didn't really fit in with other roles there...PPHC seemed to be at the centre of where any action was.

Siobhan worked on the Family Health Project from 1992 to 1996, and subsequently wrote up the evaluation for her PhD at John Moores University (Reilly, 2000).

The Family Health Project was deliberately designed as action research, with three aims:

1. To improve care for temporary residents registered at PPHC, promoting accessibility, health needs assessment and advocacy work by the FHP team based at the practice.

2. To explore formal assessment of the effectiveness and efficiency of health advocacy with homeless people and hostel residents, using patient-centred assessment of quality of life and health as well as workload statistics.

3. To reduce workload and stress for medical and reception staff associated with the care of this multiply deprived client group, by means of the Family Health Worker taking a holistic view of the client and using a team approach to separate 'medical' from 'social' needs.

Ways and means had to be found to fit a research study into a busy practice. Methodology evolved during a month-long pilot phase. The team tested questionnaires on 50 new temporary residents as well as a sample of permanently registered patients. They familiarised themselves with medical records and the computer. They visited hostels, women's refuges and bed and breakfast hotels in the area to introduce the project. Susanna worked with the team on design and methodology, and Lis Davidson later acted as a second project GP.

Health advocacy: the research project

Of 35 Homeless Services projects funded under the NHS Act 1977, only PPHC's was ever formally evaluated (Williams, 1995). The results of the health advocacy intervention were compared with outcomes from a control group of similar patients not supported by the Family Health Worker. Efficacy and cost effectiveness were investigated. Baseline questionnaires collected health needs and demographic data, and measured quality of life (QoL) using validated measures (Life Fulfilment Scale, Nottingham Health Profile and a 'Delighted-Terrible Faces' scale). Follow-up questionnaires were to be filled in by patients still contactable after three months. The all-important outcome measures were changes on the three quality of life measures and the health service workload associated with each patient.

A controlled trial was implemented by alternating the service month by month. In 'health advocacy' months, the FHW would meet with new temporary residents, preferably before they saw a GP. She would complete a needs assessment, do a health check, compile a list of medical problems for the GP, and encourage each patient to complete the QoL questionnaires as well as the usual new patient questionnaire. During 'control' months, however, new temporary residents did not meet the FHW. Instead, their baseline questionnaires were administered by the support worker as soon as they had registered at PPHC, and they attended the practice in the usual way.

The project team worked effectively with patients, practice staff, hostel staff and local services over the full three-year period, despite some real challenges. First, Susanna moved to a university lectureship in Oxford a few months after setting up the project. Lis Davidson took over as project GP, with Susanna visiting regularly to meet with the team. Next, Liverpool's housing policy changed fundamentally halfway through the recruitment period; homeless families were no longer placed in bed and breakfast accommodation. A commitment to rehousing the homeless within three months, whilst being a very positive move by the council, meant that recruitment to the trial slowed down and follow-up was more difficult. Finally, Liz Gaulton went on maternity leave towards the end of the recruitment phase. Her role was taken on temporarily by the support worker, Siobhan Reilly. The project team met each of these challenges head on, and the demonstration that a lay support worker could provide effective health advocacy was a significant factor in the later decision to roll out the intervention beyond the trial period.

Project evaluation

The results of the trial were first reported as 'Effective Health Care for Homeless People: an evaluation of the Family Health Project' (Reilly et al, 1996). Of 326 temporary residents recruited, 222 (68%) provided valid questionnaires. A similar proportion (68%) completed follow-up at three months. Altogether, baseline and follow-up questionnaires were collected for 117 patients. 72% were women, 74% were under 30, 91% were white British, 86% were single or separated, and 41% were living with children in women's refuges or family hostels. The report demonstrated that quality of life was improved for homeless patients supported by the FHW compared with those registered in control months, on all three QoL measures. Benefit was greatest for patients seen by the FHW soon after arrival in the area, and the best change scores related to self-esteem and mental health. QoL at follow-up was still worse than that of permanently registered patients, but showed modest, statistically significant, improvement. Obviously, the main sources of stress for homeless patients could not be removed by a health advocate. However, her support did seem to make a difference, particularly to newly arrived women living with their children, those with a longer history of homelessness, and those with major psychosocial burdens (Reilly et al, 2004; Gaulton, 1994).

The third project aim had been to protect practice staff and GPs from the stress associated with managing the complex needs of homeless temporary residents. Lis Davidson had reported initial concerns about running a controlled trial at the practice, with the possibility that workload for reception might increase. But GPs interviewed as part of the research later confirmed that 'knowing we've got someone we can call on' was helpful. They appreciated the clear problem lists patients produced after their interviews with the FHW: 'The feeling that there was someone trying to make order out of chaos diminished the perceived stress.' Statistical analysis of practice workload (health service usage) showed that the intervention was cost neutral. Spending on additional staff for the FHP was balanced by savings in health service usage, especially lower referral rates to secondary care, in the intervention group. For the project team and the funders this was a further indicator of success. The investment had paid off: 'Given that early intervention with health advocacy appears to confer at least moderate short-term benefit, the model of additional in-house provision within mainstream primary health care is a credible option for inner-city health care providers with responsibility for homeless families' (Graham-Jones et al, 2004).

What happened next?

Once the trial was completed, Siobhan Reilly applied for a research assistant post in Manchester. She is still working as a health services researcher:

> I am now a professor at Bradford University. Over 20 years later I am still doing primary care related health service research. Research simply hadn't been on my radar, and I didn't feel I was academic enough to even consider it as an option. But the experience of working at PPHC gave me the confidence to carry on. I was also fortunate to have the FHSA fund my fees...I managed to get my PhD in 2000...I still reflect on how practices need to operate and what they are dealing with. Reading academic papers just doesn't give you that.

Christine Wall, who by 1996 was Deputy Chief Executive of the merged FHSA and District Health Authority, felt that the results from the controlled trial justified a roll-out of a similar project at neighbouring practices in Liverpool 8 and 17. Liverpool Director of Public Health Ruth Hussey supported this idea and Liz Gaulton was employed to lead the Primary Care Deprivation

Initiative (PCDI). Liz trained link workers and other lay workers in needs assessment and health advocacy work with disadvantaged people, homeless or not. The PCDI also aimed to reduce workload and stress for GPs and other primary health care staff (Abbott and Davidson, 2000).

Looking back on this time, Liz recalled, 'PPHC and its team were held in high regard by the universities and FHSA. I became known as the 'homeless nurse', and through the high profile of the project was given opportunities that wouldn't normally be expected at the level I was working at...This project influenced future provision throughout Liverpool and beyond' (Gaulton, 1998). Liz left in 1997 to work as a public health specialist in Knowsley:

> I wanted to put my Master's to more strategic use...but also I know I was becoming burnt out with the level of deprivation I was seeing every day, and needed to get upstream of it...The team ethos at PPHC and the Master's in Public Health that the FHSA funded me to do...was the light bulb moment that tuned me in to public health. I am now Director of Public Health and Wellbeing for Coventry City Council (See Chapter 12).

Later, in 2002, when the numbers of refugees and asylum seekers arriving in Liverpool increased sharply, the Liverpool Social Inclusion Team was set up with a similar remit (see Chapter 9). Its work built on the lessons learnt in the Family Health Project, and the link-workers and support workers were redeployed in this new team. Michelle Cox was appointed team manager:

> I was interviewed for the 'Social Exclusion Team Manager' to be based in the portacabin at PPHC. At the interview with Gideon Ben-Tovim, Chair of Central Liverpool PCG, and Margaret Thomson, Chief Executive Officer, I advocated that the role should be not be the 'Social Exclusion' team, which I believe reinforced lack of participation but rather 'Social Inclusion', where I could lead the agenda to ensure all those who identified as being 'disadvantaged' had an opportunity to participate in society: the Social Inclusion Team was born. My vision was to bring together existing teams, i.e. Health Link Workers, Community Development Workers, specialist GPs, a health visitor, HIV and community nurses into a resource that could be accessed by those patients and communities struggling to access primary health services across Liverpool. This was a significant milestone in my nursing career, working with a skilled and compassionate team at Princes Park Health Centre, who...would go above and beyond the call of duty to navigate policies, highlight injustices and address issues impacting on health inequalities.

Cyril Taylor election poster (1950).
Top right: Cyril's house and surgery at
7 Sefton Drive. Right: PPHC under
construction (1976)

June Crosby on Reception (1980s)

Sheila Abdullah in surgery (1980s)

Cathy Hogan at her desk (1980s)

Cyril Taylor and Katy Gardner (1980s)

Lis Davidson in surgery (1980s)

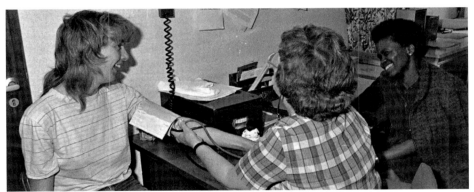

Health Day (1980s) Doreen Vernon checks a BP while Pro Torkington looks on.

Bottom Left: Cyril as Santa (1980s). Bottom Right: Sheila Abdullah, Alan Forbes, Katy Gardner, Mike Ross & Cyril Taylor celebrate prizewinning leaflets (1985).

Sylvia Hikins demonstrates the Birth Box at UB40 fair (1983)   *HART poster (1986)*

*Left: Ceilidh band at UB40 fair (1983). Right: David Blunkett MP with councillor
Gideon Ben-Tovim, GPs and community members (1990s)*

Women in White march (1985)

Margaret Simey opens the refurbished health centre (1995)

Health Thru Arts festival (1992)

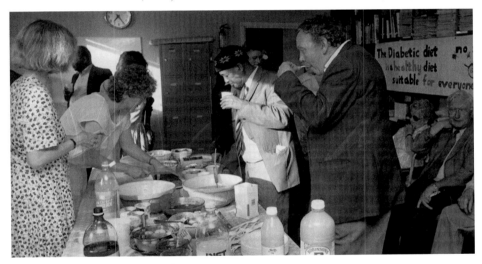

Above: Diabetic health day (1990).

Right: The Rhythm Angels at festival launch (1992).

Prinny Post: New appointments system (2001)

Poster for Public Meeting (2014)

Social Inclusion Team members Rahima Farrah and Leila Saeed enjoy the 40th birthday (2017)

Top: GPs Kate McKinnell and Debbie Faint (2019). Middle: The waiting room (2019). Bottom: Princes Park Health Centre (2019)

CHAPTER 8

Medical audit, troubleshooting and research

The Liverpool Medical Audit Advisory Group

Problem-solving, troubleshooting and research

The Liverpool Medical Audit Advisory Group

One disruptive innovation arising from the NHS and Community Care Act 1990 had a positive impact: the requirement for practices to carry out clinical audits as part of quality assurance. This was an effective stimulus for computerisation, as only with computers could practices collect both baseline and follow-up data on a wide variety of practice activities. Computerised records, in turn, opened the way to analysis and hypothesis-testing within and between practices.

PPHC was known to have a history of auditing practice activity and carrying out research. So, when the Department of Health selected Liverpool to host one of four pilot projects in England, tasked with testing different ways of promoting medical audit among GPs and practice managers across the country, practice GP Alan Forbes was invited to chair the Liverpool Medical Audit Advisory Group (MAAG). Reflecting on the decision to select him, Alan commented, 'I did ask Ian Bogle why he chose me to chair it. He grinned and said that had I not been part of the process, I might have made myself too much of a nuisance.' Other popular MAAG advisors were GPs Len Ratoff and John Hussey at The Elms practice, and Janet Heyes, an old friend of Cyril's.

Liverpool MAAG took a subtle and facilitatory approach that succeeded, against the odds, in attracting many apparently research-averse practices. Introductory meetings were held across the city, during which the audit advisory team met a predictable storm of protests about the additional workload associated with audit activity. They persisted, managing to set up groups of practices to take forward audit projects.

One successful collaboration between the MAAG and the medical school was led by Dr Peter Campion, a GP lecturer based at The Elms, and Susanna Graham-Jones. Practices were encouraged to identify topics for audit. Groups of third-year medical students went to each participating practice to do a week-long feasibility study on the chosen topic, using resources from the Department of General Practice for data analysis. The students presented their findings at meetings attended by practice representatives, the MAAG and university staff. Feedback from practices was almost entirely positive. One GP commented, 'More projects like this would help to change the practice' (Campion et al, 1992). Another innovative MAAG project targeted GPs who said flatly that they could not find time for audit. Dr Ali Al-Shehri encouraged these GPs to make a reflective diary, devoting just five minutes at the end of each surgery to note one ordinary and one unusual event or case. This paradoxical injunction to devote just a small bit of precious time to reflection worked well. Most participating GPs found themselves identifying genuine questions that they could address through audit projects (Al-Shehri et al, 1993).

PPHC and several other practices had already established regular clinics for patients with common chronic conditions and were recording information on computers. The MAAG consolidated this work, facilitating multi-practice audits of diabetes and asthma, setting targets and monitoring results, aiming to improve outcomes for patients by implementing local or national evidence-based guidelines. These audits provided a stimulus for many more Liverpool practices to use computers. MAAG facilitators kept in contact with practices, and groups of practices began to work together, breaking down traditional barriers. One group of single-handed practitioners - nationally regarded as resistant to innovations in practice -

became particularly active. This success story is a tribute to the skilled and sensitive work of the Liverpool MAAG.

In 1989, Paul Thomas left PPHC to take up the post of Primary Care Facilitator for Liverpool, 'consciously intending to apply PPHC values of whole person, whole community health and care throughout the city.' He worked with the FHSA, the MAAG and the Healthy City 2000 Project to develop local multidisciplinary facilitation teams (LMFTs). These teams encouraged and enabled neighbouring practices to work together to drive innovation in primary care throughout Liverpool (Stanley et al, 1993; Thomas 2006). Later, Paul extended this work in Liverpool to other areas nationally and internationally. He developed the West London Primary Care Research Network through Imperial College, and successfully promoted community-oriented integrated care in Ealing (Thomas, 2018).

Problem-solving, troubleshooting and research

Research projects came and went throughout most of the 40 years covered in this book. Some studies were undertaken entirely within PPHC, others in collaboration with other practices, public health departments or universities (see Chapter 12). Relatively few projects resulted in formal publications, but the findings were often disseminated locally. Research at PPHC generally took the form of troubleshooting. A GP would identify a problem, lead discussions in the practice and elsewhere, and then embark on research to understand and address it. Troubleshooting was more stimulating than mere collaboration with research from the ivory towers, in which GPs were often used to recruit patients for projects designed by university academics. Troubleshooting also went beyond audit projects, such as those linked to the MAAG, which aimed to raise health care standards to comply with previously defined objectives.

The evaluation of the Family Health Project described in the previous chapter followed an urgent troubleshooting phase. This led to a three-year controlled trial of health advocacy for homeless patients funded by the Department of Health, a systematic review, a PhD thesis, four published papers, a book chapter and several conference presentations. Another of Susanna Graham-Jones' research projects focused on the quality of life and quality of care of patients with epilepsy. This Merseyside study of epilepsy care in general practice was an interdisciplinary collaboration with clinical psychologist Gus Baker, social scientist Ann Jacoby, and Professor David Chadwick's Department of Neurology at Walton Hospital in North Liverpool. The starting point was observation and analysis of aspects of quality of life for patients with chronic health conditions (Jacoby et al, 1996). The study found that some patients with epilepsy felt let down by the way GPs issued their repeat prescriptions as a matter of routine, failing to offer any medical review. The research findings may have contributed to the decision to promote and incentivise a yearly face-to-face review for patients with epilepsy in the 2004 Quality and Outcomes Framework (see Chapter 13).

Katy Gardner's research into angina, as part of a Master's in Primary Care at the University of Manchester, arose from concerns about inequalities in access to treatment. Katy had seen a patient struggle with her angina over many years, resolutely refusing to be referred for investigation or treatment. PPHC had set up a heart disease register and dedicated clinics, but there were fewer patients on this register than expected. Why was this? Granby, Abercromby and Smithdown wards in the practice area had extremely high mortality from ischaemic heart disease, manifested as a high standardised mortality ratio (SMR) of 156, compared with the average of 100 for England and Wales (Liverpool Health Authority, 1996). Practice patients were dying young. There was marked variation across Liverpool, with wards like Woolton and Allerton having SMRs just over 100. The Inverse Care Law was at work here. There was more heart disease in deprived areas, but patients living there were much less likely to be referred for definitive treatment than better-off people living in the leafy suburbs.

As part of her research, Katy investigated 'barriers to referral' by interviewing patients who had angina diagnosed by a GP, but who had not been investigated by specialists. She also interviewed the GPs. She identified several reasons for referral avoidance. First, as one GP noted, there was a fear of hospitals: 'They give you stories like: my friend went in there and died, or: my brother went in and came out in a pine box.' Second, there was a fatalistic acceptance of angina pain, described here by a 58-year-old patient: 'I sleep a lot in the day, there's nothing else you can do.' A third reason was that some middle-aged patients perceived themselves as old. A patient aged 54 said, 'As far as the heart goes it's probably old age.' The partner of another patient said, 'He says he's in his twilight years, doc.' This patient was 53. Diagnostic confusion was a fourth barrier, especially in the presence of other morbidity: 'I get these feelings in my neck, probably when I get upset about something or when I've eaten a heavy meal. I get a lot of indigestion. Whether that's indigestion or truly a symptom of... you know.' A GP commented, 'It's just not neat and tidy.' Finally, cultural and language gaps between doctor and patient resulted in confusion. Thus, doctors did not always pick up the extent of patients' suffering, which could be submerged in a host of other problems. One GP admitted that 'the consultation tends to get crowded with a variety of things and the point of exit is: can I have my angina spray? The longer you know a patient, the more you get into their social and psychological problems and they become higher up in most of their consultations.' A patient from the Yemen, interviewed through an interpreter, described pain as 'in the chest, the ribs, under the chest and all my body.' This patient was unable to read English, was not taking the drugs prescribed and had a history of missing outpatient appointments. The GP felt she had angina but was unlikely to accept referral to clarify the diagnosis or instigate investigations.

Katy's angina study was published in the *British Medical Journal* (Gardner and Chapple, 1999). The findings were replicated in several northern cities (Tod et al, 2001), and used to inform the development of the Liverpool Heart Health Action Zone. Katy worked with the Healthy Communities Collaborative, a national initiative encouraging local health champions to disseminate health promotion messages (Coulter, 2009). In Liverpool, coronary heart disease (CHD) and cancer were the topics chosen. Barriers to seeking treatment were discussed with volunteers in training sessions specifically aimed at overcoming fear and fatalism. Katy went on to become heart disease lead for Central Liverpool Primary Care Trust.

Central Liverpool PCT manager Michelle Timoney remembered working with Katy at PPHC:

The National Service Framework for coronary heart disease was published in 2000, for the first time setting national standards around heart disease management. A cardiac advisory nurse worked with PPHC practice nurse Clare Corless to build on what the practice was already doing and create structured CHD clinics, so people with a diagnosis or history of heart disease had regular reviews...The practice had fully computerised records, so codes were added to ensure anyone with a history of heart disease would get an invite to the clinic. Everything was recorded on a template. We got more organised as we went on, sending patients for blood tests before their appointment so that results were ready for the discussion with the nurse. We did regular audits to identify people whose care could be further optimised. Princes Park had been working on patient profiling; so there was the chance to identify ethnicity, spoken language, and history of heart disease and tailor care for practice patients. Research and experience demonstrated that people couldn't always recall the signs and symptoms of heart disease, so we produced a straightforward information leaflet, initially in English/Arabic and later in different languages, describing possible symptoms of a heart attack, and asking people to call 999 [see Chapter 9]. The leaflet was distributed around Liverpool practices and pharmacies and publicised in the Echo. We got many calls into the office requesting it.

By 2002 most Liverpool practices had implemented a call-and-recall system for patients with coronary heart disease (Wilkinson, 2003). Cardiovascular disease mortality decreased nationally and locally between 1997 and 2005, and National Heart Tsar Dr Roger Boyle reported that the gap between Liverpool and the England average had narrowed (2005).

Dr Judith Hindley's most memorable heart patient described his angina in dramatic terms, as a 'galvanic' chest pain. However, Judith's research focussed on depression. She had trained in Manchester and was also interested in somatisation - psychological distress manifesting as physical symptoms: 'There was a buzz about being a practice linked with other high-profile inner-city practices through AGUDA, and with the University. We felt we had an experienced voice that was listened to. I was encouraged to complete a study on recognition of patients with depression by GPs based in three different practices.' She wanted to gather reliable information about recognition and management of depressed patients in primary care settings, to provide participating practices with a baseline for audit and allow them to identify areas for improvement. A sample of 296 patients were screened with the 28-item General Health Questionnaire (Goldberg, 1979). High scorers were interviewed by a research psychiatrist to obtain a formal diagnosis (103 were invited, 53 attended). GPs completed a questionnaire detailing their assessment and management of each patient. One third of the high scorers were not identified as depressed by

GPs. All those who were recognised as having depression had discussed antidepressant medication with their GP, but one third were found to be taking inadequate doses. Psychological help was given by the GP to most identified patients and was highly valued by over 50% of them. GPs were solely responsible for management in 75% of cases.

Reflecting on the experience, Judith concluded:

> We established some guidelines in the participating practices: i) all patients with major depression should be recognised; ii) antidepressant therapy should be considered in all patients with moderate/severe depression; iii) GPs should be aware of the psycho-social circumstances of all patients with depression. Areas identified as requiring further consideration were the effectiveness of psychotherapeutic interventions offered by GPs and…by other primary care level mental health workers, and the relationship between primary health care and psychiatric services. The study was never published, but I did have meetings with the other practices, and presented it to a psychiatry meeting at the Royal Liverpool Hospital. Reading it again, it is a snapshot of how we were managing patients with mental health problems then. I get the sense we were doing a lot more in-house than nowadays.

CHAPTER 9

Anti-racism, ethnic monitoring and health (1977-2012)

An Equal Opportunities policy

Ethnic monitoring at PPHC

Ethnic monitoring becomes mainstream (1992)

The Service Development Initiative and patient profiling (1997-2004)

Demographic changes in Liverpool 8 after 1990

MAAN, the Liverpool Somali mental health project (2002-2012)

PPHC as the lead practice for asylum seekers in Liverpool

PPHC spearheaded several separate ground-breaking initiatives relating to anti-racism, ethnicity and health. In 1977 most Liverpool Black, Asian and Minority Ethnic (BAME) people lived in Granby, Abercromby and Arundel wards, many of them in poverty and with poor housing. Unemployment rose steeply from 15% to 30% in the post-industrial doldrums of the 1970s, with containerisation cutting out labour from the docks. The young were even more at risk; a survey of Granby school leavers revealed unemployment rates of 47% for young black people and 43% of young white people (Roberts, 1980).

The problems of delivering equitable health services for BAME communities were clear to all PPHC staff from the outset and were even more evident after the riots and distress of 1981. Existing initiatives supporting BAME communities in Toxteth included the Pakistan Centre in Mulgrave St, Liverpool 8, set up in 1977 as the first purpose-built Pakistani community centre in Britain. Among others were the Caribbean Centre, the Methodist Youth Centre, and Charles Wootton College, opened in 1974 to train young black people in office skills. PPHC worked with all of these.

Pro Torkington, a postgraduate at the University of Liverpool, interviewed Cyril Taylor about primary care in the inner city in 1979 and used this material in her PhD thesis, published as *The Racial Politics of Health - a Liverpool Profile* (1983). This was a fortuitous meeting of minds. Pro had worked with Katy, delivering women's health workshops at Home Link, a voluntary organisation working with women and children, based in a soulless block of flats in Netherley, east Liverpool. At PPHC she was impressed by 'the attitude of doctors to their work and their commitment to their patients... the usual gap between doctor and patient was not there.' Pro further commented:

> Health is a political issue. I cannot understand how doctors can fulfil their professional work outside political considerations...I was pleased to find out that Princes Park Health Centre was right at the centre of the NHS and political landscape. In those days PPHC had a very positive impact on not just the health but the lives of people who were patients...Apart from the impact on patients, the centre was willing to work with anyone whose aim was to improve the health and lives of people in the city centre.

Pro was involved with the Racial Minorities Health Group set up in 1982 in response to the Toxteth riots. Following further discussions at PPHC, she led the Liverpool Health and Race Project (1985-1986), funded by the Area Health Authority and Inner-City Partnership:

> It was that supportive relationship with PPHC which enabled researchers to introduce the screening project - checks for high blood pressure, weight, height, urine testing and blood sugar testing. The doctors offered to train the researcher on how to do blood sugar testing, with the approval of the Local Medical Committee. In addition to screening, a questionnaire and a general discussion on health-related factors such as smoking, diet, alcohol, exercise and any other health topic on which a

patient wanted information, were carried out. All these activities provided an opportunity for doctors to find out if the primary health care service they provided was adequate and acceptable to patients. The Centre was in an area predominantly occupied by black and working-class residents. It was quite satisfying to find out that they are getting a good health service.

The project team included the Neighbourhood Health Project workers (see Chapter 2) who had been trained to take blood pressures. 40 PPHC patients were screened, of whom two had high blood pressure. 70% of those screened had already had blood pressure checks in the last three years, reflecting good care at PPHC. Screening was also carried out in the Hindu Centre, the Somali Centre and the recently opened Abercromby Health Centre nearby. The results of a questionnaire given out during the project were instrumental in making the case for a Liverpool interpreting service and for Mary Seacole House, a support and advocacy project for people from BAME groups with mental health issues (Torkington, 1991).

In 1984, PPHC health visitor Dorothy Zack Williams moved to Abercromby Health Centre as Clinical Lead Specialist at the Centre for Inherited Blood Disorders, which covered sickle cell anaemia, thalassaemia and G6PD deficiency:

> This was the first attempt to address the specific health needs of the Black and Minority Ethnic Community in the Liverpool and surrounding areas. However, once it was set up I had little support from health authorities throughout my time there. The clinic's aims were to provide screening and counselling services for children, teenagers and adults. I also provided information and advice to statutory and non-statutory groups, with leaflets designed to explain the various conditions. An important aspect of my job was to raise awareness of these conditions among colleagues and members of the public. I developed training for parents and health professionals, including nurses and medical students, throughout the North West. In 2004, due to my work, the idea of a Sickle Cell Support Group (SCSG) emerged, consisting of parents and their children as well as community volunteers. I am the patron of this group, which is still active and recently won Big Lottery funding.

An Equal Opportunities policy

In 1986 PPHC invited Rashid Mufti and Pro Torkington to hold a series of race awareness training sessions for all staff, in protected time during working hours. This was the first such initiative in primary care in the city. It demonstrated the commitment of the practice and set a precedent for later away-days and training sessions. Rashid went on to be the first Race Relations Officer in Camden, London. The training focused on prejudice, as well as direct and indirect racism. One young receptionist was fired up enough to go on to university and train as a social worker; on the other hand, there was resistance from a couple of long-established receptionists, who thought the training unnecessary. Lis Davidson co-ordinated an Equal Opportunities Policy Group at the practice, in consultation with the Merseyside Racial Equality Council, the Area Health Authority Equal Opportunities Officer and other local agencies. The group drew up an Equal Opportunities Policy for both staff employment and patient access, aiming for visible representation of black people (not just a token one, but at least two or more people) on the practice staff, though fears of inappropriate positive discrimination also needed to be dispelled. Working with local recruitment agency South Liverpool Personnel, efforts were made to advertise staff vacancies in places where black candidates would see them. Before long PPHC had recruited several BAME administrative staff, trainee doctors and GP partners.

Dorcas Akeju wrote:

> As someone born and raised in Liverpool 8, I am lucky to have used PPHC for as long as I can remember. The community and the city benefited greatly from this innovative and unique approach of care, understanding and genuine need to make sure people received the best care at a time when racism was rife, established and new communities were trying to understand and live with each other, and the city was facing many issues, especially in the 1980s and 1990s.

Low uptake of health and social services and educational opportunities by black people was a major concern. Several reports and studies had suggested direct and indirect discrimination and a failure to promote equality of opportunity. Lord Gifford highlighted the 'harsh reality of racism' black people in Liverpool 8 had experienced over many years (Gifford et al, 1989). With the 'great leap forward' towards computerised medical records (see Chapter 5) the practice began to collect information to document the needs and health care provision for patients from different BAME groups. The Commission for Racial Equality (CRE), created by the 1976 Race Relations Act, had set the agenda. The CRE publication *Monitoring an equal opportunity policy: a guide for employers* (1978) outlined the rationale for ethnic monitoring. It made the important point that voluntary self-classification of ethnic group should be used for the 1991 UK Census. Proxy indicators that had been used previously, such as surname or parents' country of birth, were to be set aside. The 1981 Census, which had used those inadequate tools, suggested that 37% of BAME people in the UK could be categorised as Black British. Other minorities were estimated as follows: Chinese (15%), West Indian (13%), Arab (13%), African (12%) and Asian (10%).

The 1991 Census introduced self-reporting of ethnic group with standard codes suggested by the Office of Population Censuses and Surveys (OPCS). As in other inner-city areas, the results raised concerns, especially about under-reporting. The Granby Toxteth Community Project, based in Liverpool 8, produced its own analysis of the Census, and meetings were held to discuss the results (Small and Moore, 1992; Granby Toxteth Community Project, 1991). However, information about local BAME groups was still patchy.

Ethnic monitoring at PPHC

In the years since PPHC was established, many journalists and researchers had approached GPs with requests for information about the needs of the area's ethnically diverse population (Wilson, 1978; Torkington, 1991). Over time, these questions became more probing. Without any hard data, GPs were uncomfortable about choosing between giving impressionistic and potentially misleading views, and unhelpfully, if justifiably, protesting their lack of information. The practice therefore began to move towards including self-reported ethnic origin in their patient questionnaires and documenting it in manual and computerised records. By 1992, Susanna Graham-Jones was able to report on 5 years of self-report ethnic monitoring in primary care. She described the feasibility of this painstaking pioneering work at several conferences, but her report (see below) remained unpublished.

Self-report ethnic monitoring by patient questionnaires at PPHC: methods and preliminary results, 1987-1992

In 1987 a group of postgraduate students from the Liverpool School of Tropical Medicine, some of whom were Black, tested the acceptability and feasibility of ethnic monitoring in a two-week project. They distributed a questionnaire to a sample of attenders in the waiting room at PPHC. This included the question "Would you have any objection to answering a question about your ethnic origin?" Of approximately 80 respondents, only six raised any objection to this question. These were white people, some of whom worried that raising the issue of race would of itself cause discrimination (Commission for Racial Equality, 1984). In the absence of significant objections in this pilot, we felt the advantages of obtaining self-report data for our information system would far outweigh the disadvantages.

Implementation was relatively straightforward. This coincided with our acquisition of a computer in 1988. With 'self-report ethnic origin' as one of many variables coded on the computer, associations between ethnicity and many other relevant variables could be explored. Data gathering involved the following steps:

1. Registration under the Data Protection Act (1984).

2. Decision about which ethnic origin categories to use (modified in the light of local concerns about the OPCS ethnic group categories used in the 1991 census), and about handling of non-responders and 'other' responses.

3. Modification of new patient questionnaires given to the 17% of patients joining the list annually.

4. Employment of new staff to work with the computer and set up an expandable, flexible information system.

5. Attempt to screen all male patients via our Well Man clinic (1989-1991) using a lifestyle questionnaire including the self-report ethnic group question.

6. Introduction of a lifestyle questionnaire for existing patients, including the ethnic group question. Patients aged over 65 were screened by post with the help of a grant from Liverpool University. Subsequently all attenders at the health centre were offered screening via questionnaires distributed at

reception.

7. Gradual accumulation of morbidity, referral, investigation and prescribing information from notes summaries and surgery consultations. At this stage neither GPs nor other staff had access to funding for the time-consuming task of desktop data entry. As of 1992, the database remains far from complete.

What have we learnt? [by 1992]

It is too early to come to any conclusions about associations between ethnicity and morbidity in Liverpool. We have however demonstrated the feasibility and acceptability of gathering such information by self-report questionnaires. We feel any other method is dubious. Because of the limited time devoted to data-gathering in a real-life practice and the very gradual computerisation of our medical records, only about a fifth of patients have ethnic group coded on the computer as yet, and only a minority have usable medical record summaries on the computer. However, the system is in place and we have been able to respond to queries from several researchers by providing useful, if limited, anonymised information on small samples of patient data, as follows:

a) Workload associated with new patients investigated; ethnic group used as an independent variable.

b) 'Health needs of ethnic elders' research project

c) Practice morbidity data: looking for differences in prevalence of depression, psychotic disorders and other chronic medical conditions across ethnic groups

d) A local voluntary agency working with problem drinkers asked about alcohol consumption patterns in ethnic minorities. We were able to show differences between whites and all-ethnic minorities (non-whites).

Future work plans: [as of 1992]

Data Gathering - We have applied to the FHSA for funding more staff clerical hours to computerise questionnaires and summaries.

Data Analysis - We will explore further the associations between ethnicity and many of the 'lifestyle' variables from the growing database - such as housing, employment, religion, language barriers, disabilities, tobacco and alcohol consumption, carer status, age, family history of major disease, and emotional problems. This information should be of use to service providers/ users in the assessment of health needs. Further work should enable us to relate these variables to service uptake.

Morbidity Database - This awaits further GP input. Transcription of referral/ investigation requests by secretaries is no substitute for GPs routinely updating computerised medical records during surgeries. We need further training sessions to enable all doctors to become confident with desktop consultation recording. Running a partially computerised system alongside manual records causes much duplication of records and paperwork.

References

Commission for Racial Equality. 1978. *Monitoring an equal opportunity policy: a guide for employers.* London: CRE

Ethnic monitoring becomes mainstream (1992)

PPHC's Annual Report for 1992 acknowledged that the investment in computerisation, including recording of ethnicity, would be slow to demonstrate returns. One GP commented to Susanna at the time, 'This has taken a lot of work and a lot of figures to prove what we already know to be the case!'

However, the thorough preparation for ethnic monitoring at PPHC set a good precedent. From 1989 the Department of Health issued a rapid sequence of directives about ethnic monitoring, but with no resources attached. The Departmental Adviser on Ethnic Minority Health, Veena Bahl, declared, 'Information is essential if ethnic minority groups are to benefit from, and influence the planning of, appropriate health services' (Health Trends, 1991). It became compulsory for hospitals to record ethnicity; the 1990 GP contract required all GP referral letters to include ethnicity from 1992, but no additional resources accompanied these demands. Iona Heath, a GP in central London, who supported the concept of ethnic monitoring in principle, pointed out that without training and support, practices would be unlikely to comply with these good practice guidelines. She worried that their efforts would be wasted and possibly counter-productive. GPs might well regard this as 'yet another case of the Department of Health offloading work onto general practice' (Heath, 1991).

In parallel with the largely unfunded work at PPHC, a few other pilot projects were undertaken in inner cities. Chris Horton, Ethnic Monitoring Officer at the Thames Regional Health Authorities, reported good response rates and acceptance of ethnic monitoring in his region (1992). Like Iona Heath and PPHC, Horton supported the use of sub-categories of the OPCS codes for areas with specific ethnic minorities, for example Yemenis and Somalis, and he too emphasised the need for funding. In 1993, as part of its *Health of the Nation* strategy, the Department of Health proposed setting up an Ethnic Health Unit 'to help to redress differences between ethnic groups', focusing on health improvement targets in five clinical conditions (1992). Baroness Cumberlege announced that health authorities would not actually be penalised for failing to meet the needs of ethnic minorities, but that 'they will be heavily leant on' (BMJ News, 1993). However, there was still no ring-fenced funding for this work.

Campaigner and public health specialist Taher Qassim was teaching at the Liverpool School of Tropical Medicine in 1992, when he first heard about the work PPHC was doing:

> A group of students were doing the first ever Yemeni Health Profile in Liverpool and I was their supervisor. I was advised then by key Yemeni contacts that PPHC could be the best place to meet Yemenis, as many were patients there. We used a snowball research method to find where Yemenis lived, as there was no other documentation about them. Five years later in 1997, I worked with PPHC on two other research projects. The first was phase two of the Yemeni Health Profile from 1992, and the second was Patient Profiling.

The Service Development Initiative and patient profiling (1997-2004)

Building on the pioneering ethnic monitoring initiative and Family Health Project (see Chapter 7), GPs at PPHC realised that creating a high-quality database would facilitate further funding applications for improvements to patient services. Susanna Graham-Jones had left in 1993, and by 1996 only 16% of new patients had filled in the New Patient Questionnaire, with 21% identifying themselves as BAME. Katy Gardner and Lis Davidson realised that with adequate staff time and training, uptake of ethnic monitoring could be improved, and other relevant data could be collected and analysed. They were put in touch with Bennett Lee, an enthusiastic researcher at Liverpool John Moores University. In 1997 he obtained funding from the Department of Health for a patient profiling project, which would collect information about ethnicity, as well as other data that could be used to improve patient care. This project was known as the PPHC Service Development Initiative (SDI). Taher Qassim, now chair of the Liverpool Arabic Centre, was ready and willing to help: 'The Department of Health required a public body to have a community organisation as a partner in a grant-funded project. As chair, I agreed straight away. Work started in 1998 and I joined the steering group.' The steering group of patients, staff and link workers was chaired by Michael Chan, Visiting Professor of Ethnic Health at the University of Liverpool, who was made a 'people's peer' in the House of Lords in 2001 for services to BAME health.

Patient profiling required questionnaires to be developed and distributed. These included a section in a variety of languages, explaining the purpose of the questionnaire and encouraging people to ask for assistance to complete them if necessary. They were filled in at the practice with support from the link workers and were also distributed by post. Ben Jones, son of district nurse Pat Jones, became the data manager. The database included languages spoken, country of origin, religion, interpreting requirements, employment status and access to a car and telephone. Uptake was good. By 2004, 70% of adult patients registered at PPHC had been profiled. 46% of the profiled patients were from BAME groups, comprising 18 different ethnic groups with 16 different spoken languages, the main non-English languages being Somali and Arabic. 16% had English as an additional language (EAL). Patients reported 84 different countries of birth. The project funded IT support to enable language, ethnicity and religion to be displayed prominently on patients' computer records, aiding communication between staff and patients. Patients were also consulted on issues affecting the use of health services, and differences became apparent. Overall, BAME patients reported that they felt they had less time and were less able to talk about their problems than white British patients. 40% of Somalis found it difficult to understand their GP, compared to 5% of white British patients.

The case was made for more readily available paid interpreters and more bilingual and BAME staff. Additional link workers were employed to work in the practice and were often able to step in when patients arrived without an interpreter. In 2000 Central Liverpool PCG commissioned the interpreting service, Language Line. Link worker Rahima Farrah remembered:

> Health workers used interpreters and Language Line willingly (money was not an issue) and patients with EAL had longer consultations so that their voices could be heard. The practice met people where they were at. This was not the same in all surgeries...The Somali cervical smear clinic stands out for me. We wrote to women in English and Somali, and I sat in the clinic talking with the women and explaining the importance of the smear test. We did improve uptake, although sometimes we would send for six women and two would turn up, even if I reminded them by phone. But two is better than none!

District nurse Pat Jones recalled, 'Working with interpreters was a new and challenging experience for me. At least in district nursing we were able to adjust team members' workloads to take that into account. It seemed that our GP colleagues just had to work longer hours to cope.'

Najib Al-Hakimi was based at PPHC from 2002:

> When the Liverpool Arabic Centre was approached to take part in patient profiling for the Yemeni Community, I was working there as a part time project manager. Working with the Service Development Initiative we identified a need for Arabic speaking Health Development Workers to address the barriers that the Arabic community experience in accessing the NHS. I was appointed as one of these workers by the Primary Care Trust. For me the best thing during my time at PPHC was the involvement and interaction between us as Health Development Workers, and the health professionals working to serve our community. I remember delivering the Expert Patient education programme to Arabic speaking patients with long term health conditions. I felt, working in this way, that I made a big difference to the health of our local community.

Katy added, 'The patient-led Expert Patient Programme, initiated by Central Liverpool PCT in 2001, provided six-week courses for people with long term health conditions, aiming to give them more control over their own health and wellbeing. We were particularly keen to involve people from BAME communities and Najib was a vital part of that work.'

The Service Development Initiative encouraged patient involvement, with a patient-staff group generating ideas for further improvements.

As described by Rahima, 20-minute appointments were arranged for patients with English as an additional language. Computer alerts notified receptionists of the patient's primary language when they booked. Pictures and role descriptions of staff were displayed at reception. Patient leaflets were provided in Arabic and Somali along with audiotape versions. The practice held training for all staff to improve access to health care for BAME patients. Profiles of Somali and Yemeni health were created from the practice database and used in the planning of health days organised with these communities. For example, because smoking rates were found to be very high among Yemeni men, a smoking cessation programme was developed specifically for them. Staff from other Toxteth practices were invited to education sessions about Somali and Yemeni health, and a booklet about Somali health issues was produced for local practices. User involvement meetings continued through the mid-2000s but were later discontinued because of competing management priorities and the loss of Bennett Lee, who moved to London to take up a permanent university post.

The SDI raised awareness of health issues affecting BAME groups across Liverpool health services. In 1998, steering group members collaborated with the health authority on the first of several seminars entitled 'Improving Primary Health Care of Ethnic Minority Communities' (Liverpool Health Authority, 1998). The SDI produced a comprehensive report, *Ethnicity Profiling in Primary Care - The Princes Park Health Centre Model 2000*, and was recognised by the Department of Health as a beacon of good practice (Lee et al, 1999; Jones and Gardner, 2003). In her 2001 report, *Black and Minority Ethnic Health Service provision in Liverpool Primary Care Trusts*, public health researcher Katharine Abba reflected, 'Patient profiling has become mainstream at the practice and has brought about changes in service delivery. Differences in morbidity profiles and satisfaction for patient groups defined by ethnicity and socio-economic status were highlighted. This has since been extended to other practices by Central Liverpool PCT, and approximately 25,000 patients have so far been profiled' (2001). Gideon Ben-Tovim, chair of Central Liverpool PCT, and public health specialist Margaret Thomson supported patient profiling, and in 2003 the PCT's Diversity Equality scheme won national recognition (Central Liverpool Primary Care Trust, 2004).

In 2000 Dr Richard Williams, a Lambeth GP, began patient profiling, having obtained money from North Lambeth PCG. Richard remembered, 'We took lots of lessons from your work at Princes Park - in fact Bennett Lee who'd worked with you moved to London and joined our implementation steering group.' He was able to continue this work successfully: 'By 2010 all practices in Lambeth were profiling with the same model - about 355,000 patients. The potential of patient profiling to address inequalities in health care access and outcomes was achieved through the establishment of the Lambeth Community Datanet by Lambeth PCT.' The challenge was also taken up by a group of practices in East London, which embarked on ethnic monitoring for patients on chronic disease registers from 2001. They rolled this out to their entire practice populations in 2005 by taking advantage of a 'local enhanced service' payment scheme (Hull et al, 2011; Robson et al, 2020). However, a research project involving eight practices concluded,

> Collecting data on patient ethnicity in primary care appears a considerable challenge, and the scale of work and costs for practices may be underestimated. In some practices, particularly in deprived areas, the realities of organisational and staff resource constraints may preclude practice-initiated ethnicity data collection and require external administration. A combination of methods and attendant resources to achieve comprehensive profiling of patient populations in primary care is needed. (Jones and Kai, 2007)

Nationally, the Department of Health failed to follow through on ethnic monitoring. When the Quality and Outcomes Framework (QOF) was introduced in 2004, incentivising the use of computerised monitoring and audit for specified target conditions, a derisory single QOF point (see Chapter 11) was awarded for ethnicity coding, in contrast to much heavier weightings for other practice activities.

Nowadays, with new IT solutions, data recorded in primary care can be retrieved when patients attend hospital and other settings. However, while the low-key incentive in the QOF has increased ethnic monitoring of new practice patients, its potential remains largely unrealised. This is due to inadequate resourcing in primary care and elsewhere since the early fanfare in the 1990s. Avoidable problems continue. Health workers rarely have advance information about their patients' ethnicity and main spoken languages, and the need for an interpreter is not routinely ascertained ahead of important appointments (Mathur 2013).

Demographic changes in Liverpool 8 after 1990

The practice population changed greatly during the 1990s. Midwife Dorcas Akeju worked with PPHC during this time:

> The practice was and still is unique, as it caters for diverse patients and the GPs were interested in ethnicity and related health diseases such as sickle cell disease and female genital mutilation (FGM)...During my time with PPHC, my knowledge of the diversity at Liverpool increased and I became more interested in sickle cell diseases and FGM. This shaped my work, and I became Lead Midwife for Inherited Blood Disorders and FGM.

Dorcas received a lifetime award from the Royal College of Midwives, and an OBE, for her work in raising awareness of FGM.

The arrival of Chilean refugees in the mid-1970s had given Katy Gardner a foretaste of working with distressed families fleeing trauma, but much more was to come. The increasingly unstable situation in Somalia after the outbreak of civil war in 1986 led to an influx of Somali refugees, many coming to join families long-established in Liverpool 8, where Somali seamen and traders had put down deep roots. Some new arrivals were academics, doctors and other professionals; others were from a much more rural background, and many were in poor health. Link worker Sirad Elmi described a problem often encountered in registering recent arrivals at reception:

> Everyone seemed to be born on the 1st of January. People only knew their year of birth, not the date, as births were not being recorded in Somalia or Somaliland. There was no registry office where parents received a certificate and when they entered the UK, the 1st of January was decided for them by the Home Office. A doctor was having trouble finding the patient's date of birth and the receptionist said, 'It must be January 1st!' She was right.

Sirad went on to describe her role working with the Liverpool Somali community:

> I helped to register people, gave benefits advice and filled in forms for benefit applications. I helped with housing problems and acted as an interpreter, not just for PPHC patients but for people from the area. I

often went to help patients in hospital and with hospital appointments, as, in the early days, there were very few hospital interpreters. Women used to drop by to meet up outside my room and chat; it was very social.

Health Development Worker Afrah Qassim commented: 'Sirad had a very small room and every time I passed it I would see community women in her small room gathered together, laughing and chatting while she helped them with their enquiries, or many times they just came to chat. It was beautiful.'

There was much untreated disease and psychological distress amongst refugees as a result of war and violence back home. Somali groups recognised this early on, and in 1991 took part in a seminar with the Children's Hospital on the health needs of Liverpool Somalis (Royal Liverpool Children's Hospital, 1991). Through the Equal Opportunities Policy Group and the ethnic monitoring projects, the PPHC team had become more skilled and confident at engaging with BAME patients. Even so, dealing with the clinical, psychological and social needs of refugees meant a steep learning curve for individual clinicians and interpreters. Psychosomatic illness needed to be sensitively addressed with patients for whom the stigma of mental illness could be disastrous; post-traumatic stress disorder could present in a variety of disturbing ways. Chris Dowrick, a professor of primary care and Liverpool GP, commented on the difficulties faced by refugees and their GPs: 'What we see here is a tremendous collision between undifferentiated alienation and despair, and the everyday business of clinical problem-solving' (2009). In the midst of this collision, serious illnesses were occasionally missed. Katy was mortified when she failed to diagnose TB of the hip in a patient complaining of bone and joint pain.

Severe vitamin D deficiency was common within the Somali community, and this took time for GPs at PPHC to recognise. Sirad Elmi remembered the attempts to understand the health issues affecting Somalis:

We had a day on Somali health for practice staff, link workers and interpreters. We worked with a group from a health centre in Bristol with similar attached workers, as we had the same issues: four out of five Somali people came to the doctor with the same symptoms and they came 'looking for a cure'. We did role-play, and I was the doctor! It gave us a much better insight into what GPs and nurses were thinking, and for them what Somali patients might be thinking. For example, doctors sometimes thought patients were depressed, but there was no notion of this in Somalia at that time. Mental health issues were seen as 'madness' and there was stigma. There was no 'in between'. We also talked about vitamin D deficiency as a possible cause for depression and of bone and muscle pain; this led to research with the Tropical School [see Chapter 12]. I found that day very helpful. I think many of the problems experienced by Somalis were also due to coming to a cold climate from a hot, dry climate. It changes your whole body; I know, as I have just come back from a few months in Somaliland.

The language barrier was certainly problematic. Many new arrivals, especially elders, spoke little English and found the NHS difficult to negotiate; many did not read English or Somali. However, as patients began to learn English, they wished to consult in English rather than use interpreters. Although this was encouraged, misunderstandings could arise as patients and health workers struggled to communicate. As Katy pointed out, 'Even if the person spoke very good English, there could still be gaps in the consultation.'

However, young Somalis who grew up in the UK learnt excellent English, and Somalis gradually became involved in organisations such as the Toxteth Health and Community Care Forum. Support groups flourished and many became involved with vitamin D research (see Chapter 12). Later, Katy worked with a group of young women and a Somali health activist, Samsam Salah, to address the high incidence of high blood pressure, weight gain and diabetes in Somali women. This research focused on understanding the reasons for weight gain as women grew older and on increasing awareness of the benefits of healthy diet and exercise amongst women in the community (Gardner et al, 2010).

Katy spent much time organising the computer records of Somali patients to make sense of their different health issues. In 2005 she wrote to the PCT asking for more support for the Somali community in accessing health services: 'Many Somalis have had terrible experiences. They are separated from their families and have often lost many friends and relatives. They are living in a different culture in a cold damp country.' She described examples of issues encountered in the consultation:

Zainab, a Somali refugee doctor, assigned to the practice as part of her induction course, attended the diabetic clinic. The practice nurse spent 30 minutes going through diabetes, medication and health education with a Somali patient who spoke some English. At the end, the patient asked Zainab, 'What did she say?' Another patient was attending hospital for his poorly controlled diabetes. His medication was increased but his diabetes remained badly controlled. I found he had not collected a repeat prescription for some weeks, and he told me frankly that he had not been taking his medication, as it had not made him feel better. The Somali link workers tell me that people want instant improvement and do not understand the concept of prevention. (Katy Gardner, pers. comm., 2005)

Katy also explained how some people found it difficult to follow a medication regime because they did not read English. As Zainab had told Katy, 'They bring a small paper which comes with the medicine. They ask other people to read it for them and then they say, "Oh my God, there are a lot of problems. It could affect my kidneys. I don't want to take it."' Katy concluded her letter, 'Knowledge of NHS services in the Somali community is very patchy. They often miss their hospital appointments. This could improve if patients were given a hospital appointment during their GP consultation, under the new 'Choose and Book' booking system, though I am not certain patients with EAL will have anything like a fair crack at 'choice'.'

MAAN, the Liverpool Somali mental health project (2002-2012)

By 2000 the Liverpool Somali population was estimated at between 3,000 and 5,000 (ICARUS, 2006). As mentioned above, the Somali language has no term corresponding to 'depression' and there was little understanding of mental health problems, which were associated with considerable stigma, much as they had been in the UK well into the 20th century. PPHC supported the development of MAAN, a project set up to address mental health issues in the Somali community and to build bridges with NHS services. The manager, Mohamed Ashour, who had trained as a doctor in Somalia, had a good grasp of the problems. Maan, a Somali word meaning 'mind' was also the name of a Somali self-help project in Sheffield, with which the Liverpool MAAN was linked. Launched in 2002 with lottery funding which continued for 10 years, MAAN helped to communicate with and care for people with mental health problems. The project also liaised with and trained mental health workers. MAAN enabled some grieving

Somali refugees, ill and afraid in an alien environment, to seek help. One client said, 'The war affects everyone in some way. When I think of what is happening, I can't eat or sleep, and I feel sick. Your body is here but your brain is not' (ICARUS, 2006). Katy remembered helping a refugee with a psychotic episode: 'Through working with MAAN, he accepted help from the mental health services, while at the same time taking comfort from friends from the Mosque, who recited the Q'ran around him. He made a full recovery.'

Many Somali men in Liverpool chewed khat, which they imported. Although addictive, the amphetamine-like stimulant drug found in the stems of the plant was not subject to regulation in the UK at that time. Katy remembered a visit to a house where all the men were chewing khat: 'They were very friendly but could not explain at all which of them was the patient and what was wrong with them.' Katy left none the wiser. Khat could be particularly problematic for patients with poor mental health, and MAAN ran an awareness campaign about its use. Khat was later categorised as a controlled drug (class C, along with benzodiazepines, ketamine and anabolic steroids) under the Misuse of Drugs Act in 2014.

Although MAAN was unable to continue once its Lottery funding ended, mental health services for Somalis have continued to improve, and the stigma associated with mental health issues has considerably decreased.

PPHC and the evolution of the Somali community - Khadra Mohamed

When I arrived in Liverpool in January 1994 with my family, I had no idea how my life would change from everything that I'd known. We settled in Toxteth, as my father had told us there was a large Somali community in the area and we'd feel more comfortable living there. We got a house on Granby Street, and the first thing I noticed was how diverse the area was; there were people from all over the world, but also a lot of Somali families who had, just like us, come to England for a better life.

Many people did not speak English and it was quicker for the children to learn English and to translate for our parents and relatives that didn't speak English. Times were a lot different then. Ethnic minorities didn't have opportunities. The Somalis who settled in Liverpool were left to fix their own problems, and to find their place in a new environment with a different culture and way of life. One of the only places people could get help, almost a one-stop shop if you like, was the local GP surgery. Princes Park Health Centre was a place where people in the Somali community felt heard.

I remember going there with my mother, and her catching up with other ladies from the community, sharing problems, ways of helping each other and information. It wasn't just a GP surgery - it was a community centre with information in Somali to help people, and a place where you felt welcomed and listened to. There was this sense of community spirit. Everyone pulled together to help one another. If you ask any of the older generation like my mother about the surgery, she will name all the doctors by their first name. This is the impact Princes Park Health Centre had.

Over the years the Somali community has progressed and changed immensely. The first generation of Somalis to settle in Liverpool, like my father and mother, had a lot more hardships and faced many difficulties, from language barriers to lack of employment, health and education. There was no provision to help people navigate through what would've been one of the hardest moments in their life. Without places like Princes Park throwing them a lifeline, my parents and others like them would've struggled a lot more.

The second generation of Somalis have fared better, especially young women, who have succeeded in higher education and gaining professional jobs in their chosen fields. Somali women are leading the way in changing things socially and culturally for a community left behind. In the Somali culture the male family members are seen as heads of the household and breadwinners. That was the case in the first generation, but in the second generation this doesn't seem to be the case. Elders like my mother now encourage their daughters to be financially independent, to make their own decisions and to be and become whoever they want to become. This is a big shift from how my mother's generation were raised. Unfortunately, Somali men have often struggled to find their place, and unemployment within Somali males is one of the highest rates compared to any other ethnic minority. Some have sadly found it difficult to identify with both cultures and have become part of a forgotten generation.

However, overall, things have come a long way within the Somali community. Some issues from the past have remained but others have greatly improved. The community is now empowered and informed; they have displayed that they can adapt in any situation. I work as a counsellor in a local youth project; people are open about their problems and much of the past stigma has gone. To this day the community spirit and willingness to help one another has remained, and long may it continue.

Khadra Mohamed, counsellor at Kaalmo Youth Development Project

PPHC as the lead practice for asylum seekers in Liverpool

By 1999 PPHC was part of North Mersey Community Trust (NMCT, see Chapter 11), which agreed to provide services for refugees and asylum seekers. The war in Kosovo resulted in a large group of refugees arriving on May 1st at a reception centre in Sefton Drive. Katy Gardner was there:

> Most of the clinical team at PPHC came out on a Sunday morning to check over a large group of 120 newly arrived Kosovan refugees in a reception centre near Cyril's old surgery. One girl was so very ill with a heart problem that she was transferred almost directly to Birmingham Children's Hospital. Another man had advanced TB. Many of those refugees stayed with us for several years. For most there was a happier ending as they were able to return home. That has not been the case for many others, e.g. many Somalis, Syrians, or Iraqi Kurds.

PPHC counsellor Ria Hayward recalled, 'We all went to greet and help the refugees, who had lots of medical problems. Rotting teeth were common, due to not having had access to dental care for some time. Everyone did their best to be very welcoming, hoping it would make a small difference to people in such tragic circumstances.' A second and third group of refugees arrived a month later.

Jenny Knowles, a senior nurse working for NMCT, wrote in a paper about provision of services to asylum seekers based on experience in Liverpool:

> The workload has increased tremendously in certain areas of the city, particularly in primary care, but no additional money is allocated...The acute consultation or unexpected visit is the most difficult to deal with, and health workers have to explore if [new patients] have been registered elsewhere, involving a number of phone calls...No one has a complete database of asylum seekers coming into the city or knowledge of who is coming when and where. (Ghebrehewet, 2002)

In 2000, PPHC was designated as the lead practice looking after newly arrived asylum seekers in the city. A support team was at last put in place, with GP Dr Helen West employed to work specifically with asylum seekers and refugees. In 2001, as a result of a community campaign and the work of the Service Development Initiative, another tranche of Somali and Arabic health link workers was recruited to work in local practices (Abba, 2001).

Afrah Qassim trained at PPHC as a Health Development Worker. She was the first trainee from the Yemeni community in Liverpool and was employed by Central Liverpool Primary Care Group from 1999 onwards. Although she enjoyed the work she was very much thrown in at the deep end:

> PPHC didn't feel like a workplace, but more like a second home. When I started my training, I used to go on visits with the district nurses. I found this difficult because some of the patients suffered with bad ulcers and wounds and many of them were older people who lived alone. There was one in particular - when the nurse was cleaning his wound it was so bad and painful, but the patient still had a smile on his face and thanked the nurse for her help. He asked me if I was going to be a nurse. It took me a while to stop thinking about that patient. Another difficult thing that I had to deal with was the death of a Yemeni patient, who came in with his wife. He had had a heart attack during the night, but didn't phone for an ambulance, because neither he or his wife spoke English, so they waited till the morning and came to the surgery. Katy Gardner rang for an ambulance. Katy asked me to go with them to help with interpreting. The time from PPHC to the Royal Hospital felt a lifetime. When we got there, I sat with his wife, then the doctor came out and told me he passed away and needed me to tell his wife. I froze and just kept staring at him with the hope it wasn't true. I felt so scared as I had never been in this situation. His wife was looking at me to respond, she asked 'Afrah, what happens - can I go and see him?' Once I told her, she held onto me so hard and was yelling at me to tell her it wasn't true. Then the doctor took us to see him. I didn't want to go, but I had to be with her. A while later her family arrived, and I then went back to PPHC. I just cried non-stop. I remember fellow workers Michelle Cox and Val Ravenscroft comforting me - they were really lovely - and sending me home to be with my family. Normally I am an emotional person, but that day I seemed to have kept it together from the outside, but inside I was lost. I still feel anger and sadness in me today. What would have happened if they did call for help in the night? Would he still be alive? - and the importance of being able

to communicate.

Following this episode, the PCT produced a leaflet about heart attacks in different languages (see Chapter 8) and organised a series of targeted education sessions for Yemeni patients.

In 2002, when the Social Inclusion Team was formed, Afrah joined it:

> It was managed by Michelle Cox and based at first in a portacabin behind the centre. I shared a room with Jan, another advocacy worker. The conversations we had were priceless. One strong memory is the Friday lunch times. The four of us in the team, and anyone else from PPHC who could join us, would either bring food from home or get a takeaway and share it. This moment was so appreciated. We got to know everyone, share and laugh together.

Afrah subsequently founded Savera UK, a charity combatting honour-based abuse and other harmful practices including FGM, and supporting those at risk.

Achievements of the Social Inclusion Team

- Working in partnership with Health Action Zone (HAZ) to access baby milk for asylum seeker mothers who were not entitled to milk vouchers, identifying this as an issue and responding to a pressing need.

- Working in partnership with Refugee Action who held clinics around the city to address health, housing and financial needs that were putting individuals and families into extreme poverty and poor health; working with Asylum Link Merseyside, dealing with anything from food, clothes and weekly vouchers to immigration issues.

- Working with Liverpool Women's Hospital Link Clinic supporting pregnancy and maternity services for women whose first language was not English; advocating for and supporting the Women's Multi Cultural Clinic [based at Abercromby Health Centre] for BAME women who would not access traditional Well Women clinics for specific cultural reasons.

- Developing incentive schemes to encourage and empower GP practices to make effective improvements to patient access.

- Training providers and employers on how to give individuals chances, particularly those with qualifications and skills not recognised in the UK. Developing strong links with local organisations such as L8 Law Centre, A.S. Law, Toxteth CAB, Toxteth Tigers Basketball Programme, Kingsley United Football Team.

· Developing appropriate health promotion initiatives within national programmes, e.g. chronic kidney disease, diabetes, hepatitis, Anthony Nolan Charity for blood disorders, organ donation and blood transfusion services.

· Providing educational seminars on a range of issues, with specific emphasis on safeguarding vulnerable adults and children; supporting Safeguarding Boards with expert advice on cultural issues and addressing racial discrimination.

Michelle Cox

Michelle Cox managed the Social Inclusion Team throughout its time based in the PPHC portacabin and oversaw its move to the Kuumba Imani Millennium Centre. She remembered one episode that summed up the PPHC days:

The Social Inclusion Team were often given generous donations of clothes by local communities. This was much appreciated, as many second hand charity shops did not cater for their cultural needs, particularly Hijabs and Abayas. I would take them home and wash them and store them in the portacabin should any requests come in. One day Katy had a patient who was haemorrhaging and she quickly needed something to get her to hospital and maintain her dignity. I gave her a long Abaya dress to use. Weeks later the patient made contact to thank me, as she didn't know what she would have done otherwise and was surprised that we would have such a thing in a health centre. I always remember that patient as illustrating the uniqueness in the service we were able to offer.

Michelle left in 2006, going on to become a senior nurse in NHS England's Improvement and Innovation initiative, and the Chief Nursing Officer's Black and Ethnic Minority North West Regional Lead for Nursing.

War and unrest in Iraq, Afghanistan and several African countries resulted in a further stream of asylum seekers arriving in Liverpool 8 from 2003 onwards. Almost all of them registered with PPHC initially (900 in 2003), although some subsequently moved to other practices. The practice list had shrunk in the late 1990s, but in 2005 there were over 8,500 patients, and almost 50% were from BAME groups.

Despite the provision of dedicated resources and support for work with such vulnerable patients, the demands on PPHC clinicians' time continued to increase. When Katy spoke about the plight of Somali refugees at the annual NHS service at the Anglican Cathedral in 2004, she insisted that 'in this time of government targets, we in the NHS owe it to this community to see that they are not disadvantaged further simply because they are not a National Service Framework target, and to ensure they are able to benefit from this society that is their new home.'

Michelle Charters, a patient who became the CEO of the Kuumba Imani Millennium Centre in Liverpool 8, was well aware of the practice's efforts:

> Thankfully, due to the care of these amazing doctors and staff over the years, many culturally specific illnesses and personal issues were researched, addressed and explained to a diverse community. For example: Princes Park made people aware of Sickle Cell Disease when it was not widely known. They brought to light issues like FGM, vitamin D deficiency and mental health issues specific to the BAME community, creating a feeling of better understanding which addressed feelings of isolation...FGM then was a taboo subject, but I am proud to say that I knew about the issue and was able to incorporate that into my work as a community activist...PPHC not only looked different when you walked in due to the diversity of its users, it was also somewhere you felt understood. 'Care in the Community' was really established from this one place...It felt like a place of safety too. It was a little radical for its time, but these doctors went out of their way to fully understand the complexities of physical and mental issues faced by all, and took time to explain it to you as a patient.

Michelle Cox agreed:

> Working at Princes Park Health Centre brought into sharp focus that tackling health inequalities required a partnership commitment from all. By harnessing and spreading the good practice that I observed, it was possible to make equality and justice a reality. We can ensure that we create not just an inclusive NHS culture, where everyone is respected and valued, but one where staff and patients are able to participate and thrive. We all have a duty to amplify voices, share patient stories and offer different perspectives. Almost 20 years on, I am proud that the initiatives which bore seed at PPHC continue to this day providing a legacy for

PPHC and the communities of Liverpool.

Throughout the 2000s the practice continued to look after refugees and asylum seekers as part of a still under-resourced Liverpool-wide service. Meanwhile, refugees have contributed greatly to the diversity, richness and 'magic' of Toxteth, as one of its residents recently described it (Tom Cardwell, pers. comm., 2019).

CHAPTER 10

Low pay for patients and their GPs (1990s)

Health inequalities persist (1980-1997)

Impending crisis: the difficulty of recruiting new partners (1995-1997)

Out-of-hours work and the Liverdoc GP co-operative (1996)

Early attempts at GP commissioning (1996 onwards)

Health inequalities persist (1980-1997)

Decades of determined efforts by the primary care team at PPHC could not alleviate the basic problems of an under-funded, overstretched NHS. Julian Tudor Hart's articulation of the Inverse Care Law (see Chapter 2) remained highly relevant to inner-city practice in the 1990s. Despite notable improvements in health and health care in the first 30 years of the NHS, health inequalities persisted across society. Marmot and McDowell highlighted the increasing gap in coronary heart disease mortality between manual and non-manual workers (1986). Furthermore, Richard Wilkinson's research suggested that differentials in stress, self-esteem and social relations might have even more of an impact on health than material wealth (1992). The Acheson report of 1998 demonstrated the catastrophic worsening of health inequalities in the 18 years since the Black Report. In 1977, 7% of the UK population had an income of less than half the national average. By 1996 that proportion had risen to 24% - a shocking demonstration of the widening gap between rich and poor. A third of children were living in poverty, and over one million children were living in families with no wage earner (Acheson, 1998).

By the mid-1990s, the statistics in areas like Liverpool 8 remained grim. In Granby and Abercromby wards unemployment was high at 30%, while the death rate for people under 75 years of age was 66% higher in Granby ward than in England as a whole (Liverpool Health Authority, 1997). Katy wrote, 'Our impression is that the lives of our patients have become much worse in the last 10 years' (Gardner, 1996). No less than 87% of PPHC patients met the criteria for deprivation payments to practices, but the resulting supplementary income was inadequate to support the costs of GP initiatives (PPHC, 1997). Unsurprisingly, Toxteth continued to be a daunting workplace for health professionals. At the 1997 Merseyside RCGP conference, titled 'Can inner city general practice survive?', Katy proposed strategies for avoiding staff burnout, such as ensuring protected time for personal and career development, mentoring schemes, flexible employment and moves towards a salaried option for GPs.

The high incidence of petty crime in the 1990s reflected the poverty in the area. Thanks to loyal patients and good community links, the PPHC building was subjected to less damage than other buildings in Liverpool 8, though there were occasional acts of vandalism and theft. Windows were broken and the practice safe was once removed in a wheelbarrow.

As Katy said at the RCGP conference, 'haggling with the authorities over a bit of vandal-proof paint and a window shutter is soul-destroying.' On one occasion, a young boy playing on the roof fell through a skylight and was trapped in an examination room. Fortunately, he was unhurt and was swiftly rescued by the fire service. The practice even became uninsurable for a time. Katy Gardner's car was repeatedly broken into outside her flat, which was round the corner. She took a pragmatic view and was delighted when the car was finally burnt, as she was able to buy a more vandal-proof one.

The practice successfully campaigned to prevent the PPHC building being sold off to the GPs by Liverpool Health Authority in 1990. This would have saddled the overstretched GPs with buildings of low monetary value that needed much care and attention. As Lis Davidson said in the 1991 Annual Report, the GPs at PPHC had never aspired to being property owners. Instead, in 1995, with support from both the Regional Health Authority and Rosemary Hawley, FHSA chair, the practice premises were refurbished and expanded. Lis Davidson took the lead on this project, working with local architect Bill Halsall, who remembered patients being involved at every stage of planning. The waiting area was much improved, with comfortable seating, subtle lighting, a gently curved wooden reception desk, a separate repeat prescription booth, and a space for confidential conversations. As well as clinical rooms, there were rooms for counsellors to run therapy groups and office space for the Family Health Project workers. The practice received funding for a 24-hour security guard for the year following the refurbishment. The new Princes Park Health Centre was opened in 1995 by Margaret Simey, a retired Labour councillor for Granby ward and renowned campaigner for social justice.

Patient turnover remained high. The 1991 Annual Report documented 1,230 patients joining the practice and 1,200 leaving in the preceding 12 months. Despite this, consultation rates remained close to the national average of 3-4 consultations per patient per year. The practice continued to hold its own. Dr Angie Forbes had joined the practice as a registrar in 1988 and returned as a partner in 1992. Her experience as a rheumatologist enabled her to offer rheumatology and joint injection clinics and valuable help to other GPs with rheumatological diagnostic conundrums. Martin Smith reflected: 'I still think of the early 90s as a 'golden time' at PPHC. It was very hard work - we still did all our own on-call - but, despite the inevitable conflicts between a group of people with strong personalities, we worked well as a team, working closely with district nurses, health visitors, practice nurses and counsellors.'

Health promotion activities continued. Two diabetic evenings were each attended by over 30 patients, with a chiropodist and an optician present. Activities included a quiz about diabetes and healthy food. A Saturday morning asthma event, open to patients from neighbouring practices, also drew over 30 people. The practice continued to audit its systems and collect patient feedback. Of 80 Well Woman Clinic attenders surveyed in 1990, 71 had read at least one of the health education leaflets in the waiting room and an impressive 52 said they remembered what they had read! Lis Davidson organised a survey about the appointment system, which showed that 71% of the responders saw the doctor of their choice. However, the practice had set a standard of 80%; there was still much to do. 86% of patients surveyed were satisfied with the outcome of their consultation, but only 41% were seen within 20 minutes of their appointment time. This feedback was fed into the practice goals for the next three years.

PPHC in the 1990s: looking back

From my daily ride to work, cycling up Upper Parliament Street to flying home down Bold St on my bike, I enjoyed everything about my work at PPHC. The health visitors were given opportunities that were totally innovative at the time, including Arabic lessons and training on FGM. Plays were performed by refugees to explain their stories. Learning opportunities arose all the time: during weekly meetings, over a cup of tea, following a discussion with a client. Looking back, it was pretty cool how quickly those ideas were transformed into actions...Alongside this ran a feeling of deep friendship with colleagues which I think arose from us all being on the same page, as far as our understanding of the impact of politics, poverty, housing and education on the health and wellbeing of our patients. I think it's rare for a workplace to consist almost entirely of people who liked each other and could converse on any topic pretty much in total agreement with each other.

Amanda Onwuemene, health visitor, 1989-1996

Culture shock and puzzlement probably best describe my reaction to my first days at PPHC. I mistook one general practitioner for a handyman (sneaking a cigarette outside the back door and trying to fix a lock) and heard another wailing with frustration. Later that day a receptionist reprimanded me for killing a wasp buzzing around the waiting area...All three of these individuals became treasured friends and colleagues...I was no shrinking violet when I moved to this working environment...Never, though, had I encountered such a diverse, compassionate, tolerant, competent, caring and challenging group of people.

Pat Jones, PPHC district nurse from 1990

I have lived in Liverpool 8 all my life. It has always been a vibrant area, lovely people, and good neighbours. While my children were at school I worked in jobs during school hours including as a Lollypop Lady outside Admiral Street Police Station in all weathers, and then at local GP surgeries. I joined PPHC in 1990. It was my last job prior to retirement and I loved it. Due to the practice covering a wide area with patients of differing backgrounds, health problems were also complex. There was respect between reception staff, the doctors and other clinical staff. We were like one big family, always a good atmosphere - including some good social gatherings! Though there were some confrontations when patients were unhappy about appointments. We tried various appointment systems but there was usually someone unhappy with changes. Receptionists were advised to be polite and to explain things to patients to defuse any confrontations. I remember at that time there was a small room off the reception area, where patients could obtain low-cost baby milk. Once, when I was in charge, a young lad started an argument. I can't even remember what it was about, but he left saying he was going to get a gun, come back and shoot me. Scary at the time, though he never came back, I am glad to say.

Mary Huxham, receptionist and prescription administrator

I absolutely loved the job, but in the beginning I thought I had joined a madhouse. Everyone, including the doctors, was a little unique and some people's quirky ways took a bit of getting used to, I think they will know who they are...But the doctors gave their patients 100% at all times. Even though sometimes it was difficult, they went out of their way to get the best treatment/care possible, and the patients knew this and felt well cared for...We had some really lovely patients who would bring us sweets, chocolate and biscuits, and when Katy was pregnant a patient brought lots of her maternity clothing in for her. As I live in the area, I would bump into them on a regular basis and got to know quite a lot of them really well. I still see some of them now, 14 years after leaving.

Ann Cunningham, administrator from 1990

I found PPHC at just the right time. I think I was so disillusioned with medicine, and also having to cope with renal dialysis [Kathrin joined PPHC whilst on dialysis for a kidney condition]; this combination could easily have tipped me into giving up at this point and dropping out of medicine altogether. When I visited PPHC for the first time, I walked into a waiting room, packed, except for the seats around an elderly Chinese man who was slowly lighting one match after another and throwing them over his shoulder. The receptionists just calmly dealt with him and carried on. In Katy's consulting room I looked at all the political posters on the wall and the embroideries from Nicaragua. I watched her consult and felt I had found a role model that I could identify with for the first time. I had never seen any doctor have such conversations with their patients, with trust on both sides. I was looking for a second six months' GP placement with no idea what I really wanted to do, but I went home that evening and thought Princes Park would either make medicine fun or be the last straw!

The practice sometimes felt quite overwhelming, with too many patients, not knowing what was going to happen next, and too many problems that I had no idea how to help with. All staff worked very hard and expected the same of each other...Staff were not always protected from themselves, as many were driven people with high principles, and wouldn't put themselves first. I learned that kindness is essential, I think everyone in PPHC operated on this principle without always articulating it as such. But patients were top priority, and staff came second, which I learned was too high a price to pay sometimes...It was also maddening to be in an organisation that was comfortable with chaos in a way that I am not. I did want effective meetings and decisions that were stuck to, and less debate. But it taught me that there were many other solutions and resources, and PPHC attracted so many of these: Citizens Advice Bureau, alcohol and substance misuse services, brilliant health visitors and so many community groups. I felt I was in a place that was at the cutting edge, providing primary care in the community in the tradition of Peckham, and people were committed and proud of the jobs they were doing.

Kathrin Thomas, trainee from 1991

I targeted the practice, as I had met Susanna at academic clinical meetings, and shared her ethos [Clare took over Susanna's university lectureship and role in the partnership in 1993]. I grew up in the US and chose to train in the UK because I had strongly held beliefs that the NHS system was the right way to deliver care... I worked at PPHC for five years before moving to Wales to become a Senior Lecturer in General Practice. Here are some little stories that stick in my mind: [Being] out on home visits, realising the only other people in the street were police in riot gear with shields... feeling vulnerable that my little flowery shirt would not protect me from much. Holding a young woman in her acute grief after her brother had been shot and killed two streets away from the Health Centre. Somali women saying 'I have pain everywhere', and feeling so inadequate about how to help them - trying hard though, like all the other staff. Learning from a translator that Somali women are often thought of as a chattel with no soul and realising this could be a part of why they suffered so much. The terrible day when a young mother lost her baby to meningococcal meningitis, AND her young child was killed on Princes Avenue in a road traffic accident. The stark contrast of the women's refuge next to a fancy private school. Just being fully tuned in to the suffering and poverty of the area whenever I was there; knowing I would just drive home later made me extra sad - realising that I was a champagne socialist. Noticing there were always books and pictures even in the most deprived homes, which was very different from the areas of social deprivation in Cardiff where I had worked previously. The practical joke the receptionists played on me once when I asked for the next patient. Me: 'Hello, what can I do for you today?' Him: 'I dunno love, I'm one of the builders.'

Clare Wilkinson, GP at PPHC from 1993, now Professor of General Practice at Bangor University

I was an attached health visitor for six years, latterly specialising in Child Protection and Safeguarding. Several health visitors shared an office upstairs, some geographically based, and some attached to a nearby practice, a common arrangement at that time. PPHC provided a unique 'Health' service to the community...This was well known amongst health visitors and community nurses, and on securing a role within the team, this style of care didn't disappoint. The team approach, where every member was valued and respected, ensured that patients had the best possible care, and morale was invariably good...Being in a practice with high density of poverty and all the associated problems meant health visitors' caseloads were heavily weighted with safeguarding and child protection concerns. Working with vulnerable groups, such as victims of domestic violence, drug users, people with mental health issues, etc, was both challenging and rewarding. However, having the added security of knowing that the GP's were supportive and always available to discuss cases was invaluable. My slight reservations would be that I felt that safeguarding concerns were sometimes left a little too long before action was taken. I believe this was more about giving people 'a chance to change' before engaging social services, but I felt that at times this may have been naïve. Or maybe I am just too cynical! I left in 2002 to take up a position in Halton as Safeguarding Specialist Nurse and then become the Designated Safeguarding Nurse across the Merseyside Clinical Commissioning Groups until I retired. These specialist roles were heavily shaped by my time and experience at PPHC.

Trish Drew, health visitor at PPHC, 1996-2002

I remember a patient who was a an alcoholic and diabetic, a lovely guy with liver problems who used to be an accountant but fell on hard times. This particular day Karen, the manager, said the patient was in 6a. I immediately thought of ward 6A at the Royal Liverpool Hospital, as he had not been too good, but Karen said, 'No, Clare - he is in 6a - the side room' (alongside a consulting room). He'd come for an appointment and the cleaner had said to Karen, 'Do you want to look around the other side of reception and see what I can see?' This poor man had locked himself out getting his milk in, and only had his shirt and underpants on. He thought if he came to the health centre, and pretended he wanted to see me, we would sort it. I found him sat there with a blanket around him, feet up, having tea and toast. He was laughing when I walked in. He said, 'Any chance you could go and get me the Daily Mirror?' Thank god he did not say the Sun, or he would have been marched! It took me half the day sorting him out. When we got his flat opened, we found it infested with cockroaches, so I had to deal with this and then do a full surgery of irate patients because I was late starting. But they were good times for me.

One Christmas I was seeing a Romanian woman for her diabetes. The interpreter told me she had no money for food as she lived with her son, his wife and five children, and his wife was having her sixth child. I called at their home and it was in a derelict building off Granby St. The windows bricked up, the children had nothing, and the house had one electric fire. The husband worked nights as a security guard. I went back to PPHC and told of the plight of this family. The staff collected clothes, bedding and toiletries and contacted KIND, a local children's charity, who supplied food and presents for each child. It was an honour to take all this to the family at Christmas, and very humbling.

Clare Corless, practice nurse 1996-2015

Impending crisis: the difficulty of recruiting new partners (1995-1997)

Maintaining stamina and stimulation whilst avoiding overwork and burnout is a real problem for all GPs. During its first fifteen years, PPHC had been able to retain its workforce moderately successfully, with an extended team of clinicians and backup staff. Increasingly, while some GPs continued to work full-time, others worked part-time, doing other activities or jobs on their days off: in education, campaigning, or in the wider NHS as portfolio GPs. As the 1990s progressed, it became more difficult to recruit GPs. The main factors appeared to be the relatively low pay because of the small patient list size, the unwillingness of recently qualified GPs to work in the inner city and the fact that GPs were responsible for their patients day and night, even with a practice-based on call rota. Difficulties in recruitment meant that the practice had to employ locum GPs whose pay came out of the GP partners' pockets, resulting in even lower incomes. Although most GP partners at PPHC were far less interested in making money than in providing an excellent service, even the most dedicated of them expected a respectable income.

Moreover, because of its well-earned reputation as a listening practice, extra work piled up and the PPHC list grew to over 8000 patients. The practice had hosted district nurses for neighbouring practices since 1984. Practice-attached district nurses Rita Potts and Maureen Newton, and later Pat Jones and Liz Hunter, also covered other nearby practices. When, in 1997, the nurses reported issues with unacceptable care in a neighbouring single-handed practice, the FHSA asked PPHC to take on its list for a year.

This rescue mission was rewarding, but stretched the practice further. Many of the neglected patients had multiple problems, including addiction to benzodiazepines and codeine-based drugs. Most of these patients later chose to stay on at PPHC as permanent patients.

Psychiatrist Rob Poole recalled,

> My enduring impression of PPHC from that time is of vibrancy but also high levels of stress. When I made a list of all the doctors I'd worked with there, I was surprised to see how long it was, due to high stress and high turnover. The 1995-1996 Liverpool gang wars were a particularly stressful time, with regular shootings and armed police patrolling in bullet proof jackets. One afternoon, an interview with a patient in PPHC was interrupted by gunfire close by, unmistakable, loud and, as I remember it, lasting a good 15 seconds. The gang war was not anonymous and distant; it happened around us, and it affected everyone. Anyone who thinks that these events only touch criminals is wrong. Local people, staff, everyone; we were frightened for ourselves but, more so, we were frightened for, not frightened of, the people around us.

The practice was unable to recruit a new full-time partner to replace Alan Forbes when he left in 1994 to run his own practice in Halewood. The vacancy was re-advertised three times. Angie Forbes and Judith Hindley also left in 1994. In 1995 Katy wrote to Steven Dorrell, the new Secretary of State for Health: 'Not only is there a crisis in recruitment of GPs in our practice, but colleagues in other inner-city practices are having similar problems. Indeed, we have had to treat people as emergencies here because they could not find a doctor to register with in this area.'

The FHSA recognised the practice's plight and employed Kerry Marson, a newly qualified GP, to help out as a salaried associate from 1995-1998. Despite the challenges of working in Liverpool 8, Kerry remembered the patients at PPHC with affection:

> As a young woman I never felt threatened going out on home visits alone, I remember doing a home visit on an elderly patient and having to walk through a gang of youths to get to their front door, which could quite easily have made me feel threatened. Instead I was greeted with warmth and enthusiasm, as it was their elderly relative that I was visiting. I remember when the computers got stolen and one of the patients 'arranged' for them to be returned.

But there was a darker side: 'I also remember sometimes feeling quite helpless when trying to treat people with depression, when what they really needed was a decent home, a job and some hope.' Kerry also recalled 'hearing some of the heart wrenching stories of the lives of the Somali refugees, of the trauma many of them had experienced before they left Somalia.' There were some surprising encounters too: 'On a lighter note, I remember seeing a University lecturer in linguistics, who pinpointed my place of birth to within a few miles by the accent which I thought I had lost years before! I was mightily impressed.'

This 'associate GP' scheme was a recognition of the need for additional resources to combat burnout in inner-city primary care. Martin Smith felt the strain: 'Towards the end of the 1990s things were beginning to fragment. Several partners left in quick succession and we struggled to recruit new partners who shared our philosophy. However, we had a good relationship with Liverpool Health Authority and they supported sabbaticals for Katy, Lis and myself, allowing us to undertake postgraduate courses to recharge our batteries.' Christine Wall's input was crucial in facilitating these sabbaticals:

> Complex patients with complex problems, coupled with long hours and dedication to doing the very best for people, took its toll on PPHC staff, particularly the GPs; I recall the burnout the dedicated GPs suffered. I remember organising many a visit of various Health Service 'dignitaries' to PPHC to hear from the grassroots what it was like to work in inner-city practices, to show that it was possible to deliver a better service and to make a difference to the lives of patients struggling with much more than just ill health. Not many wished to hear that to do so required a different way of funding, that smaller list sizes and more time with patients was essential, or indeed that targets for health promotion, admirable in themselves, were difficult for inner-city practices to achieve. In 1993 legislation was introduced to allow mergers of FHSAs and District Health Authorities. As Deputy Chief Executive of the new Health Authority, I continued to champion primary care and used innovative ways of funding general practice to facilitate new ways of working and attract new general practitioners to Liverpool. A new practice in Vauxhall, involving community representatives in the appointment of two job-share female practitioners, was an example of such an innovation and indeed became the forerunner of salaried practitioner status.

GP Kit Oi Chung, who had previously worked at PPHC with Katy, was one of these Vauxhall GPs:

> In 1992, I was involved with setting up a new health centre-based practice in North Liverpool, with Helen McKendrick, who had trained in Princes Park. The new practice, Vauxhall Primary Health Care, very much shared the ethos of Princes Park Health Centre, which Helen and I believed in strongly and tried to develop in the Vauxhall area. Culturally, the areas are different, but both experience a high level of poverty, disadvantage, and the associated problems. Like in Princes Park, we wanted local people to be actively involved with the practice and we involved them in the recruitment of our staff and doctors. We set up a multi-disciplinary team, had an in-house counsellor, and later developed co-location with Social Services. Women from the neighbourhood offered a tea and toast service, and the practice became seen as a community asset. These are the values that we learnt at Princes Park and, in turn, are instilling in the GP trainees who come through our practice. Even in the worst times for PPHC, there was a comfort that in Vauxhall, we were keeping its spirit alive.

The worst times for Princes Park Health Centre were yet to come. Despite the new initiatives, the shortage of doctors continued. Katy's view was, 'I don't think with this population you could do good health care and have low costs, that's my thinking and I don't think that's ever been really addressed.' In 1996 the practice had to close its list and stop registering new patients, whilst the partners continued to pay for expensive locum cover.

Out-of-hours work and the Liverdoc GP co-operative (1996)

From the late 1980s onwards there had been enough GPs in the practice, including trainees, to enable PPHC to run its own in-house on-call rota, instead of sharing the rota with other practices. GPs were on call overnight once or twice a week and every few weekends. In contrast, many Liverpool GPs were paying to use private locum services of variable quality. PPHC patients were usually helpful when they called GPs out to potentially high-risk areas at night. Nevertheless, one trainee admitted at her leaving party how terrified she had been doing night calls. In retrospect, Susanna Graham-Jones, who regularly covered Thursday afternoons and nights single-handedly, recognised that she had coped 'by putting on an invisible cloak of bravado' in preparation for visits to intimidating tenement buildings. She was once threatened with a knife by an alcoholic patient on a home visit, and on another occasion had her doctor's bag stolen by a group of children while getting out of her car. The bravado cloak did its work well - these episodes didn't leave her feeling too vulnerable. She was furious, however, when her microscope was stolen from the windowsill in her consulting room in broad daylight!

The PPHC in-house rota was helpful for ensuring continuity and consistent quality of care, but GPs were expected to do a full day's work the next day, and this was exhausting. Alan Forbes' contribution to the 1991 Annual Report mentioned the slog of working days after nights on call: 'So if we [doctors] look as bad as you feel, be kind to us, we are human too.'

Soldiering on in this way seemed reminiscent of life as a junior hospital doctor in the 1970s. There didn't seem any alternative - the work had to be done. Breakfast meetings at PPHC provided an opportunity for the occasional rant. Kathrin Thomas remembered meetings during her trainee year: 'Many an anxiety was eased by sharing it informally, which was especially important for trainees and younger doctors. But there were sometimes arguments, and one morning Katy impressed me by throwing a sugar bowl...after one GP walked out in the middle of a heated discussion. It shattered against the wall and there was sugar everywhere... fantastic!'

Mark Burns, remembered as the partner who provided fresh coffee for the breakfast meetings, was one of the founders of Liverdoc, a GP co-operative set up in 1996 to provide high-quality out-of-hours care. Over time, most Liverpool practices became involved. GPs worked in shifts between 6.30 pm and 8 am, offering GP appointments at a Liverdoc base, as well as home visits. Drivers were employed to accompany GPs on home visits, massively reducing the stress of being on call. Katy remembered telling a friend:

> Before the out-of-hours service started, I was sleepwalking for most of my life. How I managed to do a night on call and then a surgery next day I will never understand. I dreaded 'on call'. I never got over the worry that something drastic would happen - and sometimes, of course, it did - but working with others in Liverdoc made it much more bearable.

There was much debate at the time about loss of continuity of care. Nevertheless, the co-op developed into a successful social enterprise, UC24, with Mark Burns remaining a medical director for many years. Difficulties in recruiting GPs to work at PPHC persisted, but the co-op did at least enable doctors to plan their week and to work more safely. Its successor organisation, Primary Care:24, is still operating today.

Early attempts at GP commissioning (1996 onwards)

In 1996, Katy Gardner joined the National Association of Commissioning GPs (NACGP), which opposed GP fundholding (see Chapter 6). She found the members 'really helpful, as a peer group.' The NACGP envisaged alternative commissioning models. Liverpool was an early adopter of 'neighbourhood commissioning', which built on the work of the MAAG and LMFTs (see Chapter 8). This involved groups of practices working together to plan, agree and monitor services, as an alternative to fundholding. It was intended to ensure equitable distribution of services in the area and prevent fundholding practices from monopolising access to secondary care services.

Katy became lead GP for a group of practices in Liverpool 8 and 15. The irony was that the 'redistribution' of existing resources under neighbourhood commissioning often took services away from patients who had earlier benefited from PPHC's vigorous advocacy. Hard-won physiotherapy, chiropody and counselling schemes for PPHC patients were examples. Katy accepted this reluctantly: 'The result was that everything got watered down and we had less of it - but at least it was fairer, and to me that was important.'

Similarly, the focus on 'equal access' resulted in the withdrawal of the successful weekly practice-based child psychiatry sessions run by Carla Thompson and Chris Kennedy in the mid-1990s:

> Our service was intended to offer families a more accessible place than our base near Lime Street station. Children and young people were referred by the GPs, and it was a successful and enjoyable project with good attendance rates. We attended GP meetings to find out more about the referred children and realised how well the doctors knew them. We quickly got details, pooled between GPs, about the children's families - often across three generations. We met with the health visitors and occasionally went on visits with them. We'd never had such quick

and useful background information before (or since)! It was a good way to work. Unfortunately, it stopped because we didn't have the staff to offer it to all GP surgeries in our patch, and therefore the service was considered 'unequal'.

Child psychiatrist Dr Julia Nelki reflected, 'This was, in my view, sad and short sighted. It would have been far better to try to make it accessible to all, or even to continue with health centres that wanted it.' Katy agreed that commissioning was not always thought through in enough detail, but she felt that 'however creatively commissioning was carried out, regrettably, without extra resources from government, this type of occurrence was inevitable.'

CHAPTER 11

Salaried at last (1998)

The Primary Care Act Pilot

Not everything in the garden was rosy

A temporary reprieve for the NHS: The Labour government (1997-2010)

The Primary Care Act Pilot

The Tory government's 1997 NHS Primary Care Act offered GPs a variety of new contractual options. This opened up the possibility of the practice becoming a salaried service as a Primary Care Act Pilot (PCAP). This was not an entirely new idea, as Cyril Taylor and his comrades had long envisaged salaried GPs working from health centres (Socialist Medical Association, 1964). In the 1990s many left-wing GPs throughout the UK, particularly in deprived areas, were considering their options in the light of an impending shortage of GPs. Some felt that the small business model of general practice was outdated and that in future there might be a general switch to a salaried service. This could be run either by GPs or by the newly emerging hospital and community trusts, established under the NHS and Community Care Act 1990.

The GPs at PPHC had never been business orientated. Giving up the partnership model and joining a salaried service seemed a pragmatic way of opting out of responsibility for the financial aspects of the practice. Lis

Davidson, Mark Burns and Katy Gardner were members of the Medical Practitioners' Union (MPU), which favoured the salaried option. They met with interested MPU members from Liverpool, Sheffield, Newcastle and London to take these ideas forward. Lis commented:

> There was that element of thinking that we (GPs) should all be part of the same NHS organisation and not 'independent contractors'. Of course, the difficulty was that we went into it at a time of increasing corporatisation and of seeing the NHS as a business model. This was started by the Tories and continued by a prime minister who I felt was really a Tory.

There were discussions about larger-scale salaried service models; practices might collaborate or merge into a mutual organisation or co-operative. The GPs at PPHC envisaged being part of a network of practices that would share learning and good practice. They were encouraged by Ron Singer, an MPU inner-London GP, who wrote that these models would 'allow us to tailor services to a deprived population, while assuring the economic stability of a traditionally low earning practice' (Singer, 2000). This seemed highly relevant to PPHC, so in 1997 the GPs pondered the pros and cons of a future as salaried employees, rather than as partners and employers in their own business. They recognised that PPHC had become increasingly complex as an organisation and was probably beyond the capabilities of a practice manager who had grown up through the system. They thought there would be benefits in being part of a larger organisation which already managed district nurses, health visitors and other staff. At one GP partners' meeting, Katy described the freedom of the previously highly prized independent contractor status of GPs as an 'illusion'. Little did she know that subsequent events would force her to reconsider this view.

In 1998, after much soul-searching, the practice did become a Primary Care Act Pilot (PCAP). All practice staff, including GPs, were to be salaried employees of the newly created North Mersey Community Trust (NMCT), which provided both mental health and community services. The GPs worked extensively with the team setting up this trust. They were looking for shared values and the potential for support, expertise and networking, particularly in the areas of mental health, pharmacy and research. The practice was to be part of a new Primary Care Directorate within the trust, along with another small practice, Garston Under the Bridge. Martin Lloyd-Jones, a PPHC partner who had joined the practice in 1996, was excellent at negotiating what felt like a mutually beneficial contract. Sadly, he emigrated to Australia shortly afterwards.

The PCAP application stated, 'The Inverse Care Law has been aided during the past decades by changes to the NHS which have allowed resources to move towards the more affluent areas of our society. This bid suggests a way to support and develop an existing high-quality service which has survived within an area of high deprivation' (PPHC, 1997). A planning meeting defined an overall aim for the PCAP: 'To provide improved health care for people in the area, while providing a supportive and adequately rewarded working situation for staff.' The list-based 'capitation' payment system for GPs in the General Medical Services contract, which had proved so unfair for inner-city practices, was replaced by salaried contracts. These included provision for protected time for reflective practice, previously squeezed into the working week and often abandoned due to work pressures.

Lis Davidson joined the NMCT board as the clinical lead. Katy wrote at the time, 'It doesn't feel problematic having a former colleague as the 'boss', as we have always worked in a non-hierarchical way' (Gardner, 1999). Practice manager Sheila Scott, who had been at PPHC for many years, moved to a different position within the trust. Not everyone was happy with this, but it was part of the new management structure agreed by the GPs. There were downsides for other staff too. Pip Abraham, a longstanding receptionist formerly employed by the FHSA and attached to the practice, was discomfited: 'The PPHC GPs used to top up my wages, and when we joined NMCT I lost that money.' On the whole, however, morale was good. District nurses, practice nurses and health visitors also became employees of NMCT. One team together - exciting times!

Working in the PCAP benefited the GPs almost straight away. Recruiting GPs to vacant posts became easier. As intended, staff were freed up to focus on services for patients, as well as development and training. Under the protected time provisions, GPs had one surgery-free day per week: half for development work and half as free time. Staff appreciated having NMCT policies in place, such as those for health and safety and for protection against bullying and harassment. After the first year's pilot phase, the practice became a fully-fledged Personal Medical Services (PMS) practice.

Having one salaried team, with background support for administrative and finance matters, meant that there was time for reflection on some lasting difficulties, such as unmet demand for GP appointments. Appointment systems are always problematic in primary care; few practices have resolved problems of access without losing continuity of care, as demand invariably exceeds supply. Katy reflected, 'Whatever we tried, and we tried many things, we never quite succeeded in cracking the issue of our patients' need for time.'

Through the Service Development Initiative (see Chapter 9) the practice was able to try out various models, attempting to take on board the increasing diversity of languages spoken, especially from 2000, when PPHC became the lead practice for refugees arriving in Liverpool. A report from a 2001 practice development session stated, 'We had recently introduced a morning triage system but were still facing 'extras', people ringing later in the day wanting to be seen. We were looking at a GP call-back system, or an extra lunchtime triage system.' Although this worked well for some patients, it was more difficult for those with little English and those without access to a telephone. The practice in effect ran two parallel systems. PPHC continued to experiment, including holding a drop-in session for Somali patients with Sirad Elmi on hand to interpret. The triage system was reviewed and reorganised in 2004. Practice manager Karen Hewitt remembered, 'When we initiated the updated triage system, I personally met with community groups...to allay fears that patients who did not have English as their first language would not get medical treatment.'

The practice was also an early adopter of new educational tools. For example, Brenda Nasr, temporary practice manager in 2000, remembered that 'the practice was very committed to documenting Significant Event Analyses [a recently developed way of reflecting on significant patient events, for example if a diagnosis had been delayed or missed] and using them as a learning tool.'

Not everything in the garden was rosy

The PCAP had envisaged several more practices joining the directorate so that it would be a more substantial, and effective, organisation. The agenda at the first away-day of the pilot project in 1999 included plans for greater collaboration between the two founding practices, as well as between the practices and NMCT. However, PPHC and Garston Under the Bridge had never previously worked together, had little in common and were geographically distant, Garston being several miles from PPHC. Despite attempts to work collaboratively and share resources, it became clear that Garston Under the Bridge had a different ethos from PPHC. The collaboration foundered, and NMCT found it easier to work with each practice individually.

After a short honeymoon period during the PCAP pilot, the heavy hand of bureaucracy began to be felt by Lis Davidson in her role as clinical lead. NMCT was a new organisation on a steep learning curve. Lis felt that its staff never really grasped the essence of primary care:

> I was on the NMCT board for three years until 2001...I wasn't ready for the different culture. It was much more political (small p) and more cloak and dagger than I expected. I needed to be more strategic than I was. I am too straightforward. There was a sort of tribalism; nurses, doctors, physios etc., all in their tribes. We had tried so hard at PPHC to work across boundaries, and that didn't seem to be the case at NMCT. Rosemary Hawley was now Chair of NMCT, which was partly why we had thought it was a good idea to join the trust, as she had always been supportive. Looking back, I think at PPHC we had got where we were by standing up for what we believed in, and not by being strategic. NMCT management, including the senior doctors, had learnt to manoeuvre, and I felt that certain managers undermined other people. I remember one senior doctor saying 'you have to choose your battles.' He seemed to play the buffoon, his way of managing the system and getting on with the managers. However, when he wanted to get a point across, he got serious.

Jack Czauderna and other GPs at the Darnall Practice in Sheffield experienced similar issues after becoming a salaried PCAP in 1997, and later a PMS practice:

> We had a whole team of committed medics in the 1990s, but when we needed to recruit new doctors they did not come forward for financial reasons, and we were faced with bankruptcy. The salaried option allowed us to survive and thrive with excellent new doctors, continuing to innovate, e.g. by early employment of a pharmacist to help with our prescribing. This lasted for perhaps ten more years, before financial pressures meant the community trust was unable to support us well enough. I was the

lead GP in that period. I agree they did not fully understand primary care. Managerialism slowly took over.

By 1999 PPHC was established as a PMS practice and had 7,777 patients, served by the equivalent of five full-time GPs and one half-time GP, with three part-time practice nurses. List size was therefore 1,414 patients per whole-time GP, whereas the average across Liverpool at the time was 1,625. NMCT initially appeared to acknowledge the added value provided by PPHC, with its willingness to 'go the extra mile'. Brenda Nasr recalled an example:

> A lady came into surgery and she did not look very well. I made her an appointment for later that day, but I felt reluctant to let her leave. It was lunchtime and there were no doctors about. Then in walked Katy, who was on annual leave...I explained about the patient, and she took her down to the consulting room. Next minute Katy rang me to get an emergency ambulance; the patient was having a heart attack. That day proved to me the care and commitment the patients in Princes Park received.

However, as Karen Hewitt reflected, 'I think they [NMCT] had the impression we were a bunch of socialist nutters who were expensive!' This label, and the stigma attached, was damaging. Lis Davidson remembered:

> There was a health service view, on taking over Princes Park, that we cost too much and had attracted good nurses and health visitors, and it cost them to get the nurses into other places. There was a suspicion of us as GPs, which we weren't aware of, that we had managed to overturn the Inverse Care Law for ourselves. We were felt to be creaming off good staff for our patients; services were inequitable and there were other areas of deprivation that deserved them...But I feel that the way you address the Inverse Care law is by having champions in an area on the ground, like ourselves and the Vauxhall GPs, who demand better services in those areas.

Overall, Lis felt, 'You don't get equality through a big organisation like North Mersey Community Trust, as in the end the people who shout loudest will always get the best care. I think that could still happen in the present Clinical Commissioning Group structure.' The cultural stand-off and suspicion of PPHC soured working relationships throughout the practice's time under NMCT. This persisted when the practice was repeatedly placed under new management, as NHS 'reforms' were imposed with bewildering frequency.

The 1997 Labour government embarked on a series of health reforms. Following publication of the 1997 white paper *The new NHS: modern, dependable,* fundholding was abolished and FHSAs disappeared. In 1999 GP practices in England were formed into Primary Care Groups (PCGs), each with a budget for general practice and community health services, under the umbrella of health authorities. PCGs were to be led by primary care professionals and were charged with improving the health of their populations, addressing health inequalities and contributing to commissioning. But as it turned out, PCGs were short lived. In 2001, Liverpool's PCGs became Primary Care Trusts (PCTs) and began to commission hospital and community services directly, in addition to managing primary care services (see Chapter 13).

A temporary reprieve for the NHS: The Labour government (1997-2010)

The outlook for inner-city Liverpool residents improved under the New Labour government. Liverpool's bid for European Objective One funding was successful, and residents in Toxteth benefited from Neighbourhood Renewal projects and the creation of more public sector jobs after 1998. The post-Militant Labour council (1987-1998) introduced positive action and local training programmes. Many Liverpool-born black people had moved out of Liverpool 8, to areas such as Smithdown Road and beyond, although most remained on the PPHC list. While Granby Street had died as a community hub in the 1980s, Lodge Lane began a spectacular revival in the 1990s, with the advent of various projects including the Toxteth Community Health and Care Forum (see Chapter 6), Liverpool Arabic Centre, Granby Toxteth Development Trust, the Greenhouse Project and the Somali Women's Centre. Housing had also improved. Steve Munby could remember delivering leaflets in the walk-up blocks in Coltart Road, near the practice, in the 1980s 'while sewage ran down the stairs.' By the 2000s many such blocks had been replaced by social housing, much of it owned by housing associations, for which Labour provided funding. The 'heroin alley' estate off North Hill St (see Chapter 1) was transferred to a housing association and completely transformed following a campaign by residents.

The 1999 white paper *Saving Lives: Our Healthier Nation* (Department of Health, 1999) explicitly aimed at 'improving the health of the worst off in society and narrowing the health gap.' In 2000, Liverpool established the first public health observatory in England, hosted by John Moores University, collecting data on health and health inequalities. Facilities such as Granby Sure Start (later Granby Children's Centre) opened in 2003 to alleviate the impact of childhood poverty. Liverpool, declared a Core UK City under New Labour, was pronounced a 'rising star' by the government (Parkinson et al, 2006). Investment and employment increased, and in 2008 Louise Ellman, Labour MP for Riverside, was hopeful: 'There is optimism. Liverpool is becoming successful, even if there is a long way to go' (Parkinson, 2019).

There was indeed a long way to go. Inner-city Liverpool lagged behind more affluent areas of the country. Little of the significant investment and visitor spending during the city's Capital of Culture year in 2008 trickled down to Toxteth, and Granby Ward remained one of the most deprived in the country (Communities and Local Government, 2007). The 'Health is Wealth' Commission, of which Katy Gardner was a member, noted, 'Life expectancy for residents of the Liverpool City-Region is typically seven years less than in some parts of the South-East...Incapacity Benefit levels are almost 75% higher than the British average' (Woodward and Devaney, 2010). And after 2010, funding cuts by the Coalition and later Tory governments effectively reversed many Labour initiatives, resulting in great hardship (see Chapter 15). Liverpool's regeneration did continue, but huge disparities remained between more and less affluent areas (Parkinson, 2019).

CHAPTER 12

Primary care and public health: a joint agenda

PPHC as a cradle for public health specialists

Health promotion in the 2000s

Further collaboration with academic public health departments

PPHC as a cradle for public health specialists

In *A New Kind of Doctor,* Julian Tudor Hart proposed that the task of medicine was to 'serve whole populations according to their needs, rather than be merely available to individual demanders or purchasers of care' (1988). This reflected the shift from pre-NHS care to the socialist aspirations of the post-war Labour government. As Marshall Marinker has pointed out, Tudor Hart's Inverse Care Law was a GP's 'articulation of the two linked themes of public health - prevention of excess morbidity, and social justice' (1998).

These concepts were alive and well at PPHC. It is not surprising that two of its clinicians went on to become directors of public health: Liz Gaulton in St Helens and later Coventry, and Dr Sarah McNulty in Knowsley. As a GP registrar at PPHC, Sarah had been inspired to write her report *Princes*

Park Health Centre as a Public Health Organisation (McNulty, 2004, see Appendix). It demonstrated how the practice covered all ten designated areas of specialist public health practice, including collaborative working, reducing health inequalities, research and development and promoting population health. The report was circulated to all practices in the Central Liverpool PCT as part of a strategy to align primary care and public health more closely (Gardner, 2003). Kathrin Thomas became a consultant in public health in Wales, and an enthusiastic supporter of the role of primary care in population health (Thomas 2020). Taher Qassim, who had collaborated with PPHC on patient profiling (see Chapter 9), was a public health specialist in the Liverpool Primary Care Trust (PCT): 'For me PPHC became synonymous with Katy, who was then on the PCT board, and [public health manager] Margaret Thomson. The PCT held meetings with local organisations at PPHC, and the room was crammed with participants.'

Some PPHC staff continued to have a foot in both public health and primary care camps. Paul Thomas' roles as a Primary Care Facilitator and with the Liverpool Healthy City 2000 project enabled him to work across the divide (see Chapter 8), and he also helped to set up an Occupational Health Service for the city. Susanna Graham-Jones joined the Department of Public Health and Primary Care at Oxford University in 1993, pulling together an integrated course across both disciplines. The course used experience in general practice as a microcosm for developing students' thinking about improving the health of populations. Katy Gardner did a Master's in Public Health at John Moores University after leaving PPHC and, as a Macmillan GP, worked in prevention, screening and early diagnosis of cancer. Mike Ejuoneatse spent a sabbatical year working in public health, gaining certification from John Moores University, and later became deputy Chair of St Helens Clinical Commissioning Group. Siobhan Reilly made her career in health service research after working on the Family Health Project. In Manchester she produced several systematic reviews for the Cochrane Collaboration. She then taught at Lancaster University, and became a Professor at Braford University in 2020.

These career choices reflected the questioning and problem-solving attitude at PPHC; the attempt to see the bigger picture. Several GPs took up other challenging roles in health care and management after leaving PPHC. Ed Gaynor and Kit Oi Chung joined Liverpool Clinical Commissioning

Group (CCG) when it was formed in 2013, and former PPHC trainee Helen McKendrick was awarded an MBE for her work for the people of Vauxhall.

The benefits of linking public health work and primary care were recently reaffirmed by the Medical Practitioners Union: 'We believe there is a need for training programmes which will train doctors to practice part-time in general practice and part-time in public health. This would create doctors not only for the neighbourhood public health leads but also for population health management' (Doctors in Unite, 2020).

Health promotion in the 2000s

From 2000 a portacabin in the PPHC car park housed bicycles that could be loaned out through the Regeneration Through Environmental Action Cycling project (REACT) project. Cycling lessons, including sessions specifically for Muslim women, took place in nearby Princes Park. A bike was made available for staff to use for short journeys to and from the practice, and staff were encouraged to visit the park in their lunch hour. Michelle Timoney, PCT heart disease manager, recalled:

> We were keen to try to prevent heart disease. So, as well as structured treatment in primary care, work was ongoing at community level to help reduce heart disease risk. We worked with the council to tackle smoking, leading the campaign which led to smoke-free legislation in 2007. We successfully bid for funds for a Sport Action Zone, which Julie Curran was appointed to manage. A working group was set up with the council to improve coordination of and access to physical activity in targeted areas of Liverpool, including Liverpool 8. It was an exciting time. A lot of work went into engaging community groups to think through barriers and opportunities to become more active, and to help to tailor solutions and options for those groups...We had a partnership project with the Mersey Forest, called REACT, and Liverpool 8 was one of the target areas. People asked, 'Where is the forest in central Liverpool?' but the project was about all green space, not just forests. Its aim was to promote use of outdoor space for physical and mental wellbeing. Gill Weston, project manager, got people planting, using allotments, cycling, and walking, making connections across groups and individuals...PPHC worked closely with Julie and Gill to promote ways patients could be involved and help shape these developments.

Dr George Fairbairn, who had joined the practice in 1999, was a huge cycling enthusiast and was often to be seen cycling to home visits in all weathers. He was a great role model for all PPHC patients and staff. George worked with REACT and wrote about it in the local health newspaper, *VOICES*.

With support from Liverpool City Council, a group of Liverpool 8 residents and health professionals secured Millennium Lottery funding to create a virtual Healthy Living Centre, called Heal8. It was launched in 2003, with Karl Smith, a former Toxteth Health and Community Care Forum board member, as manager. Heal8 continued many of the initiatives spearheaded by the forum (see Chapter 6), including health fairs, fruit and vegetable stalls, exercise classes, environmental health projects and provision of health information. PPHC worked with Heal8, referring patients to support groups, a green gym (gardening as exercise) in Princes Park, and vegetable-growing projects. A PPHC/Heal8 recipe book with contributions from patients and staff was published at Christmas in 2003. Ideas from a workshop with PCT public health representatives that year included 'Walking for Health' and provision of low-cost fruit in the practice waiting room. These were later introduced into other local practices. Carmel Dersch, former chair of the Toxteth Health and Community Care Forum, became a walk leader for Walking for Health.

Further collaboration with academic public health departments

PPHC had been raising awareness about chlamydia as a sexually transmitted disease since the 1980s (see Chapter 3) and the practice continued to care for a considerable number of young single people. In 2000 the practice was invited to pilot opportunistic screening for chlamydia, working with the North West Public Health Laboratory. This pilot project followed on from research by family planning clinics in Merseyside and provided evidence for the feasibility of chlamydia testing in primary care (Harvey et al, 2000).

Postgraduates on the University of Liverpool's Public Health course were often hosted by the practice as they embarked on their dissertation projects. Master's students from the Liverpool School of Tropical Medicine (LSTM) were encouraged to investigate hepatitis B infection and anaemia in the Somali community (Aweis et al, 2001). Hepatitis B was found to be surprisingly prevalent; practice findings contributed to a campaign for testing and vaccination of babies, which was later taken up nationally.

A meeting about the health of Somali patients, particularly the high prevalence of joint pains, had highlighted the possibility of vitamin D deficiency and symptomatic severe osteomalacia, a type of bone thinning often causing severe pain (see Chapter 9). In a subsequent collaboration with LSTM, led by a Somali researcher working with paediatrician Dr James Bunn and members of the Somali community, 292 Liverpool Somalis were invited to complete a lifestyle and dietary survey, provide blood and urine samples, and have bone mineral density (BMD) measured in their heels. This confirmed the high prevalence of vitamin D deficiency; over 80% of the sample were deficient or severely deficient, 37% had symptoms of bone pain and 28% had back pain. These results led to a wider study in 2002, and to a programme based at Princes Park and Abercromby Health Centres, providing vitamin D supplementation as needed (Bunn et al, 2004). Katy Gardner remembered, 'We held regular health sessions in the late 1990s for Somali patients. Community dieticians showed us an NHS Healthy Food Plate picture, including foods containing vitamin D. But much of this food was not eaten by Somalis, including oily fish and mushrooms, which were considered poison!' As a result of this experience, Somali campaigner Samsam Salah, already involved with the vitamin D study, carried out research with dietitians and Somali community members to discover which foods containing vitamin D Somalis ate regularly (Maxwell et al, 2006). Samsam then created a pictorial Somali Healthy Food Plate which the dieticians could use when working with Somalis.

From 2003 Dr Paula Grey, Director of Public Health for Central Liverpool PCT, collaborated with Katy and Samsam Salah to produce vitamin D guidelines for the Mersey Region (Pan-Mersey Area Prescribing Committee, 2018). The group campaigned to raise the profile of vitamin D deficiency and ran a Liverpool-wide education programme for communities and health workers. Public health specialist Annette James took the lead. In 2013, after further lobbying, the newly formed Liverpool Clinical Commissioning Group (CCG) agreed to provide free universal vitamin D supplementation for pregnant women and children, in an extension of the national Healthy Start vitamins programme ('Liverpool Children Developing Bone Disease', 2012). The 'targeted' Healthy Start programme had been inequitable and bureaucratic and had very poor uptake, but the PCT had considered a simplified, free programme unaffordable. Katy felt that 'the GP-led CCG understood this in a way that the PCT had not, despite Paula Grey's efforts.'

However, in a senseless reversal, free supplementation was stopped in 2017 - again due to alleged funding constraints. This was an example of the 'one step forwards, two steps back' trajectory of various health initiatives after 2010, caused by lack of coordination in the fragmented NHS and public health systems. At PPHC, frustration was only mitigated by the knowledge that, by 2017, many Somalis had already been tested for deficiency and treated as necessary, and that health workers and residents in Liverpool 8 were by now aware of the issue. Despite the guidelines on prevention and treatment published by the National Institute for Health and Care Excellence (NICE) in 2018, vitamin D deficiency is still affecting BAME communities in Liverpool and beyond (NICE, 2018).

CHAPTER 13

Living within a fragmenting NHS (2000-2012)

The Primary Care Trust takes over salaried practices: autonomy ebbs away

Opting out of 24-hour responsibility for patients

Targets: the Quality and Outcomes Framework (2004)

PPHC suffers further as a salaried practice

We can't go on like this: longstanding GPs look elsewhere

The Primary Care Trust takes over salaried practices: autonomy ebbs away

Under the NHS Plan of 2000, the new Primary Care Groups established in 1999 morphed into Primary Care Trusts (PCTs), preparing the ground for the full purchaser/provider split. Primary Care Trusts paid for GP services and their drug costs. They commissioned and directly purchased hospital, community and mental health services, for which bids (tenders) could be submitted by NHS or private sector 'providers' (Turner and Powell, 2016). PCTs were also permitted to take over 'failing' GP practices, i.e. those which were unable to meet their contractual obligations within their allocated budgets.

In 2002 Central Liverpool PCT took over the management of PPHC and Garston Under the Bridge from the North Mersey Community Trust, under a new PCT Medical Services (PCTMS) contract. The PCT then rolled out the salaried model to a further eight struggling practices threatened with closure. As Chief Executive of Central Liverpool PCG, Margaret Thomson had been keen to use PPHC's experience to rescue and improve these practices, and Katy Gardner endorsed this move as a PCT board member. However, it had unforeseen adverse consequences for PPHC. The other practices taken on by the PCT arrived in various stages of decline and distress, with low standards of care for patients. PPHC staff felt their aspirations undermined; their umbrella organisation seemed to be functioning at a 'lowest common denominator' level, with most constituent practices 'just getting by'. Furthermore, as nurse Clare Corless said, 'The PCT tried to equate PPHC to another practice, say in a more affluent area like Childwall. It was a struggle to get them to realise that we needed more staff because our patients needed more time and had high expectations.'

It was soon evident that the PCT's managerial strategy was compromising the all-important teamwork at PPHC. Staff became increasingly frustrated. District nurse Pat Jones left in 2002: 'The 1997 Primary Care Act appeared to offer new opportunities to teams, and PPHC initially embraced it, but with the advent of trust managers taking over senior roles, creativity and co-operation were stifled. Formalisation of the co-operative relationships between different groups of staff made them stilted and less coherent than previously.' Practice-based district nurses and health visitors, integral to the primary care team since the 1970s and regarded as essential elements of the 1998 pilot (see Chapter 11), were forced to give up their rooms at PPHC. Soon after Pat Jones left they were moved to a different base, no longer attached to the practice, in the name of 'streamlining' the workforce. Daily face-to-face contact between nurses, GPs and others at PPHC became a thing of the past. Instead, any communication required time and effort. In a miserable paradox, at a time when health promotion activities that PPHC had pioneered were being adopted, mainstreamed and rolled out across the UK, the practice itself lost many of the special characteristics which had enabled those innovations. GPs whose self-esteem had been based on creative energy felt increasingly stifled by the oppressive aspects of working for a large organisation. They continued to do their best to combat this. Katy remembered one example of rule breaking: 'We were told we had to charge patients for writing supporting letters, for example relating to housing benefit. So we simply wrote them 'under the radar'.'

After 2000, turnover of inner-city GPs across England increased further because of the punishing workload. Dr Rob Barnett, secretary of the Local Medical Committee, predicted a long-term shortage of GPs in inner-city Liverpool (pers. comm., 2001). Although GPs no longer had to be on call out-of-hours, the stress of following the latest prescriptive guidelines and attempting to reach targets in order to generate income, while dealing with patients' complex problems, made the working day ever more intense.

Over the following decade, different models of primary care were developed throughout England. The changes within the Merseyside NHS were chaotic, and the practice was transferred from one newly invented authority to another. The accompanying rapid turnover of senior NHS staff resulted in loss of continuity and trust between clinicians and managers. PPHC's identity as a flagship practice was under threat. In becoming salaried and directly employed, GPs had indeed been liberated from the administrative burden and responsibility of managing the practice. But the increasing fragmentation of the NHS meant that, having given up their autonomy, the GPs were then subject to a succession of less than competent managing authorities.

In 2003 PPHC lost another ally when community health councils were abolished by the Labour government with little explanation or consultation. Although the government created a new scrutiny role for local authorities, the CHCs' close interaction with NHS bodies and, in particular, their ability to take up issues on behalf of patients and community groups, was lost. Staff at PPHC, and GPs nationally, were very unhappy about this and lobbied against it. The practice had enjoyed close links with Central and South CHC since its formation in the 1970s. Weaker forums set up subsequently, such as Patients Liaison Services (PALS) and Healthwatch, have generally proved toothless, with fewer resources and less clout. Martin Rathfelder, then secretary of the Socialist Health Association, commented, 'It is now clear that the abolition of CHCs was a mistake. The elaborate and expensive machinery which replaced them has not delivered an effective voice for patients' (Socialist Health Association, 2006).

PPHC continued as a training practice for GP registrars until 2008, when Martin Smith, the last longstanding GP trainer left. Loss of training status was deeply regretted; trainees and registrars had always added their own colour and perspective to the team. Dr Ralph Brussatis, Katy's registrar in 2000, had some vivid memories of his time at PPHC.

Remembering PPHC: Dr Ralph Brussatis

You never know

Mr. S, elderly with a long beard, suffering from double cataract in his eyes, finds his way into the surgery. He carries a big stick, around which is wrapped a large black bin bag. He complains about itchy hands. When this is sorted, I ask him, 'What about the cataract operation?' He answers, 'Yes, but not now. I've got business to do.'

'What kind of business?

'I've got to see someone,' he replies with a conspiratorial undertone.

I ask what he carries in the bin bag.

'Oh, it's me documents, Doctor. I always carry them with me.'

'But why?' I dare to answer.

'Well, otherwise someone might steal them from my room in the house.'

'Who, besides you, lives in the room?'

'Only me, Doctor.'

'And who lives in the house?'

'Oh, only my father. But you never know - do you?' he answers with a twinkle in one of his eyes.

I never found out what he meant...

Miracles: it's always worth a try

Home visit. 86-year-old D-Day veteran. Early Alzheimer's, and a right shoulder injury from a German gunshot during the war...

His wife is despairing as he can't do anything with his arm anymore. On top of that he becomes forgetful, frustrated and angry at times.

There is not much I can do about his shoulder but despite the obvious illusory outcome, I offer to give him a short acupuncture trial. After all, he has not used this arm for nearly 60 years and there is not much muscle left either... but miracles are always worth a try.

After the session, with the needles in for about ten minutes, we carefully try to mobilise. His face lights up for the first time. To all our amazement, we manage some very basic shoulder rotations, some abduction and also actually lifting the arm to nearly 90 degrees.

His wife 'beats herself up', never having thought of going for this option in all those years. It had become a 'no go' area and she was always fearful of inflicting more harm.

His arm had been dangling like a limp appendix for many years.

Now he is somehow, apparently for the first time, moving his shoulder again and using his arm to lift a can of beer. Triumphantly he grins with both ears and I thank him for risking his life to save the world from an evil and brutal Hitler dictatorship.

Of course, I don't know how long this newfound glimpse of shoulder freedom of movement will last, but when leaving, he amazingly manages to give me a wave, with his right arm.

His wife beaming next to him.

I will never forget that scene.

A few days later I discover an email from one of the doctors, telling me that I am not entitled to do any acupuncture, as it is not evidence based and I am not insured...

Time flies when pregnant

Another emergency appointment. A young woman storms into my room.

'So, what's up?' I start the conversation.

'Doctor, doctor, I am pregnant!'

'Congratulations! How many weeks?'

'About three weeks,' she replied.

'But why do you make an emergency appointment?'

'Well, don't I have to be admitted to the hospital?'

'Hospital? Do you have any serious health problems?'

'No Doctor, but this is my first pregnancy.'

'Well, most people wait nine months before they go to the hospital to deliver the baby.'

'Oh, is that so? Ah well then. Thank you, doctor,' she replies, gets up, shakes my hand and disappears...

The practice had been doing video assessment and consultation analysis for many years in an educational and supportive way (see Chapter 4). Accreditation of registrars now included this as a formalised process which Ralph, amongst others, both trainers and registrars, found a stressful challenge.

Grabbing the world by its horns

Yes, I will grab the world by its horns and shake it until it gives me what I want!!!

Not wasting any time anymore. No, No No !! I'm going to be pro-active and full of power and energy, making the best of life and my current situation...

Friday, 9 am. I start...in front of my computer, ready for action and writing a summary of my patient video consultations, which has to be handed in in five days.

Suddenly my computer crashes and freezes all my personal and professional documents, leaving me in utter disbelief, helplessness, despair and finally panic.

Ten hours later, by 7 pm - no progress!

I am shattered, but on my way to a meditation workshop in Wales, driving through heavy rain and snow in a tiny car with no heating and a very tired windscreen wiper.

Maharishi talks about the absolute and relative aspect of life, the beauty of a flower and other manifestations of this higher intelligence, and I meditate... on anti-virus software, firewalls and frozen computer screens.

So much for taking my destiny by its horns!

Ralph passed the assessment. He went on to work as a freelance GP in Liverpool, and as a volunteer in developing countries.

One of the last PPHC registrars, Dr Kishore Krishnamurthy, known as Krish, became a salaried GP and provided enthusiastic support to Lis Davidson.

Remembering PPHC: Dr Kishore Krishnamurthy ('Krish')

I did my GP training with George Fairbairn and Martin Smith in 2006. I returned to PPHC as a salaried GP in June 2008 and worked there till October 2011; I would still recall these as my 'wonder years'. I can honestly say that I learnt what it is to be a GP at PPHC. I had the pleasure of working with the best GPs you could ever imagine, including the likes of Drs Lis Davidson, Martin Smith, Michael Ejuoneatse and George Fairbairn. We had a fantastic team of nurses including Clare Corless, Jane and Carla, blessed with some of the best nursing skills you could have prayed/wished for. Karen Hewitt our practice manager could never be fazed by anything in life! We were fabulously supported by the reception staff including Dotty and Nicky to just name a couple, who were the face of the practice to the world.

PPHC was the best place you could you imagine starting your career. The support of the whole team was unwavering in the most difficult of circumstances. The team at PPHC would go out of their way to be understanding and supportive of the needs of vulnerable patients and help them to the best of their abilities. These included asylum seekers; patients with English as not their main spoken language; patients fleeing from persecution and war-ravaged places in various corners of the world with the associated complex psychological and medical issues that accompany these circumstances; patients on a methadone replacement programme - complex groups of patients, to just name a few! I strongly felt and still feel that PPHC was, and hopefully still is, the backbone of the local community and L8 area. My favourite memory of PPHC was the surprise 'mock wedding' I had in the surgery meeting room! All the staff colluded and organised a surprise party during lunch time, between the morning and afternoon clinics, on my return to the surgery after my home visit. This was planned and executed on the day before I was to take a flight to India to get married in 2010. It was a complete wedding with a fully laid out lunch for all the staff; the practice manager Karen Hewitt was the 'mock' bride (in her white wedding dress), and bridesmaids thrown into the picture too!! This was an experience that will remain etched in my memory forever, for all the right reasons!!

Opting out of 24-hour responsibility for patients

In 2003, government legislation enabled GPs to opt out of providing 24-hour care to patients. This meant handing over care from 6.30 pm to 8 am to out-of-hours services separately commissioned by the PCT. Previously, even if out-of-hours calls were handed over to locums, GPs retained ultimate responsibility for their patients. Susanna Graham-Jones, a GP adviser to the NHS Chief Medical Officer at this time, remembered being shocked when the proposals were first presented. She felt strongly that the individual GP's 24-hour responsibility was beneficial to patients, but she was in a small minority. Most GPs were happy to opt out, paying a nominal sum for out-of-hours cover, and GPs at PPHC followed the trend. Their decision was influenced by the fact that several of them already worked for the GP out-of-hours service UC24 (see Chapter 10). Some GPs at PPHC continued to work for UC24 for many years, including auditing out-of-hours consultations and teaching GP registrars. So PPHC patients could be reasonably confident of a high-quality service. This was not the case in many inner-city areas, where the quality of out-of-hours services varied widely.

The introduction of fixed daytime working hours reduced the length of the GPs' working day. But increased paperwork and the expectation of improved record-keeping meant that they were still working long hours, often taking large bundles of letters home to read, or arriving early in the morning to view endless lists of documents on the computer.

Targets: the Quality and Outcomes Framework (2004)

The impact of New Labour's policies on NHS services was mixed. The shorter waiting times demanded by PCTs in hospital contracts benefited patients with serious health conditions, while improvements in admission procedures removed many of the endless waits on the phone to admit a sick patient. However, the culture of target-setting was problematic. Lis Davidson remembered, 'We went to a Labour meeting in Manchester discussing target-setting and competition for service provision, and we argued against. But I do also remember a Labour MP saying how much leverage the NHS has been able to get by competition, e.g. with greatly reduced waiting lists in dermatology in Liverpool.'

Targets became a major concern for GPs in 2004 when the points-based Quality and Outcomes Framework (QOF) was imposed (King's Fund, 2011). Funding for GPs was changed radically, moving some critical financial goalposts. Once again, inner-city practices were effectively penalised. Postcode-based deprivation payments for practices serving poor households, intended to compensate practices with hard-to-reach patients, were removed. The QOF deliberately increased the element of performance-related pay, powerfully incentivising evidence-based chronic disease management. Payment for health promotion activities was withdrawn in favour of payment by results. Running a hypertension clinic no longer attracted payment. Instead, the practice had to record successful outcomes of treatment - for example, normal blood pressure readings in a large majority of patients - to score maximum QOF points and attract the financial rewards. GPs and practice nurses at PPHC had long been committed to chronic disease management, audit and prescribing reviews. As before, however, it was hard to reach pre-set targets in a multilingual, deprived inner-city area. While suburban practices, with their stable lists of relatively compliant and healthy patients, reaped the benefits, PPHC struggled to score QOF points, and was paid less for its pains.

A QOF assessment team from the PCT visited PPHC in 2004 and noted the high turnover of patients and the obvious difficulty of keeping record summaries of new patients up to date. However, national guidance allowed no leeway in relation to criteria for earning QOF points, nor were any additional resources provided. The practice was again stigmatised as a low earner compared with others, and as expensive for its employers. As mentioned above (Chapter 5), the pressure to meet targets and score QOF points interfered with relationships between clinicians and patients. Katy Gardner protested: 'If a patient comes to see me and discloses rape or child abuse or has no money for food, am I going to say, "Your smear test is due, and we need to check your blood pressure?"'

The QOF was intended to raise standards and reduce inequalities, using evidence-based care protocols. It markedly increased the workload of practice nurses, administrative staff and GPs. But subsequent research showed that the impact on patients was limited. The Inverse Care Law remained true; the most deprived patients benefited least from health service provision. A report by the King's Fund concluded that 'there has been little evidence of health improvement and reduction in health inequality from the QOF Framework: [this was] a tick-box exercise that failed to encourage doctors to examine the health of the wider community' (2011).

PPHC suffers further as a salaried practice

In her 2004 annual appraisal, Katy complained that the high turnover of middle managers at the PCT meant that practice priorities were neglected and plans were not followed through. The practice wrote to the PCT as follows: 'Managers have put down a spate of poor staff appointments to bad luck. We disagree. There have been many staff related issues that have been poorly handled. To whom and for what are the managers accountable? We feel we must institute a vote of no confidence in the current managers.' Karen Hewitt, who valiantly continued to manage the practice at ground level, felt her hands were tied by unhelpful meddling from above: 'We were managed by trusts who didn't really understand primary care or care about the philosophy of the team. More and more restrictions were placed on us, not allowing us to be the creative PPHC we once were...With each new employer that came along, a little bit of the old 'Prinny' was chipped away.' The constraints imposed by working for an NHS trust tightened. For example, Katy remembered that GPs were instructed to account for every hour of their 'development' time, logging where they were and exactly what they were doing. This was dispiriting and counterproductive.

Despite these difficulties the PPHC team continued to provide excellent patient care. Jim Hamilton remembered:

> I had enjoyed good health until I reached the age of 60. I had a party in a church hall and a lovely meal which a good friend prepared. She was good at cakes and puddings and I think I sampled every one of them! Shortly after this I went to the surgery with a bit of cough and the doctor who saw me did a blood test. Much to my surprise and the doctor's, I was diagnosed with diabetes, which was strange considering I was not overweight. Over the coming months I developed a heart condition...I was having to go for lots of tests, but was determined to carry on working as I was a self-employed painter and decorator. However, one afternoon a

nurse rang me and when she heard how breathless I was, advised me to see the doctor. I think it was Katy I saw, who was concerned that I was out of breath from just walking up the corridor to her room and signed me off with fluid round the heart...After two weeks, I felt well enough to return to work, but as I loaded my gear into the car, I slipped and fell. There was a sickening crack from my ankle, and I ended up on my back. After a minute or so I started to feel better and went to work, but it became increasingly harder to climb the ladder. By evening I could hardly walk, so my wife and daughter took me to A and E, where they discovered I had broken a bone in my ankle and put my leg in plaster...Next day I hobbled into the surgery to get a sick note and saw Lis, who asked 'What have you been up to now?' followed by 'Do you think someone up there is trying to tell you something?' Well, I think on this occasion, she was right, although, as I understand it, she doesn't think there is anyone 'up there'.

PCTs were given further powers from 2004. The Alternative Provider Medical Services (APMS) contract enabled them to negotiate with diverse organisations to provide primary medical services, opening the floodgates further to private providers (Williams et al, 2001; Barnett, pers. comm., 2008). More practices across the UK followed PPHC's example and gravitated towards salaried contracts in search of steady income and reduced responsibility, administrative burden and financial risk.

GPs at PPHC, meanwhile, were worried by these rapid changes to the rules on who could provide health services. The day-to-day pressure of their work did not leave them with much room to scan the horizon for solutions, but it was evident that many of the new models of primary care provision were located firmly in the private sector. In 2006 it became clear that PCT operations would be definitively split into provider and purchaser functions. PCTs would be purchasers, commissioning health services, and would no longer be permitted to manage practices. This prompted the ten Liverpool salaried practices to meet informally to look at their options in these new circumstances. In the event, however, they were given no choice. In 2010, under the NHS Transforming Community Services programme, Liverpool PCT was forced to hand over its role in service provision, including GP practices and district nursing services, to another new entity, Liverpool Community Health Trust (LCHT), which took over the management of PPHC (Gardner, 2012).

We can't go on like this: longstanding GPs look elsewhere

Loss of autonomy during the 2000s eroded the motivation of the longstanding GPs to maintain the enduring doctor-patient relationships championed by Cyril Taylor and his successors. In 2005 Katy left PPHC after 28 years, feeling she had given everything she had to the practice. She also resigned from her post as PCT heart disease lead. She was deeply apprehensive about an impending merger of all the Liverpool PCTs, each serving a population of about 100,000, into a whole-of-Liverpool PCT: 'It was massively big. I thought it was a step too far, and that's when I resigned.'

Katy hoped to follow Cyril's example and become a city councillor:

> I was exhausted. It wasn't just the bureaucracy. When I started out at PPHC, I felt as if I was in the front line of a war zone. There was so much suffering; I just had jump in and do my best. Sometimes it wasn't good enough and that left an indelible mark. But as medicine became more complex, and we could do more to help people, my uncertainties seemed to grow. Meanwhile, the burden of distress endured by patients never seemed to shrink. I needed a different challenge, but I was still passionate about serving the local community. I applied to the Labour Party to stand as a councillor for Granby Ward when a vacancy came up. I knew I could not 'do a Cyril' and be both a councillor and a GP. I felt unable to reduce my time at PPHC further without a great loss of continuity and, of course, an advantage of being salaried meant I could change practices within the PCT organisation. In the end I was not selected by the Labour Party, pipped at the post by one vote. So I did a Master's in Public Health instead and then moved to Marybone Health Centre in Vauxhall, one of the 10 salaried practices, as a part-time salaried GP.

In fact, it turned out to be 'out of the frying pan into the fire'. Until recently Marybone had been run by a single-handed GP, and it suffered many of the problems that beset small practices in deprived areas. Luckily, Katy was able to use her PPHC experience to help turn it around.

Mike Ejuoneatse and Martin Smith, both innovative and thoughtful GPs, left the practice in 2007 and 2008, having put in 13 and 20 years respectively. Quite apart from workload issues, they both left to escape the stress of working for a bureaucratic and often dysfunctional organisation. Martin remembered:

> Inevitably there were teething problems with becoming salaried, but as

far as I was concerned matters deteriorated rather than improving. The final straw for me was in 2007, when we were refused any part in the process of appointing a replacement doctor. We had already run into difficulties with doctors who didn't share our ethos and didn't seem to want to work as a team.

Mike explained his own decision to move on:

The move from partnership to a salaried model was necessary at the time, given the challenges faced with recruitment, but led to the erosion of the ethos and camaraderie that made working in a challenging area tolerable and manageable...I left because of a growing desire to regain autonomy and control in my working environment, which had been gradually eroded. However, my time at PPHC provided perhaps the best and equally most challenging experience. I felt that if I could make it there, I could make it anywhere, and that has certainly proven to be the case.

Like Katy, administrator Ann Cunningham left in 2005. She too took her skills and experience from 15 years at PPHC into her next job:

The practice was slowly losing its ethos and GPs began to leave. As much-loved GPs moved on, patients became disgruntled, were not happy with the replacements, and used to speak about the good old days and how things used to be at PPHC. I left as an after-effect of the changes, and now work at PC24 Asylum Service as Practice Manager. My experiences at PPHC equipped me with many skills that I can bring to my post now; the main ones being the capability to deal with people from many different backgrounds, treating each one as an equal, and an understanding that how we converse with our patients has a direct effect on them and how they feel...My fondest working memories are of PPHC and the rest of the team, which was evident at my and Katy's leaving party, when I cried my eyes out because I didn't want to leave.

As doctors who had been partners left, they were replaced by GPs who had only ever worked as salaried doctors. Despite being attracted by the PPHC ethos, they tended not to stay for the long haul. Lis Davidson, now the longest-standing GP at PPHC, summed up the prevailing attitude at this time:

[It always seemed to be] 'What is my job?' - a rigid approach to how we shared the workload. There was friction between different personalities. Some GPs did not function as a team or pull their weight. Everyone came to me to complain and sort it out, and it drove me mad. It was so different from when we were a team and took responsibility for ironing out differences. Most of these GPs were blaming someone else. I think that was the thing that started to make me feel I couldn't carry on.

In 2007 Lis Davidson became official lead GP at PPHC, as did Katy at Marybone. The PCT, and subsequently Liverpool Community Health Trust (LCHT, see Chapter 14), apparently expected them to perform this role unsupported, without reimbursement or protected time for the additional work. Both protested that their role was being undervalued, Lis struggling valiantly to keep the PPHC ethos going, and Katy helping to rescue the failing Marybone surgery. In 2011, supported by the British Medical Association, both were awarded compensation by LCHT.

Fortunately, PPHC did continue to attract dedicated staff who helped Lis to keep standards high. Sheila Altes joined the team as a practice nurse in 2007:

> I had previously been employed in surgeries with only one or two GPs and small populations. Although I enjoyed my work, I was beginning to feel isolated as the lone nurse. All this changed with my transfer to PPHC. I heard that it had a large and diverse practice population and that I would be one of a team of four nurses. I was apprehensive about adapting to my new surroundings, but I was immediately put at ease...The lead nurse, Clare Corless, had arranged an induction programme to familiarise me with the health centre. This was in stark contrast to other surgeries, where I had been expected to start clinics on the first day. The atmosphere was warm and friendly and the other nurses, Carla and Jane, patiently showed me the ropes despite their busy workloads. I soon became one of the team. Teamwork was essential in such a busy practice; we all had our areas of expertise but could call on one another for advice. We would help each other out if we were struggling to complete our clinics. The doctors could be relied upon to come to our aid if we encountered a problem that was not within our remit...I welcomed the opportunity to work with patients from other countries and learn of their cultures and felt staff were committed to meeting their diverse needs. Many staff had worked there for years and knew the patients very well, as I did with time. One receptionist had been here for 28 years and had seen some of them grow up. This commitment towards patients and their families leads to understanding and adaptability to deliver care...It was not all perfect, and

not without its ups and downs, but my first years at PPHC were happy ones and my overriding memory is of laughter among the staff.

CHAPTER 14

Out to tender (2011)

The tortuous tender process: SSP Health takes over

How could it have come to this? The Care Quality Commission inspections

The tortuous tender process: SSP Health takes over

The practice fared no better under new management. In 2010, Liverpool Community Health NHS Trust (LCHT) took over PPHC and other salaried practices from the PCT. LCHT turned out to be a dysfunctional organisation. In 2018 a retrospective independent review chaired by public health physician Bill Kirkup concluded that LCHT had been set up with a 'new and inexperienced management team; their leadership was inadequate from the outset' (Kirkup, 2018). The review concluded that the trust board had been preoccupied with over-ambitious financial goals - its aim was to become a foundation trust. As a result, it failed to respond appropriately to emerging staff concerns about poor management and inadequate service provision for patients: 'LCHT not only failed in its duty to provide safe and effective services, it concealed this from external bodies. Both patients and staff suffered harm for too long as a result' (Kirkup, 2018). Lis Davidson felt that the managers had washed their hands of PPHC: 'We were seen as 'too difficult' (not fitting neatly into the boxes defined for us).' At Marybone practice, Katy Gardner also found LCHT bureaucratic and risk averse. She retired in 2012, and at her leaving interview described it as a 'can't do' organisation.

Meanwhile, in 2011, Liverpool PCT put the salaried practices out to tender without any consultation with staff or patients, inviting bids from both NHS providers, including local practices, and private providers. One reason given at the time for this unexpected move was changes to European competition law on the rules governing NHS procurement; but Liverpool's salaried GPs suspected that this was a spurious argument and that PCT politics played a role in this decision. The cover-up by LCHT, described above, was presumably a further source of obfuscation, as, without explanation, LCHT failed to bid to continue managing the practices. Salaried GP Krish left in 2011:

> I have nothing but fond memories of my time at PPHC and do sometimes wonder if I had left this fabulous place a bit earlier than I should have! But I left because the whole team were unhappy with the tendering process. Many of the colleagues I had worked with in the previous years left one after the other. Morale at PPHC was so low and none of us was keen on working for a private provider in the long term.

Further chaos ensued when, just as the tenders for the salaried practices were about to be awarded in January 2012, the whole process was aborted (Gardner, 2012). Again, no explanation was provided; the silence and suspense was excruciating for everyone at the practice. The tendering (bidding) process started again, taking nine more months. The circumstances of this debacle are still shrouded in mystery and rumour, obscured by yet more reshuffling of NHS organisations. As a result, practice morale plummeted, and yet more staff deserted an apparently sinking ship. Practice manager Karen Hewitt resigned: 'I felt the climate within LCHT made it no longer the PPHC I knew and loved, and the writing was on the wall; another takeover was imminent.' She was right. LCHT was taken to task by the Care Quality Commission in 2013, and an interim executive management team was appointed pending further investigations.

Worst of all, when PPHC was put out to tender in the second round, local practices which had expended time, money and effort to put in first-round bids for the practice could not afford to repeat the process. These included Brownlow Health and Vauxhall Primary Health Care, both practices led by GPs who had trained at PPHC; and the nearby Elms Medical Centre, which had an excellent relationship with PPHC over many years. It was clear that larger and more profit-orientated businesses had much greater capacity to bid for such contracts - many of them employed lawyers and accountants with years of experience of takeovers and mergers.

After a period of disconcerting uncertainty for the practice, the tender was awarded in 2012 to an organisation named SSP Health (SSPH). This was a GP-run business based in the North West of England, but with no presence in Liverpool at that time. It had very little in common with PPHC as an organisation. SSPH took over PPHC in April 2013, and subsequently acquired several other practices in Liverpool and Sefton, doubling the number of surgeries in its portfolio.

Chas Clegg had left PPHC in 1993 to work as a full-time diabetic specialist nurse, but remained in touch: 'I cannot understand how the practice went from being a phoenix of health care to being owned by a conglomerate. It was a beacon of good practice. I despair of what happened to it and our NHS under the Tories...For all those involved, PPHC was our Camelot.'

Lis Davidson decided to leave at this point:

> Martin Smith had left, and we had lost our training practice status. I felt I would try to get PPHC back its training practice status, and then if things were no better I would leave...But then there was the whole bidding process, the failed tender and the rebidding. I remember thinking first time round, if the consortium including the Elms Medical Centre got the bid, I would talk to them about staying on...But the bid collapsed and SSPH got it second time round. That was my exit cue. Once I had made the decision, I felt I coped much better.

Amid this takeover turmoil, a surprising material bonanza arrived; the PPHC building was designated for refurbishment, as part of the NHS 'estate'. It became a hub for district nurse treatment room clinics - though alas, not the district nurse teams themselves - and for physiotherapy. Levi Tafari and Riverside MP Louise Ellman officiated at the re-opening. The waiting room had been further improved, but all the colourful and iconic posters and pictures were removed and never replaced, due to new health and safety concerns. Counsellor Ria Hayward remembered how she had loved the old consulting rooms: 'Each one was personalised and it gave you a connection somehow. Judith Hindley's room had pictures of mountains, as she loved walking, and Katy's had lots of health-related pictures and posters.' The refurbished consulting rooms were subsequently described by a patient as 'sterile - they lost all their character.'

Matters had already taken a real turn for the worse, locally and nationally, when the Health and Social Care Act became law in 2012. Susanna Graham-Jones, interviewed in Oxford on BBC television in 2011, had vigorously opposed the Bill, as had Katy and many GPs and patients at PPHC, some of whom joined the national campaigning organisation Keep Our NHS Public (KONP). The Health and Social Care Act encouraged further fragmentation and privatisation of the NHS, and fundamentally reduced the statutory duties of the government as regards health provision. One consequence was the abolition of Primary Care Trusts, which were replaced by Clinical Commissioning Groups in 2013. The transition to CCGs was needlessly disruptive.

Meanwhile, the deliberate Tory policy of austerity undid many of the gains made in the Labour years, blighting the lives of many PPHC patients. Unemployment and chronic ill health remained at toxic levels. An increasingly punitive benefits system caused much avoidable hardship, generating a wave of appeals against benefit withdrawals across the UK. A tellingly large proportion of these appeals were successful (BMA, 2012). Nearly 50% of respondents in a 2014 survey of inner-city GPs said that their patients' deepening financial problems had significantly increased their workload, while a report commissioned by the Mayor of Liverpool revealed the plight of low-income families in the city (Kyprianou, 2015).

Despite all this, Toxteth's regeneration was underway. It had avoided the worst of the rioting that took place in many inner cities in 2011. Youth workers organised and managed to dissuade young people from getting into confrontations with the police which could lead to arrest and damage to their future life chances. Local activists and organisations came together to form the 'Liverpool 8 Against the Riots' alliance. New shops and businesses were continuing to open.

How could it have come to this? The Care Quality Commission inspections

This was a dark time indeed for Princes Park Health Centre and its patients, exacerbated by high turnover of staff. SSPH appeared to rely mainly on locum GPs, rather than employing enough salaried GPs to work consistently in the practice and get to know its patients. Staff became worried and, despite the efforts of a few loyal, stoic receptionists and secretaries, patients became dissatisfied with the deteriorating standards of care and lack of continuity under SSPH management. Complaints were made. The Care Quality Commission (CQC) inspected the practice in January 2014 and recognised a major problem in the appointments system, quoting patients who described long delays and lack of communication by staff (Care Quality Commission, 2014).

At a follow up visit six months later, some improvements to the appointment system were noted. However, many patients were still dissatisfied, and an active group of them started meeting regularly, demanding improved services and explicitly calling for a change of health care provider. At the time, GP contracts required evidence of 'user engagement' in the form of a Patient Participation Group, with the express purpose of enabling patients' voices to be heard. But concerned PPHC patients found their practice unresponsive. The campaigning organisation Keep Our NHS Public (KONP) stepped into the gap and helped to design a questionnaire for a survey of patient opinion. Patients and staff were interviewed. Over 60 people attended a public meeting for patients, interpreters and members of the Arabic, English and Somali-speaking communities. This meeting aimed to give a voice to those not being heard, and to explore options for improving the situation. Testimonies from patients, staff and interpreters painted a grim picture. Patients were still finding it difficult to get appointments, and consequently suffered delays in receiving care. Many were forced to use A&E or walk-in centres, as they could not access the primary care service which held their medical records. An elderly patient remembered: 'We had to queue. There were people queuing down the street, several abreast. It was horrible.'

For over 35 years PPHC had provided good news stories for the Liverpool Echo. Now the headline was: 'Patients forced to queue in street for an appointment at Princes Park surgery' (Taylor, 2015). At the public meeting there were reports of interpreting services not being booked or not working properly. Numerous minor clinical errors were reported. The over-reliance on locums caused major problems. One patient described their experience: 'I am diabetic. I am still waiting for Princes Park to contact me. I ended up taking drugs without diagnosis or prescription. I've moved my family to another GP for their protection.' Another patient, who moved to a different practice, said she was 'shocked to get good treatment there, just like we used to have here.'

Keep Our NHS Public Merseyside published a report detailing patients' experiences and the survey results, under the title *Princes Park Health Centre - The destruction of community based GP services* (2015). It described 'a practice in chaos, unable to fulfil its responsibilities for patient care. Patients living in the Princes Park area of Liverpool are being let down by a system that does not care.' The report stated:

> Although on a smaller scale and of a different nature, the similarities between what happened at Princes Park Health Centre and what occurred in the Mid Staffordshire NHS Foundation Trust are unnerving. That report found, among other issues: lack of openness to criticism; lack of consideration for patients; defensiveness; acceptance of poor standards; failure to put the patient first in everything that is done.

It concluded, 'The original ethos of PPHC, where everyone worked together to meet the needs of the community, was lost. It had become a place where relative strangers came to work for a company whose primary responsibility is to maximise profits for the shareholders' (KONP, 2015).

The report contained an interview with PPHC practice nurse Jane Ford outlining her experiences, which were echoed by nurses Sheila Altes and Clare Corless. Sheila remembered:

> Several GPs had resigned shortly before the transfer and were not replaced. This created problems with continuity of care and increased the already heavy workload of permanent doctors and nurses. Many locums were not familiar with policies and protocols. Consequently, often, prescriptions were not issued on time and medication reviews were not completed. The administrative staff bore the brunt of patients' anger over the lack of appointments and the time taken to obtain their prescriptions. Soon admin staff were leaving and being replaced with agency staff, also unaware of protocols and recall systems. Nurses were told to reduce consultation times, including reviews for patients with complex needs. Practice meetings were non-existent, and training sessions discontinued.

Clare Corless, quoted in the KONP report, agreed: 'To say there was a severe lack of medical support was an understatement. Levels of administrative staff also reduced, creating huge problems...Patients weren't attended to and were left waiting in the reception area' (2015).

The KONP report's findings were corroborated by the results of the mandatory annual GP Patient Survey (GPPS) for 2014, undertaken in all practices on behalf of NHS England. That year, PPHC scored below the CCG average on the survey in every aspect of care (NHS England and Ipsos MORI, 2014).

PPHC patients' forceful expression of their longstanding concerns and frustrations about the management of the privatised practice was essential to the campaign for change. Thanks to continued lobbying and the publication of the KONP report, the Care Quality Commission decided to inspect the practice again in 2015, and the inspectors arranged to meet with patients. This time, the practice was found to be inadequate in many respects. The CQC placed it in 'special measures', calling for specific remedial actions to improve the quality of care within a reasonable time (Care Quality Commission, 2015).

CQC rates Merseyside GP Surgery as Inadequate

6 August 2015

Princes Park Surgery, operated by SSP Health Ltd, has been given an overall rating of Inadequate.

Under CQC's new programme of inspections, led by Professor Steve Field, Chief Inspector of General Practice, all of England's GP practices are being inspected and given a rating. The practice was inspected in April 2015...A full report of this inspection has been published on the CQC website today.

Although inspectors received some positive comments from patients during the inspection who said that they were treated with dignity and respect by staff, inspectors also identified a number of significant concerns.

Staff understood their responsibilities to raise concerns, and to report incidents and near misses. However, reviews and investigations were not thorough and lessons learned were not communicated widely enough to support improvement.

The provider did not deploy sufficient numbers of GPs to meet the demands of patients including in response to their urgent needs. The high usage of locum and agency GPs led to a lack of continuity of care, and increased the risk of patient incidents and complaints occurring.

The practice was not responsive to people's needs. Patients regularly had to queue outside the practice for it to open to ensure they get an appointment for that day. Many of the people inspectors spoke to stated they had difficulty arranging an appointment over the telephone and were not always able to access an appointment with their regular GP at a time that they needed.

The systems and processes to address potential risks were not implemented well enough to ensure patients were kept safe. There were no written action plans when incidents and complaints had occurred. This meant that the practice could not monitor the effectiveness of any action taken.

The Care Quality Commission has identified a number of areas for improvement, including:

- The practice must review the system in place for reporting incidents, including locum and agency GPs, because the method used during inspection was not sufficient in detail to adequately identify risks. Actions following investigations must be shared effectively with all staff in a timely manner.

- The practice must address the patients concerns about adequate GP cover and continuity of care, and should put measures in place to respond to patient's urgent needs.

- The practice must take appropriate action to ensure patient records are accurate and updated at the earliest opportunity, to ensure follow up appointments and hospital visits are supported by the most relevant information.

- The practice must ensure that GPs complete clinical audits to assess and continually evaluate their practice.

- The practice must develop an action plan to increase the surgery's performance for cervical smear uptake.

- The practice must review the appointment system to ensure there are sufficient numbers of patient appointments to meet the demands of the local population.

CQC is working closely with Liverpool Clinical Commissioning Group and NHS England to support the practice while it addresses the issues identified by the inspection.

Extract from the CQC news release (2015)

Professor Steve Field, Chief Inspector of General Practice, who led the visiting team, concluded, 'On the basis of the ratings given to this practice at this inspection, I am placing the provider into special measures...We will inspect the practice again in six months to consider whether sufficient improvements have been made. If we find that the provider is still providing inadequate care, we will take steps to cancel its registration with CQC' (Care Quality Commission, 2015).

The SSPH contract for the ten Liverpool practices was due for review by the Clinical Commissioning Group (CCG) in 2016. It was not renewed. Nurse Shelia Altes wrote of her relief at the outcome: 'PPHC was lucky to count among its patients Sam Semoff, a founding member of Keep Our NHS Public Merseyside...Thanks to his and fellow KONP members' tireless efforts, the SSPH contract was not renewed.'

The CCG now asked for expressions of interest to run the Liverpool surgeries on a temporary basis for a year. Contracts for the Princes Park and Marybone practices were awarded to Brownlow Health, a local multi-practice organisation which had won the national General Practice of the Year award in 2013. Dr Ed Gaynor, a former PPHC trainee, is one of the lead GPs at Brownlow Health:

> Financial pressures appeared to lead to the demise of PPHC as it was taken over by the Community Trust and then SSPH. The loss of the core group of founding GPs meant that there was a loss of the essence of PPHC. So, when the opportunity to take over PPHC arose, I was surprised at my enthusiasm. I think this stemmed from it being in such a sorry state with patients leaving, a continuous list of complaints and a CQC rating of requiring improvement. At Brownlow we have always had a vision of creating a larger practice and this included applying to take over practices, as long as these practices were coherent geographically and in good premises. However, it was much more than that. I obviously knew the history of PPHC and was able to share with the Brownlow partners how it once was the jewel in the rather tatty crown of Liverpool general practice. We were all aware of the poor service it was currently offering and believed we could help it to return to at least some of its former glory. Under the leadership of GP Debbie Feint this has certainly been the case. We recognised that PPHC was unlikely to generate significant income because of the deprived population it served and the high demand on services. Financially it is not a viable practice on its own, but as part of a larger financial organisation it appears sustainable at present...Improving access has been one of our main focuses, but I think consultation rates are running at about 20 per patient per year which is way above the national average and probably unsustainable in the long run.

The takeover by Brownlow Health came not a moment too soon. On the last day before the practice changed hands, a huge queue of patients waiting to be seen almost turned into a riot, and the police were called.

CHAPTER 15

Princes Park Health Centre and Brownlow Health (2017)

Brownlow Health managed to improve patient care at Princes Park Health Centre within its one-year contract, and patient feedback was uniformly positive. Regular doctors were employed, improving continuity of care and standards. The appointment system ran properly at last, with a new telephone triage system. Sheila Altes, who had left in 2014 after reporting the practice to the CQC, was delighted: 'I am happy that the practice has now been taken over by a group of committed GPs and is becoming the model of primary care it once was.' The CQC revisited the practice, speaking with staff and patients, who had now formed a fully functional Patient Participation Group. The inspectors were delighted with the pace of progress. Steve Field wrote to Katy Gardner, 'I am thrilled by the improvement in Princes Park Health Centre since its change in ownership and hugely impressed by the team I met.'

PPHC began to prosper again. Open patients' meetings were held, with toast and coffee. Health promotion events were once again held in the waiting room. Welfare benefits 'Advice on Prescription' sessions run by Citizens Advice Bureau staff were funded by the Clinical Commissioning Group. Katy felt that the spirit of Princes Park was back, thanks to the resilience of staff and patients, and the helpful oversight of Brownlow

Health. A patient told Katy, 'I feel I now have easier access to medical care in a responsive, kinder and more professional way. I am no longer frightened to phone the practice, whereas before I was sometimes left shaking and crying. Former excellent GPs have returned and are working there regularly again.'

Rahima Farrah, a former link worker and now a member of the Social Inclusion Team, reflected:

> Things went downhill under SSPH. Many people were unhappy and 'kicked off' in the waiting room. I found it hard to do my health awareness sessions in this bad atmosphere and I had to pull out, but now I am back. The atmosphere has improved, as Brownlow Health value community cohesion, making changes together, working together. I am happy doing health advice/advocacy sessions and health walks. I feel I am contributing and am valued.

On St Patricks Day, 17th March 2017, an open afternoon and health promotion event celebrated the 40th anniversary of the opening of the health centre with a huge birthday cake.

The Granby area had been regenerated by this time, thanks to the drive and persistence of residents. There were lively shops, a monthly market and its own Turner Prize winning arts programme, Granby 4 Streets. Lodge Lane now boasted an award-winning fruit and vegetable shop (BBC, 2015), as well as restaurants and cafes reflecting a diverse cuisine, and thriving businesses developed by Somali and other refugee communities (Munby, 2019). Pioneering organisations set up by PPHC patients, such as Blackburne House and the Kuumba Imani Millennium Centre, continued to thrive. The local park was now a safe and welcoming place to visit. Much housing had been upgraded and homes were warmer and more comfortable than in the 1970s and 1980s. Rats were now only rarely spotted on home visits.

Despite these positive developments in the area, all was not well in Liverpool 8. Though perhaps less of a problem in Toxteth than elsewhere, racism remained an issue, despite having been confronted so forcefully after the 1981 riots. Unemployment in Princes Park Ward was still the second highest in Liverpool, and the child poverty rate was the worst in the city (Liverpool City Council, 2017). The big-screen TVs in many homes still disguised poverty and hopelessness. Welfare cuts had a devastating effect on PPHC patients, while also reducing revenue for the city (Parkinson, 2019). The infamous

Health and Social Care Act had transferred public health responsibilities from the NHS to local councils in 2013. As former director of public health Ruth Hussey noted, this was 'intended to enable more attention to the underlying causes of poor health, [but] the reality was that budgets were cut and the services weakened in the ensuing years' (pers. comm.). Robin Ireland worked with PPHC in the 1980s and went on to work in public health: 'All parts of the NHS are inadequately funded. However, the budget for public health has been squeezed more than most. People have less and less support to lead healthier lifestyles. They, and society, will pay the price.'

The council had done its best to alleviate inequalities, using innovative funding to keep children's centres, libraries and parks open. Nevertheless, life remained precarious for many PPHC patients. As Mayor Joe Anderson wrote in March 2019, 'We have lost a colossal 63% of our funding from Government, £436 million per year, since 2010. On top of that, we have to deliver £21 million in savings between now and March 2020' (2019).

In 2018, Brownlow Health was awarded the PPHC contract for the next five years. Ed Gaynor and colleagues at Brownlow understand that many of the patients on the high-turnover PPHC list are vulnerable, facing mental health issues, poverty and complex psychosocial problems. They live in an ethnically diverse area with many multiply deprived individuals and families. For many patients, English is still a second or third language. Additional resources are still needed to address the needs of patients and for the practice to meet health service targets. Fortunately, with oversight from Brownlow Health, the GPs working at PPHC feel well supported, and patient satisfaction is evident. Teresa Williamson, a longstanding patient who had campaigned for change in 2014, wrote, 'The health centre is inviting, friendly, holistic, accommodating...I am proud to be a patient, and although I don't attend very often, I hear from other patients with complex or chronic health conditions how helpful and healthy the surgery is. I also attend the patient participation group, which is informative, supportive and essential.'

Dr Kate McKinnell had joined the practice as a locum GP in 2013. Initially positive about the team and the patients, after some months under the SSPH regime, she had left. But when Brownlow Health took over, she returned as a permanent salaried GP, and greatly appreciated the support offered.

Coming back to PPHC

The first day I walked into Princes Park Health Centre for a locum shift, I felt at home. It's hard to define exactly what it is about the place, but I am sure I am not the only person who finds this. It is something about the feeling that everyone is working together with a genuine wish to improve the lives of the community members, whether that is by doing something about their health or even turning a blind eye when they yet again take a short cut through the centre between Kingsley and Bentley Road. Everybody looks after everyone else; sometimes the patients seem more concerned about the staff than themselves. It often feels chaotic and exhausting, but there is always something to laugh about or a word of understanding and comfort that brings you back the next day. PPHC feels like the place that answers the question of why I went into medicine. There is much to learn from every patient, whether it's how they have lived their lives, some strange medical syndrome, the politics of a faraway country or tips on gardening, DIY, cars.... the list goes on! The frustrations are when you fail to understand or communicate or connect and ultimately fail to help, but those times are balanced by small moments of success. And the characters! - so many, amongst patients and staff past and present...There was a time when all this seemed doomed and I had to walk away, but I feel so privileged to be back at Princes Park, now under the care of Brownlow Health, back on what feels like a path which could survive this current NHS rollercoaster. We have a lively PPG, a coffee morning once a month, and a health walk on a Friday. We are trying to get a PPHC Park Run group going on Saturdays. Our Social Prescribing worker - a member of admin staff who has been trained up - is seeing patients on a Friday to offer whatever they might need, and we are working to get the "friendly practice" status for asylum seekers.

We can contact Debbie Feint, the GP Clinical Lead [at PPHC], at any time, and she will get back to us quickly, even if not immediately available for advice. We have a weekly clinical meeting for GPs to discuss problems and complex cases, regular email debates and a monthly afternoon training session for the whole practice. The admin staff have a daily huddle to discuss any problems. If we are short staffed, we contact the main Brownlow hub and they send a member of staff to help. For example, we can have an admin member to help if we are behind with scanning [of hospital letters, etc.] The practice manager, based on site, is always available. She floats around, checking all is OK, and if there is a problem at the front desk, she comes out to help, if necessary, taking the patient to a quiet room for a discussion.

Dr Kate McKinnell

As Ed Gaynor pointed out, PPHC is unlikely to ever be profitable as a free-standing business, but Brownlow Health has shown its willingness to accommodate Princes Park Health Centre in its multi-practice portfolio, balancing the benefits and risks of tailoring primary care to the needs of a locality. It recognises that PPHC is a unique enterprise addressing the very real needs of people in the area. So far this seems a very hopeful partnership, in which the size, clout, reputation and financial oversight of a larger organisation, based and owned within primary care, allows for effective delivery of primary health care in a particularly vulnerable inner-city area.

CHAPTER 16

Princes Park Health Centre, forty years on

The story of Princes Park Health Centre reflects the turbulent history of the National Health Service over the last 40 years. The practice evolved in parallel with the relentless changes dating from the radical 1974 reorganisation of local government and the NHS. The succession of further so-called 'reforms' were driven by different political approaches to the escalating demands, achievements and costs of health care in the United Kingdom.

PPHC attracted a stream of highly motivated GPs, other health professionals and local activists, determined to nurture excellent, socially sensitive, patient-centred primary health care in Liverpool 8. It was a visionary practice, born in an era of hope which included the rise of the women's movement in the 1970s and flourishing community-based initiatives.

From 1979 the tables were turned. Thatcher and Thatcherism took their toll on the NHS, on Merseyside and eventually on the staff of PPHC. Over the 40-year history of PPHC, the one constant for the NHS has been inadequate funding. During the 1980s and early 1990s, as the newly resource-constrained NHS struggled to maintain its standards of care, national public health policy was steered away from addressing the recognised social and economic determinants of health. There was a Thatcherite regression to politically driven health service reorganisations, with expensive but largely ineffectual attempts to influence individuals' lifestyles and behaviours. Under the Labour government from 1997 to 2010 this perverse shift was challenged and partly reversed, only to be reinstated by the Coalition and Tory governments from 2011 onwards. Austerity left a trail of devastation in the inner cities. Inequalities in health have continued, scandalously, to widen rather than narrowing, with governments effectively abandoning the post-war social contract. The infamous Inverse Care Law still applies to funding for primary health care in deprived areas - the greater the need, the more pitiful the resources available (Levene et al, 2019). Princes Park Health Centre struggled bravely against the tide, maintaining its focus on social justice.

Established NHS structures and organisational boundaries for primary care in Merseyside have shrunk, disappeared, and then re-emerged during these four decades, to the bemusement of health workers. The area served by Liverpool's Clinical Commissioning Group, defined in 2017, resembles that of the old Area Health Authority when PPHC opened in 1977. The 2017 Merseyside and Cheshire Sustainability and Transformation Plan covers a similar area to the old Regional Health Authority. Have any lessons been learnt, as these wheels have been reinvented? The myriad changes in the geography, structure and function of the NHS seem to have been disruptive rather than productive, for both patients and health workers. Iona Heath's comment rings true: 'Each cycle of reform seems to have shaved off a little more of the essential core of the service that is expressed in the founding principles' (Heath, 2018).

Crucially, public accountability has not improved. In 2012 the Health and Social Care Act turned the NHS on its head, driving further fragmentation of previously coherent services, and embedding the competition and privatisation begun in the 1990s under New Labour. Whilst there is often powerful GP representation on CCGs, many primary care workers feel disempowered by administrative and financial obfuscation and perceived vested interests. A genuinely 'primary care-led NHS' remains a dream of the late 1980s.

On the positive side, primary care in Liverpool today is of an almost universally high standard, thanks in part to the legacy of activist practices like PPHC. Effective networking between practices was begun and spurred on by initiatives such as the Liverpool Medical Audit Advisory Group, local multidisciplinary facilitation teams and neighbourhood commissioning projects, in which PPHC played a pivotal role.

The decision of GPs at Princes Park Health Centre to become a salaried practice under NHS external management in 1998 was a brave experiment. The trade-off between the GP partnership model, celebrating practice autonomy, versus the benefits of leaving management and finance to a supportive umbrella organisation, is still debated by progressive socialist GPs (Doctors in Unite, 2019). The timing of the PPHC experiment, however, was disastrous. The practice became a pawn in the increasingly chaotic NHS commissioning and provider landscape over the next 17 years. When the Care Quality Commission designated the practice as 'inadequate' in 2015, the news came as a shocking blow to GPs and other staff who had worked at the practice, whether still in post or looking on from a distance.

Cyril Taylor and his successors launched numerous innovations in holistic primary care and health promotion. The practice GPs worked hard to build bridges between academic institutions, public health units and local communities. This book describes the efforts of dedicated clinicians and staff who, time after time, scraped together just enough funding from practice resources, from health authorities, or from research funds, to put a new idea into practice. In an ideal world, worthwhile initiatives undertaken locally would be taken up and promoted with sustainable funding. Some PPHC projects did indeed obtain central funding and were rolled out - examples were the Family Health Project and the patient profiling (ethnic monitoring) initiative. Succession planning for others proved problematic. Nevertheless, many PPHC ventures were rediscovered or reinvented elsewhere and are now taken for granted as examples of good practice. PPHC inspired many forward thinking and imaginative clinicians and public health practitioners to understand, nurture and safeguard the health needs of their populations (Thomas, 2020).

The Association of General Practitioners in Urban Deprived Areas (AGUDA), which several GPs at PPHC joined in 1988-1989, was a forerunner of the 2009 Scottish initiative, GPs at the Deep End. The centrality of the doctor-patient relationship as a key contributor to tackling health inequalities remains at the forefront of the Deep End agenda (Watt, 2019). For some rather envious former PPHC GPs, the success of the Deep End project is further proof that primary care teams working in deprived areas, with their backs to the wall, must be properly funded and supported to enable reflective practice and to allow them to enjoy their working lives. The principles embodied in this project provide hope and inspiration for GPs working in practices like PPHC.

At its best, Princes Park Health Centre, as a flagship practice in a deprived locality, encouraged and inspired all who were associated with it. But the energy and idealism with which PPHC stormed through its first two decades were followed by exhaustion and burnout for some doctors. The need for additional resources was clearly stated on PPHC's transition to a salaried service in 1998 and in subsequent contracts, but it was not honoured. As a result, overworked GPs and staff gradually lost the capacity and resilience needed for long-term survival in the stressed practice. Ultimately, continuity and good practice were compromised, despite the exceptional dedication of loyal staff.

The eventual rescue of Princes Park Health Centre in 2017, by a successful multi-practice organisation led by one of its former trainees, was a joyous moment. Brownlow Health has taken on the mantle of Cyril Taylor's health centre, and continues to ensure the delivery of holistic, patient-centred primary health care. Liverpool 8 remains a vibrant neighbourhood within a resurgent and hopeful city, despite huge problems, including recent catastrophic reductions in Liverpool City Council's funding. According to former PPHC GP Michael Ejuoneatse, there's hope yet: 'I think the NHS is increasingly revisiting the values that were once prioritised at Princes Park Health Centre.'

Thanks

This story ended in 2017 but we finished writing it during the Covid-19 pandemic. We would like to thank all NHS staff and key workers, including many mentioned above, who have worked so hard in these challenging times.

Thanks to all the contributors who shared their memories, insights and reflections from their time at Princes Park Health Centre. We hope the book rings true for you. We know that there are people whom we have not been able to reach or mention, but who made a huge contribution.

We are grateful to everyone who encouraged us and helped with the later drafts of this book, including, amongst many friends old and new, Pro Torkington, Paul Burnell, Julia South, Steve Munby, Taher Qassim, Chris Dowrick, Graham Watt, Sharon Messenger, Sally Sheard, Roger Jones, John and Ruth Hussey, Jack Czauderna, Steve Iliffe, Gary Hayward, Greg Quiery, Katharine Abba, Michelle Timoney, Rob Barnett and all the 'Docs' Diners'.

Many thanks to the following people for permission to reproduce their work: Levi Tafari for his poem; Catherine Marcangeli for Adrian Henri's poem; David Knopov for his portrait of Cyril Taylor; Pete Betts for his cartoons.

Our publishers at Writing on the Wall, based in Toxteth library, have been helpful and supportive throughout. Thanks for taking us on!

Special thanks to our editor Robin Munby and to Maddy Robinson for editing the photos and helping with our social media. Maddy designed the wonderful book cover.

Our book is dedicated to all who have worked at and with PPHC, and to all our brave and lovely patients. Thanks to all who fought tirelessly in the dark times, from Cyril Taylor through to Sam Semoff, longstanding patient and health activist, who played a key role in the rescue of PPHC. Katy and Sam had many conversations about this book before his death in 2018.

We also fondly remember Sheila Abdullah, who sadly died while we were writing this book.

Thanks to all who continue to make Liverpool 8 an ever-better place to live.

This book springs from, and was inspired by, the struggles of PPHC patients and everyone in Liverpool 8.

WHO's WHO at Princes Park Health Centre

Below is a list of many of the people mentioned in this book who worked at, or very closely with, PPHC. Some people were known by different names in the past and in the text we have mostly relied on our gut feeling. We hope we have clarified this here. The list is alphabetical by surname.

Dr Sheila Abdullah	single-handed GP, then GP partner at PPHC 1979-1986
Pip Abraham	receptionist 1977-2000
Pat Aglimanye	computer facilitator from 1988
Dorkas Akeju	midwife, 1990s
Najib Al-Hakimi	Arabic speaking Health Development Worker 2002-2012
Dr Ali Al-Shehri	GP and Research Associate at University of Liverpool Department of General Practice
Sheila Altes	practice nurse 2007-2014
Dr Galina Artioukh	GP registrar 1996-1998 (arrived from Russia in 1993)
Mohamed Ashour	trained as a doctor in Somalia, project manager of MAAN
Bill Barnes	clinical psychologist and psychotherapist, 1980s
Marion Barr	receptionist from 1985
Dr Mary Belshaw	GP partner 1987-1990
Dr Mark Burns	GP partner 1980s-1998, salaried GP 1998-2015, co-founder of the Liverdoc out-of-hours co-operative in 1996
Dr Ralph Brussatis	GP registrar 2000
Isla Cameron	health visitor 1991-2012

Dr Peter Campion	GP at The Elms Medical Centre and Senior Lecturer in General Practice, University of Liverpool
Prof. Michael Chan	chair of Service Development Initiative steering group from 1998
Ruth Chan	midwife, 1980s and 90s
Dr Kit Oi Chung	maternity locum GP for Katy Gardner 1990-1991, co-founded Vauxhall Primary Health Care practice in 1992
Chas Clegg	district nurse from 1983, ran Well Man clinic from 1988 and Diabetic clinic from 1989-1993
Clare Corless	practice nurse 1996-2015
Michelle Cox	worked at PPHC from 1999, manager of Social Inclusion Team from 2002
Ann Cunningham (Pettit)	secretary/administrator 1990-2005
Dr Lis Davidson	GP trainee 1983, partner 1986-1998, GP trainer from 1991, salaried GP 1998-2012
Trish Drew (née **Walker**, later **Bates**)	health visitor 1996-2002, Child Protection and Safeguarding
Pam Duff	social worker, Liverpool Personal Social Services, from 1977
Dr Mike Ejuoneatse	GP trainee 1990, partner 1994-1998, salaried GP 1998-2007, later GP in St Helens
Sirad Elmi	Somali link worker 1990-2003
Dr George Fairbairn	salaried GP 1999-2007, GP trainer, worked with REACT cycling project
Rahima Farrah	Somali Link worker 1999-2004, Social Inclusion Team worker from 2004
Dr Debbie Feint	GP Clinical Lead at Princes Park@ Brownlow Health from 2015
Dr Mark Fisher	psychotherapist 1989-2004

Dr Alan Forbes	GP trainee, then partner and trainer until 1994
Dr Angela Forbes	trained in rheumatology; GP registrar at PPHC 1988-1990, GP partner 1992-1994
Jane Ford	practice nurse 2015
Fi Francis	illustrator of leaflets produced with the Community Health Council, 1985
Dr Katy Gardner	GP trainee 1978, partner 1979-1998, salaried GP 1998-2005
Professor Linda Gask	psychiatrist in Manchester, facilitated video feedback training 1989-1990
Liz Gaulton (Gaulton-Berks)	general and mental health nurse, Family Health Worker 1992-1996, then Primary Care deprivation Initiative lead 1996-1997
Dr Ed Gaynor	GP trainee 1990, then founded Brownlow Group practice in 1994, which became Brownlow Health
Dr Barbara Gaze (Kidd)	locum GP working with Katy Gardner from 1981-1983
Noreen Gilhespy	practice nurse from 1988
Dr Susanna Graham-Jones	partner 1986-1993, Lecturer at University of Liverpool Department of General Practice
Ria Hayward	practice-based counsellor 1990-1999
Karen Hewitt	receptionist 1990-1999, then practice manager 2004-2012
Dr Janet Heyes	GP and MAAG Adviser
Sylvia Hikins	Chair of South Central Community Health Council and lecturer in creative writing
Dr Judith Hindley (Preston)	GP partner 1988-1994
Cathy Hogan (formerly **Delahunty**)	student attachment 1975, secretary 1976-1979, returned as practice manager 1983-1986

Liz Hunter	district nurse
Dr John Hussey	GP at The Elms Medical Centre, Liverpool 8, MAAG Adviser
Mary Huxham	receptionist from 1990
Robin Ireland	project director, Sports Council Health and Recreation Team (HART), 1984-1992
Lyn Jones	first practice nurse at Sefton Drive practice, 1969-1975
Pat Jones	district nurse 1990-2002
Dr Sam Jones	GP trainee
Dr Karen Kearley	GP trainee September 1984 to March 1986
Chris Kennedy	ran CAMHS sessions at PPHC, mid-1990s
Jenny Knowles	senior nurse at North Mersey Community Trust 2000-2002, worked with asylum seekers
Dr Kishore Krishnamurthy ('Krish')	GP registrar 2006, then salaried GP 2008-2011
Gwyn Lautterberg	health visitor from 1975
Bennett Lee	researcher based at John Moores University, worked with PPHC on the Service Development Initiative 1997-2000
Dr Ewan Lewis-Jones	GP assistant from 1977
Dr Susie Lewis-Jones	GP assistant from 1975
Dr Martin Lloyd-Jones	PPHC partner 1996-1999, lead negotiator during transition to salaried service
Clare Mahoney	health promotion worker, worked on Health Thru Arts festival, 1992
Dr Kerry Marson	salaried associate GP 1995-1998
Dr Ruth McCutcheon	psychiatry registrar at Liverpool Drug Dependency Unit, ran weekly clinics 2004-2006 at PPHC

Fiona McDavid	ran massage and relaxation sessions at PPHC, 1992
Dr Helen McKendrick	GP trainee 1990-19911, co-founded Vauxhall Primary Health Care in 1992
Dr Kate McKinnell	locum salaried GP in 2013, returned as salaried GP in 2015
Suzanne Morris	patient and Neighbourhood Health Worker
Rashid Mufti	race awareness trainer 1986
Liz Muir	counsellor 1993-2004
Steve Munby	patient, activist, City Councillor (Riverside ward)
Brenda Nasr	temporary practice manager 2000
Dr Julia Nelki	child psychiatrist with CAMHS from 1989, ran 'Think Family' sessions at PPHC
Maureen Newton	district nurse 1984-1988, then Macmillan nurse based at PPHC
Amanda Onwuemene	health visitor 1989-1996
Dr Alwen Parry	public health registrar, investigated attendance at PPHC Well Man clinic in 1989
Dr Vera Pettit	psychoanalyst, Balint group facilitator 1987-1989
Dr Ram Poluri	GP trainee 1987, then briefly partner 1989-1990
Dr Rob Poole	community psychiatrist, ran weekly clinic at PPHC 1988-2004
Rita Potts	district nurse
Afrah Qassim	Health Development Worker 1999-2005, first trainee from Yemeni community
Taher Qassim	campaigner, public health professional, taught at LSTM 1992; later, Chair of the Liverpool Arab Arts Festival

Dr Len Ratoff	GP at The Elms Medical Centre, Liverpool 8, MAAG Adviser
Val Ravenscroft	receptionist from late 1980s, and later worked for Social Inclusion Team
Siobhan Reilly	Family Health Project Support Worker 1992-1996, wrote up the evaluation of the Family Health Project for her PhD in 2004
Helen Rigby	receptionist 1980s until 1997
Dr Mike Ross	GP partner 1981-1988
Samsam Salah	Somali health researcher from 2000, worked on vitamin D
Carolyn Saxton	social worker 1985-1988
Mike Scott	attached social worker in 1981, while training as a clinical psychologist
Sheila Scott	administrator/secretary 1970s, PPHC practice manager 1977-1983 and 1986-1998
Dr Alex Scott-Samuel	consultant and then senior lecturer in public health 1978-2015, Chair of SHA 2017-2020
Maureen Scott-Samuel	district nurse from 1976
Dr Martin Smith	GP trainee 1986, GP partner 1987-1998, then salaried GP until 2008
Dr Cyril Taylor	single-handed GP in Sefton Drive 1950-1977, moved to PPHC in 1977, worked at PPHC 1977-1987 and later as locum.
Pat Taylor	Cyril's wife, co-founder of first women's refuge in Liverpool, 1973
Dr Kathrin Thomas	GP trainee 1991, later consultant in Public Health
Dr Paul Thomas	GP trainee 1986, then partner 1987-1994
Carla Thompson	ran CAMHS sessions at PPHC, mid-1990s

Margaret Thomson	Chief Executive of Central Liverpool PCG 1999-2001, public health specialist at Central Liverpool PCT 2001-2004
Michelle Timoney	Primary Care Trust manager, worked with Katy Gardner on heart disease and on REACT project
Pro (Protasia) Torkington	Liverpool Health and Race project director 1985-1996, race awareness trainer 1986
Doreen Vernon	practice nurse 1975-1992
Christine Wall	FHSA manager 1990, then Deputy Chief Executive of merged FHSA and District Health Authority 1996
Dr Helen West	GP based at PPHC from 2000 to work with asylum seekers and refugees
Dr Clare Wilkinson	GP partner/University lecturer from 1993, replaced Susanna Graham-Jones
Dorothy Zack Williams	health visitor early 1980s, then at Centre for Inherited Blood Disorders
Zainab	fictitious name of Somali refugee doctor assigned to PPHC for induction in 2005

Appendix

Princes Park as a Public Health Organisation

Report for Central Liverpool NHS Primary Care Trust

by Sarah McNulty

Aims of the project

- To define a public health organisation.
- To show that Princes Park Health Centre is a public health organisation.
- To examine the issues surrounding the public health function of primary care, at a practice level, and explore the barriers that may exist.
- To examine ways practices can become involved in the public health agenda.

Introduction

History of Princes Park

Princes Park Health Centre was built in 1977 in the Liverpool inner city neighbourhood of Toxteth.

Dr Cyril Taylor, a local GP active in the pursuit of equality, had a vision the centre would provide "an opportunity for many different workers involved in community care to be under one roof, meet each other every day"1.

The practice population resides within some of the most deprived wards in Liverpool. Over the past ten years, it has seen huge changes, with a large influx of refugees and asylum seekers, especially from Somalia, and more recently, from many different countries. The population experiences high levels of poverty, unemployment, homelessness, drug use and health problems.

In 1998 the practice became a Personal Medical Services (PMS) pilot and the GPs became the employees initially of North Mersey Community NHS Trust, now Central Liverpool PCT.

Four whole time and two part time GPs, a part time associate, and a GP who works with asylum seekers serve the practice population, currently 9600 (April 2003). Two practice nurses, health visitors, district nurses, phlebotomists, reception and administration staff and one or two GP registrars are attached to the practice. The practice also teaches medical students and nurses. Midwives, health visitors, chiropodists, physiotherapists and counsellors hold weekly clinics. A consultant psychiatrist holds a regular clinic. There are also advocacy workers and an asylum seekers support team.

Background to this project

Since its inception the practice has been dedicated to reducing health inequalities within the local community. Over the years, staff and patients have been involved in many innovative projects to help improve the health of the local population.

One of the GPs, Dr Katy Gardner approached me to write a report on the work that had been done, and is being done to tackle these issues, and discuss the role of the practice as a public health organisation.

I hope to show interested parties, and hopefully other practices, that public health is already a valuable part of the everyday work of general practices, and need not be seen as additional work, or as clashing with the ethics of general practice.

Public health in primary care

Public health is described as the "science and art of preventing disease, prolonging life and promoting health through the organised effort of society".2

Shifting the Balance of Power (DOH) documented radical changes in NHS structure. It described a shift towards local Primary Care Trust (PCT) based service provision and placed responsibility for public health onto PCTs, as part of managed public health networks for the region. It laid down the scope of a modern public health system and described how this will be established within the NHS. It recognised the importance of local services to fit local need.

One of the functions of PCTs is "improving the health of the community through health needs assessment, service planning and delivery. To respond to local need and national targets".3

General practice, the basic unit of the Primary Care Trust, is well placed to have an important role in this function.

The Chief Medical Officer recognised this in his report Strengthening the Public Health Function in England.4 He acknowledged that primary care practitioners "have a role in health improvement and reducing inequalities, but they need "to develop a 'mind-set', with greater appreciation of how their work can make a difference to health and well-being". He also recognised that certain professionals, health visitors, for example, spend a large part of their work on public health and many other professionals have a contribution to the public health agenda.

The report highlighted the need for multi-disciplinary working to achieve the goals of public health.

The Faculty of Public health Medicine also recognises there are many organisations which have a public health function, 'public health organisations'.

The faculty has established ten key areas of public health practice.5 These cover functions of all those involved in public health. I have used these ten functions as the basis for examining the work of Princes Park Health Centre. I intend to show that, in fulfilling these functions, the practice is a public health organisation.

Area of specialist public health practice: 1

Surveillance and assessment of the population's health and well-being

Annual practice profiles

Practice profiles have historically provided information on the practice population and included data on sex, age, ethnicity, mortality ratios, Jarman scores, unemployment Coronary Heart Disease (CHD), cancer, mental health problems, respiratory disease and prescribing information. From this data, clinical priorities for the next year were set.

These have been replaced by business plans, which contain information on health needs assessments, priorities and resources required.

The Primary Care Data Project

In the early 1990's the practice was involved in The Primary Care Data Project. Princes Park was one of six practices acting as pilots looking into targeting service provision to fit local need. Data was collected on patients with mental health problems and coronary heart disease, including postcode, age, smoking and alcohol status, and the information was fed into the commissioning process.

The Patient Profiling Project

More recently, a comprehensive assessment of local need has been undertaken with the Patient Profiling Project. This was developed in 1997 by a team based at the practice involving members of the Public Health Department of John Moores University, Liverpool Health Authority, and the City Council.

Its broad aims were to develop local patient data on a wide range of health related matters, and to use this data to influence service planning and service delivery.

The project involved a patient questionnaire, used to obtain information on patient characteristics, such as ethnicity and family origin, age, sex and marital status, smoking, alcohol, language spoken and written, housing tenure, damp housing, employment status, car ownership and religion. It also looked at self perceived health and views on factors impacting on health and diagnosed health problems, such as angina, diabetes, MI, asthma, depression and severe rheumatological illness. Patient satisfaction with waiting times, access to GP of choice, and quality of consultation was also analysed.

From this data, the practice was able to target its services to suit the practice population's needs.

Some examples included:

- Highlighting the need for education and information in the Yemeni population on cardiovascular disease and recruiting link workers and interpreters for the healthy heart clinic.

- Identifying patients who could benefit from the government assistance from the New Home Energy Efficiency Scheme and help patients to access this funding.

- Informing the proposals of a Healthy Living Centre in the area.

- Highlighting the need for language support staff.

- Linking members of black and ethnic groups to services at a local neurological unit.

Opportunistic data collection

Opportunistic blood pressure measurement, cholesterol levels, smoking and alcohol status assessment in consultations and in chronic disease clinics contributes to the ongoing surveillance and assessment of the population. If coded correctly on computerised records, these are easily accessible.

It is also possible to produce registers of other conditions. This has been done as part of the audit system, for example, epilepsy, asthma, hypertension, drug users and hepatitis B.

Well baby clinics are a form of health surveillance looking at babies and mothers. Levels of breast-feeding in the community and immunisation rates can be assessed.

The practice produces quarterly figures for immunisation rates and cervical smears.

Additional projects

The practice was involved with the Liverpool School of Tropical Medicine in a study looking at the prevalence and risk factors for hepatitis B antigen carriage amongst Somali households in Liverpool.[7] As a result of this study, a hepatitis B working group is currently developing a project with the Chinese community to look at hepatitis B prevalence and uptake of immunisation in this population.

Another joint study was the Somali Calcium and Vitamin D Study, which I will detail later.

The practice and the asylum seekers support team were involved in a mental health needs assessment for asylum seekers in 2002.

Discussion

Shifting the Balance of Power within the NHS (DOH) set out the importance of services based on local need, and the requirement for PCTs to assess the population's health needs.[3]

A study commissioned by the NHS Executive looked at health needs assessment in general practice and found that, although it was seen as important, there was poor understanding of what was involved, and was perceived to be the responsibility of public health departments.[7] The RCGP and FPHM suggest that primary care and public health practitioners "work together to devise and pilot ways of recording useful information which will allow appropriate targeting of interventions and audit of progress on alleviating health inequality".[8]

Most practices will have, or be in the process of compiling, disease registers for certain conditions, such as CHD and Diabetes, in line with National Service Framework targets. The new GMS contract will make registers financially attractive to practices by awarding quality points for disease registers of such conditions as CHD, Diabetes, stroke, hypothyroidism, COPD, long term mental health problems, hypertension and epilepsy.

Computerisation of patient notes will make the retrieval of this information much easier. However, care must be taken to ensure that the data is accurate, for example accurate READ coding of data; this involves training of all staff.

Information should be used appropriately to influence service provision. Assessment alone is not enough.

PMS may provide opportunities to utilise information gathered from assessment to influence service provision within a practice. PMS contracts may release individual practices from blanket, nationally set targets that may not be most appropriate to their patients.

One potential problem of primary care based needs assessment is that those needs easily identified may take priority over non-identified needs. It is important that clinicians stay open to look at other areas, although this may be difficult with payments dependent on achieving certain targets. There is also a cost implication in projects, time, staff and resources, and the need to sustain the work.

Practices, especially those similar to Princes Park, have a high patient turnover and a shifting profile and priorities may change over time. There need to be on-going systems in place to accommodate this.

Area of specialist public health practice: 2

Promoting and protecting the population's health and well-being

The World Health Organisation defines health promotion as "the process of enabling people to exert control over, and to improve their health."

Health visitors

Traditionally much health promotion work has been seen as the role of the health visitor. Well baby clinics provide a platform for promoting immunisation, breastfeeding, healthy eating, accident prevention and safe sleeping. They can provide an opportunity to recognise maternal problems, such as post-natal depression, and to target mothers for well woman checks, smoking cessation and general health promotion. Some of this work is also carried out in antenatal clinics, jointly held with the midwives.

Historically the breast-feeding agenda has been well supported in Princes Park Health Centre, from the presence of a breast-feeding advisor in clinics in the past, to posters, leaflets and advice from health care workers. This has resulted in very good rates of breast-feeding in the practice.

The health visitors have set up pre and postnatal support groups and host a number of innovative groups to encourage mothers to talk about things that are worrying them. They provide an opportunity for health promotion and identification of needs. Groups include baby massage and health and beauty events.

Screening programmes

The ongoing cervical screening programme provides a platform for opportunistic health promotion and can be used to trouble shoot problems and refer to another professional appropriately. The practice is active in encouraging parents and women to participate in the programme.

Well person clinics

The practice was one of the first in the UK to set up a well woman clinic in primary care. The clinic offers cervical screening, family planning services and general health information. In the past a well man clinic has been piloted, this provided services for men and looked at smoking, alcohol, blood pressure

(BP), CHD risk, cholesterol and stress counselling. Unfortunately, after review this was not continued, but the practice nurses encourage any person to come in for a well person check. A cardiovascular disease (CVD) primary prevention clinic is currently being set up, using practice information and patient profiling to target at-risk groups.

Opportunistic health promotion

GPs, practice nurses and primary health care team (PHCT) staff use opportunistic health promotion in their consultations, for example blood pressure monitoring and lifestyle advice, alcohol and drug assessment and smoking cessation advice. The specialist clinics also contribute to this.

New patient checks identify disease risk factors, lifestyle history, medical history and patients have their BP and Body Mass Index (BMI) measured and urine tested.

The yearly flu vaccination programme offers at-risk groups protection from disease and the opportunity to troubleshoot and offer advice or further care for any other worries.

Other services

Fag Ends is a smoking cessation support group, held in the practice weekly, which provides advice, prescription review and peer support for smokers aiming to give up cigarettes.

The practice is involved in an exercise for health program with local sports facilities, offering low-cost gym assessments and programmes tailored to individual needs for patients with various health problems. It also will refer obese patients to local dieticians for advice on successful weight reduction.

The practice has a number of drug users, and it is practice policy to encourage hepatitis screening in these patients and offer vaccination. This is the subject of ongoing audit.

A health questionnaire is filled in by nursing staff for each new asylum seeker to attempt identification of tropical disease, such as tuberculosis (TB) and HIV. The practice has links with the local TB nurses and HIV team. The asylum seekers team offers a weekly nurse-led drop-in with language resources covering health promotion work and other health care.

The practice holds twice monthly travel clinics for advice and travel vaccinations.

The practice has held health days for the local community, for example, the local Somali and Yemeni populations. These have provided opportunities for BP measurements, blood glucose testing and advice on a variety of relevant and targeted health matters to specific communities, for example, healthy diets and cervical smears.

The practice newsletter, The Prinny Post, has been used to promote health and practitioners have contributed health advice pieces to the local papers. There are health promotion posters and leaflets in the waiting room.

Discussion

In the past health promotion was not generally seen as a GP's role. Part of the reason for the failure of the Health of the Nation targets was that GPs saw it as someone else's agenda and opposite to the traditional, non-population focused, medical model based GP role.9 This may no longer be the case. Shifting the Balance of Power put the job of improving the health of the community to local PCTs and thus to local practices.

All members of the primary health care team can get involved with health promotion. Practice waiting rooms can be used to promote good health, encourage smoking cessation and provide information about local resources though posters and leaflets.

Some local practices sell reduced price fresh fruit in their waiting rooms to target patients and encourage healthy eating. This has been organised through the local PCTs.

Computerisation is a valuable tool for health promotion, allowing easy identification of patients. It can be used, as at Princes Park, to provide opportunistic offering of services, flagging up overdue smears, BPs, etc. On some systems, health promotion material can be printed along with prescriptions.

Practices are part of national screening and immunisation programmes. They are also involved in communicable disease control, as a statutory requirement.

The new GMS contract awards quality points for some health promotion activities, such as smoking cessation advice, cervical screening programmes, blood pressure measurements and cholesterol testing.

The Working Group on Public Health in Primary Care states that "primary care professionals should be encouraged to use every encounter with patients, their families, and carers to pursue public health goals, including the promotion of health and the prevention of disease".7

One of the problems of this approach, however, is that patients attending the surgery and health promoting events tend to be more health aware than those who do not use services. Those who need it most, use it least. Practices need to look at innovative ways to get health messages across to those who do not take up in-house activities.

Area of specialist public health practice: 3

Developing quality and risk management within an evaluative culture

Clinical Governance works to ensure quality control and rapid management of under-performance. The practice is involved in activities such as:

Audit

Members of the primary health care team regularly participate in audit. External workers additionally visit to perform performance audits, for example pharmacists.

Evidence-based practice

Specific areas have GP leads that oversee the management of certain conditions, for example, diabetes and coronary heart disease. Some of this work may involve ensuring the implementation of NSFs, developing protocols, disseminating information to other practice staff and reviewing performance. Local guidelines on specific conditions are available in every room in the practice for easy access during consultations.

Education

There are weekly in-house clinical meetings covering specific areas; outside speakers attend to feedback new work in the area, or new services. There are also monthly educational events for all members of staff. The practice is closed during this time.

Confidentiality

The practice staff attended a Caldicott teaching afternoon recently, covering best practice for ensuring patient confidentiality.

Significant event analysis

The practice has regular significant event analysis meetings where potentially, or actually harmful events are flagged up in a no-blame environment and attempts to prevent further episodes occurring made.

Accountability

The practice has a written complaints procedure that is available to patients. There is also a suggestion box in the waiting room for patients to air their views.

Patient satisfaction

Patient surveys have also been undertaken to identify concerns within the practice population on the work of the practice. There is also regular feedback on the new appointment system.

Discussion

The NHS Act 1999 made it a legal requirement for PCTs to put in and keep in place arrangements for the purpose of monitoring and improving the quality of health care which it provides to individuals.10 This feeds down to practice level with a requirement for clinical governance policy in each practice.

The CMO (Protecting Patients, Supporting Doctors) has proposed that GPs compulsorily participate in external audit and annual appraisal.11 GMC re-registration will depend upon revalidation.

An adequate facility for cascading information to health care team members from local guidelines and national guidelines is vital. It may help, as in this practice, to have clinical leads, to filter out important messages. Journal clubs are another suggestion to keep up-to-date with current evidence-based practice.

Computers can make evidence-based information more accessible during consultations. Adequate IT structures need to be in place. Staff training may be an issue.

The new GMS contract awards points for undertaking patient surveys, significant event analysis, staff appraisal, inductions, adequate complaints procedures, basic life support training for staff and personal development plans for nursing staff.

Area of specialist public health practice: 4

Collaborative working for health

The practice has a long history of working with other agencies, in the public, private and voluntary sectors.

In-house services

A Citizens Advice Bureau worker has held sessions to provide help and assistance to locals requiring information on benefits, finances and legal issues. This is currently being re-introduced. In the past social workers have also been seconded to the practice.

There is an advocacy worker on site to help patients with housing problems, benefits queries and liaison with other professional bodies.

The asylum seekers support group offers refugee patients a similar service, liaising with relevant bodies, for example, housing letting agents to help improve living standards and facilities.

The practice building is also openly available to allied health professionals. Regular sessions are held by psychiatry, chiropody, physiotherapy, community midwives and counsellors. There are close links with the local hospital consultants and invites them regularly to speak on relevant topics to the staff.

Health visitors

The health visitors liaise on a regular basis with local nurseries schools and social services, working together on child protection, and providing advice on a wide range of issues. They link in with the Sure Start programme locally.

Community groups

The practice has forged good links with local community groups, for example Toxteth Health Forum. Several community groups meet regularly within the health centre.

Other links

The exercise for health scheme was set up with local leisure centres.

The practice is involved with the development of a virtual healthy living centre (Heal 8) locally. This five year project involves a consortium of community groups and professionals to address environmental health, food and nutrition and community capacity building in the Liverpool 8 area.

The Somali MAAN healthy mind project is a voluntary organisation which aims to increase awareness of mental health issues and establish a range of community based services for the population. Members of Princes Park Health Centre are on the steering group, along with community members and other interested parties.

One of the doctors, whose remit is to work with the asylum seeker population, regularly writes specialist reports for solicitors dealing with cases where the client has been a victim of torture.

The practice has worked with the Liverpool School of Tropical Medicine on a number of projects, for example the Hepatitis B Study and the Somali Calcium and Vitamin D Study. The latter was a cross-sectional study, which determined the prevalence of rickets, osteomalacia and associated risk factors in the Somali community. It found that approximately 90% of this population were deficient in vitamin D. From this work, a community chest grant was secured to provide appropriate dietetic advice and resources to encourage changes to the diet.

The practice has worked with the Public Health Department at Liverpool University. Students on the public health training scheme (MPH) have been attached to the practice to work on projects that improve the health of the local population, for example, the development of the Heal 8 project.

Discussion

Collaborative working for health includes other health professionals and those involved in the wider determinants of health. The Health Act 1999 imposed a duty on all NHS organisations to work in partnership.10 This may involve work with local schools, police, local employers, voluntary groups, government initiatives and social services, child protection is an example.

An awareness of the roles of other professionals is vital in order to use their skills appropriately. Shadowing and invitations to speak with staff may help this. Leaflets, videos in the waiting room and education of staff, can increase patient awareness of their roles.

Area of specialist public health practice: 5

Developing health programmes and services and reducing inequalities

The Primary Care Collaborative

The Primary Care Collaborative is part of the National Primary Care Development Teams' work with practices to modernise patient services in line with the government modernisation agenda. Its broad aim is to improve quality of care to patients and improve overall patient experience. At present it is targeting CHD NSF targets, 48hr access and managing demand for primary to secondary care in the area. Princes Park Health Centre is one of five local practices currently acting as a pilot for the initiative.

A CVD clinic had already been set up, as part of the patient profiling project to monitor patients with a previous history of cardiovascular disease, working alongside NSF targets. This clinic offers advice and guidance on risk reduction, as well as ensuring optimal drug treatment and risk factor monitoring.

The practice is currently targeting non-English speaking patients and sending translated letters out to patients, whilst ensuring that language resources are available for that appointment.

The practice has switched to a same-day appointment system, in line with the 48 hour access targets, which is currently being assessed as part of the project.

Patient profiling

The Patient Profiling Project has led to a number of health programmes, based on local need.

Well person clinics

As previously mentioned, the practice has a well woman clinic, and has held well man clinics in the past. There is now a system of new patient health checks in practice.

Screening and immunisation programmes

The health visitors, practice nurses and GPs are involved in developing health programmes for children and patients and taking forward health screening and the immunisation programmes. Additional slots with language resources are being considered to target the non-English speaking community.

Other programmes and services

One of the GPs is currently looking into the practice acting as a pilot for an outreach sexual health clinic, in line with the National Strategy for Sexual health and HIV, as local levels of Sexually transmitted infections are a worry.

The practice prescribes methadone for opiate addicts, as part of a structured programme, which includes regular monitoring and consideration of other health problems as well as hepatitis B immunisation.

Tackling inequalities

The practice is committed to promoting and protecting health, preventing disease and reducing inequalities. The practice population has identified high levels of deprivation, unemployment, non-English speakers, and health problems.

One of the aims of the PMS pilot was to ensure equitable access to services for all patients. As a result the practice has extensive resources for non-English speaking patients including practice information and health care leaflets in other languages. Many of the staff speak foreign languages and receptionists can book translators. Language line is used in emergencies. Non-English speaking patients are currently being targeted for participation in the cervical screening programme by sending out letters in English and their first language to invite them in.

Time for appointments has been amended to address the problems of language. There is the provision for 15-minute appointment slots for patients who require interpreters.

The asylum team is active in reaching out to provide health promotion/ protection and assistance. They provide a weekly drop-in clinic for Kurdish and Farsi speaking patients.

There are link workers for local communities, who help with making appointments and addressing the wider determinants of health, such as housing, benefits, etc. A full-time primary care advocate is in-house; she works as part of the primary care deprivation initiative project, a post that has existed for a number of years. She takes referral from patients themselves, and members of the health care team, and acts as an advocate, liaising with other parties, to help patients with problems such as housing, social services and benefits. She also visits the local hostels for the homeless, and other vulnerable groups, and helps them register with the practice.

The Family Health Project ran for three years from 1992 and addressed the inequalities that exist for homeless patients. A family health worker visited local hostels/hotels to offer registration with the practice to the residents. A variety of services were offered, such as health checks, health promotion, counselling, advocacy and advice.

The practice has worked with other local organisations in trying to increase the provision of, and training for culturally sensitive and multilingual counselling for black and minority ethnic groups with mental health problems, for example, the Somali Maan project.

Discussion

It is important that services are tailored to fit local demand, based on accurate health needs assessment. General practice is ideally placed to be aware of local need to target health programmes and address inequalities.

Funding, as always can be a major stumbling block to setting up new services and, perhaps more importantly, keeping them up and running. In Princes Park clinics and services have been withdrawn in the past due to insufficient funding. Good advocates, who are skilled in application for funding, and a good relationship with the local PCT will help. Innovation may provide the key for programme development and new ways of tackling old problems sought. This may reduce the need for extra resources. It may also help to work with local community groups, fundraising and raising awareness of services.

The DOH has resources for ideas for tackling inequalities and gives some more ideas from practices across the country in its leaflet tackling inequalities.12

Area of specialist public health practice: 6

Policy and strategy development and implementation

Involvement on local groups

Members of the primary health care team have been, and are on various steering groups, which produce local guidelines and protocols, or are involved in strategy development. These include:

- The Mental Health Needs Assessment of Asylum Seekers Steering Group

- The Service Development Initiative. (Patient profiling)

- Liverpool Somali Healthy Mind Project Steering Group

- Heal 8 Healthy Living Centre Consortium

- Sure Start Steering Group

- The Sexual Health and HIV Strategy Group

- GUM Redesign Group

- Termination of Pregnancy Group

- The Primary Care Collaborative

- Primary Care Trust Cardiovascular Group

The patient profiling work has been used to influence service provision, as a health needs assessment tool. Feedback from this initiative has led to the appointment of two Yemeni health workers this year by the PCT.

The practice has piloted a new method of referring patients for terminations of pregnancy and it is hoping to become a pilot for an outreach sexual health clinic.

One of the practice nurses has been involved in the NSF Diabetes working group and the local heart failure group. She was also involved in the development of integrated care pathways for diabetes.

Some of the GPs have close links with the PCT. One of the GPs was the Primary Care Group (PCG) lead on mental health, and another member of the team is on the current PCT Professional Executive Committee (PEC).

Discussion

The introduction of the National Service Frameworks puts pressure on general practice to develop its services to fit in with national targets and policy. Many GPs may find this constrictive and cumbersome, especially when additional funding is not available.

Mixing Oil and Water, a paper which looked into the emerging role of primary care and public health, makes the point that, with the development of primary care organisations, primary care needs to become more involved at a strategic level, and general practice must become involved in service provision to meet local need. This may involve substantial mind-set changes in practitioners.9 Certain team members may be naturally drawn to certain groups and have their own specialist interests. This needs to be recognised, encouraged and resourced by the team. A varied career may help staff morale and help retain staff.

Links with the PCT are valuable to keep informed of funding opportunities and have an influence on budgeting for local needs. Primary health care team members have much to contribute to PCTs function, the Royal College of Nursing, for example, believes that health visitors especially are ideally placed to hold public health posts in PCTs. They are aware of local need and have strong links with the communities they serve.13

Area of specialist public health practice: 7

Working with and for communities

Toxteth health forum

The health forum brings together the voluntary and statutory organisations and the local community to work together to improve the quality of health and community care and provides information about health for locals. It produces a paper, which the practice staff contribute to.

Patient/staff group

As part of the patient profiling project a patient/staff group was established to work on issues such as access to services, the environment of the health centre and issues around language and culture. The group's findings were fed into the practice business plan, for example LED screens informing patients about appointments and activities in the clinic, translated practice leaflets and improved waiting room environment.

Advocacy work

Wider determinants of health are addressed as part of the advocacy work involved in helping with housing, benefits and social services problems.

Other initiatives

As previously mentioned, the practice has hosted 'health days' in the local community in the past, and the health visitors provide mother and baby groups, and other meeting forums. The Heal 8 project and Somali Mind project serve the local community.

The Prinny Post is a newspaper written by staff for patients, informing them of new and existing services available from the practice, accessing health care and other health related topics.

An arts festival for focal talent was hosted by the practice in 1992 to celebrate and exhibit local talent. A fun day was hosted, and workshops held on art and poetry, these continued through the month. The local community participated in the event.

The practice has multi-lingual resources, as mentioned previously for the high proportion of black and ethnic groups in the area. It has also created its own practice leaflets on a wide range of topics such as diarrhoea and vomiting, depression and eczema.

Discussion

The working party on public health and primary care recognises the unique role that general practice staff have in the community. It highlights that this makes general practice a good focus for advocacy on community issues. It suggests ways to develop the role, for example health visitors being used in community groups to discuss domestic violence, and accident prevention.[7]

Provision of room space is a good way to get local groups to work with the practice, for example local crime-stoppers, neighbourhood watch, mother and baby groups. Writing for the local press is another way of connecting with the community.

Some practices have taken the step of appointing a community strategy co-ordinator who forges links with the local population and works on promoting health. This may be something to consider. A number of practices could combine to provide funding for such a post.

Practices may choose to get involved with local campaigns, such as traffic calming areas.

It is also worth considering employment of local people in the practice. As with all the areas, an awareness of the practice population and its specific needs are fundamental to developing public health practice.

Area of specialist public health practice: 8

Strategic leadership for health

The practice has been the forefront of a number of initiatives and provided leadership by example and feedback.

Coronary heart disease work

The practice was a coronary heart disease pilot in 2000, as part of the collaborative work. Members of staff have subsequently presented their work to other local practices and advised them on how to set up a healthy heart clinic.

Well women clinics

The practice was one of the first to hold a well woman clinic, a need identified and published by one of the practitioners. Information on setting up and running the clinic, problems and outcomes were reported in The Journal of the Royal College of General Practitioners for other practices to read.14

Patient Profiling Project

Patient profiling is now being rolled out to other practices across the city and nationwide. A book detailing its work has been written.

Hepatitis B project

As previously mentioned, following on from the work from the School of Tropical Medicine, a project with the Chinese community is being developed to look at immunisation in this at-risk group.

Appointment of advocacy worker

The practice, along with Toxteth Health forum, was pivotal in the PCT's appointment of a Positive Action Trainee, a local community member who represents patients in dealing with other agencies.

Discussion

Mixing Oil and Water stresses the necessity of GPs being involved in strategic development with the shift to Primary Care Trust budgeting. Indeed, as I have previously mentioned, the primary health care team is ideally based to lead and influence local service provision.9

Strategic leadership can be achieved with involvement in local organisations and also, as I have illustrated, by disseminating good practice. To be more effective, this should be supported by evidence of benefit.

Leadership skills can be developed, for example, on one of the NHS Leadership Centre courses. These are available to all health care professionals, and help develop leadership skills, as well as covering clinical governance and evidence- based practice.

Area of specialist public health practice: 9

Research and development

Research projects

Many research projects have been undertaken by the practice, including joint ventures with other groups. For example:

- Somali Calcium and Vitamin D Study

- Hepatitis B Study

- Dipex. A patient experience, internet-based programme

- Published research by staff members

- Audit projects. Looking a wide variety of subjects, for example, CHD monitoring, thyroid disorder monitoring, drug use and breast-feeding.

Staff development

The practice has regular, protected, teaching time for staff, including administration and reception staff.

Practice staff have attended a wide variety of courses to equip them with additional skills, for example practice nurses have attended courses covering family planning, diabetes management, venepuncture and coronary heart disease.

Other projects

One of the doctors organised a conference for medical staff working with asylum seekers.

The practice trains medical students, GP registrars and nursing students. One of the GPs teaches the local salaried doctors as part of their educational needs. All the partners have undertaken sabbaticals for personal development. Some of the partners have other interests, for example, one works as a clinical assistant in hepatology.

The practice has an extensive book and journal library, which is continuously being updated.

Discussion

Audit and annual appraisal are now a requirement for GPs. It is important they are used to benefit the practitioner and patients and not just be seen as a hoop to jump through. Audit can provide invaluable information on practice performance and identify areas for change. It is vital that lessons are learnt, practice changes where needed, and the audit cycle completed. Appraisal should be seen as a continuous process to identify learning objectives, ensure patient safety and provide a platform for career planning.

It is important that practice staff are kept aware of training opportunities, and links with education providers maintained, as well as an easy application process for courses and meetings.

Area of specialist public health practice: 10

Ethically managing self, people and resources (including education, and continuing professional development)

Continuing professional development

Each practitioner is responsible for his or her professional development. They should have methods for identifying their learning needs and achieving these needs. All GPs are expected to participate in annual appraisal and prove a commitment to continuing education.

Information on local educational opportunities is delivered routinely in the practice to all relevant staff members via notice board and practice Intranet.

Staff appraisal

Staff undergo regular appraisal to identify needs and wishes for their future development.

Audit

As mentioned in previous sections, audit is an important part of the culture at Princes Park Health Centre.

Computerisation

The practice is computerised and moving towards being paperless. All staff are on the internal email list and message board and use this for effective communication. An Intranet has recently been constructed with access to information about the practice, including protocols and guidelines, for all staff.

External monitoring

The practice, as with all practices, is monitored for its prescribing (PACT data), which is then fed back to the individual prescribers for their information. Services are monitored through the PMS contract on pre-decided aspects.

Other initiatives

The doctors, admin and reception staff and nurses have regular meetings, prepare agendas, record minutes and rotate chairing.

Staff have an induction period to cover policies and the working of the practice.

Significant event analysis is regularly undertaken, and lessons learnt from mistakes or near mistakes incorporated into everyday practice.

The practice aims to be as green as possible, with recycling of paper and paper- light practice. The staff are currently seeking funding for a bicycle shed to encourage staff to cycle to work, and the building is non-smoking. Several members of staff regularly participate in charity bicycle rides. The practice hosts celebrations, for instance, recently, celebrating the practice 25 year 'birthday', this all helps to foster team spirit.

Discussion

Learning organisations should continuously take lessons from their practice and feed these back into the loop to improve patient services. Audit is an invaluable tool for this, providing, as mentioned earlier, the cycle is completed, and reviewed.

Business plans facilitate resource management and should be linked into other data, for example health needs assessment can assist appropriate management. PACT data is useful to look at individual prescribing practice. Referral patterns are another useful source of information.

Each staff member is responsible for management of themselves, but additionally there is a need for an awareness of other members, and identification of problems early enough for intervention. A good occupational health system is useful and can be used to help staff in difficulty.

It is easy to view appraisal as threatening, or a box to be ticked, but it can be used on an on-going basis for professional development and an opportunity to widen knowledge and skills.

Ethical management of people includes colleagues and patients, an awareness and respect for all is needed. Regular meetings may help build team spirit and an open culture, where everybody's opinion respected, is ideal. Patients must have their needs addressed in an appropriate manner, for example, referral when indicated.

Summary

The World Health Organisation incorporates a public health agenda into its definition of primary health care as being "a preventative, intersectoral and multi professional collaboration for population health improvements".9 Traditionally a population approach has been seen as being in opposition to the general practitioners' role as being an individual patient advocate, with a medically based focus. This is changing, and the role of general practice is gradually becoming more entwined with the public health agenda. GPs are becoming more involved in service provision and adapting a more strategic role in health. The formation of Primary Care Trusts and the implementation of NSFs are but two examples of this changing approach.

A lot of the public health agenda will fall to PCTs to provide but some of its' delivery will ultimately be down to practices. Practices are ideally based at the heart of communities to provide a local focus to strategic planning and ensure the community's needs are served.

PMS contracts may offer some additional flexibility to deliver the agenda. The new GMS contract incorporates some incentives to deliver the agenda, in quality payments but this should not be at the expense of other important areas.

Barriers to a public health approach

The Public Health Alliance (1998) identified barriers to the development of a public health approach in primary care.9

- No easily agreed definition of public health, primary care, community or locality. Primary care generally perceived as primary medical care, leading to an emphasis on health as an individual concern rather than a community issue.

- Primary care and public health practitioners acknowledged inequity contributes to ill health but lack confidence to address this.

- Genuine participation by local people in health viewed as helpful but problematic to achieve.

- Short-term funding and inappropriate timescales unhelpful. Good relationships and an understanding of communities take time to develop.

- Disease-focused outcome measures may take years to become significant; hinder innovations that seek to improve overall health and well-being rather than a specific disease process.

A study exploring GPs' understanding and perceptions of public health, in central Liverpool PCT confirmed these barriers. Telephone interviews were conducted with eleven willing GPs in the PCT looking at their understanding, perceptions, involvement and needs with regards to the public health agenda. Again, public health was perceived as a different discipline to general practice, and, in some cases, conflicted with the general practice role as patient advocate. GPs did recognise some of their work as serving a public health function, for example, infectious diseases management, audit, specialist clinics, targeted services, few recognised screening and immunisation.

The GPs interviewed were keen to have a greater involvement in PCT decision-making and felt they were well placed to inform on inequalities, but needed support from the public health department for this. They felt there was some conflict and tension in trying to meet the demands of general practice and PCTs. Funding was seen as a barrier to developing the public health role.15

I hope my work will show other practitioners that a lot of GP work already fulfils a public health function. NSFs and the new contract may shift GPs to thinking in terms of a population approach to problems, for example disease registers. Perhaps a new mind set is required for primary health care team members to see public health as part of their function and a useful add-on to their current working practice.

Addressing inequalities is well within the reach of general practice, for example the DOH toolkit, which looks at ways to target hard to reach groups, for example hosting health days and improving access to vulnerable groups.

Community participation can be hard to achieve and may take time, but it is achievable and can be rewarding.

Recommendations for practices to take a public health approach

Recognise existing work that fulfils a public health function. For example existing clinics, health promotion, audit and information services.

Recognise the roles of all members of the primary health care team. Look at the ways a multi-disciplinary approach can affect the local populations' health. Look at the role of other professionals and how the practice can support their work.

Think about encouraging ownership of projects to maximise staff participation.

Utilise individual skills, strengths and interests. This will not only ensure that the job is done by the best person but will be good for morale.

Start small. Small projects can have a huge impact on the local community and are more likely to be successful, for example fresh fruit and vegetables available at a reduced price in the reception.

Maintain a local focus. Look at the needs and characteristics of the local community and think how your ideas can fit them. Get the community involved at all levels, from planning to implementation of ideas, to feedback and monitoring. Feed into local initiatives, such as HAZ, Healthy Living Centres and Sure Start. It may be useful to have a community liaison worker who co-ordinates work in the local area with work in the local practices.

Look at availability and sustainability of resources. A lot of projects lose funding and are not continued. Most projects will need on-going input to be maintained.

Do not be afraid of innovation and creativity in developing projects.

Consider using the skills of local public health specialists, they may be able to help, for example, in needs assessments, offering advice and may be aware of funding opportunities.

Use IT. Information Technology can make projects happen, and are invaluable when it comes to, for example, needs assessment, screening, audit, research and evidence-based practice. They are useful for effective communication and dissemination of information.

Disseminate good practice. If an idea works, roll it out to other practices.

Remember performance management, in order to prove something works, and is good practice you need to measure outcomes and affectivity.

Get involved with your local PCT. You know your local community, and can act as their advocate in ensuring services that fit needs are provided. Can they provide more public health support? For example education and dissemination of information.

Funding, as a fact of life, will always be an issue. It is important to try, as far as possible, to plan future resources and ensure that good practice is continued.

Admittedly this does seem like a large amount of additional work on an, already, overloaded system, but some of this work is becoming compulsory, and some of it is done already. However, the benefits are huge and, as working as part of the Princes Park Health Centre team has shown me, the work can be enjoyable, and rewarding.

Sarah McNulty, January 2004
Acknowledgments

Thank you to all the staff at Princes Park Health Centre for their insights and information, Dr Katy Gardner for her vision and encouragement and Dr Gina Halsted and Morag Reynolds at Seaforth Village Practice for their ideas and time.

1. Ethnicity Profiling in Primary care: A Princes Park model. Public Health Sector Liverpool JMU. August 2000.

2. Acheson, D (1998) Public Health in England, Report of the Committee of Inquiry into the Future Development of the Public Health Function. DOH

3. Department of Health (2001) Shifting the Balance of Power within the NHS, London: DOH

4. Department of Health (2001) The Report of the Chief Medical Officer's Project to Strengthen the Public Health Function. London: DOH.

5. Faculty of Public Health Medicine: Good Public Health Practice. www.fphm.org.uk

6. Aweis, D et al. Hepatitis B Prevalence and Risk Factors for HbsAg Carriage Amongst Somali Households in Liverpool. Communicable Disease and Public Health 2001: 4: 247-52

7. Department of Health (1998) The Report of the Working Group on Public Health and Primary Care. London: DOH

8. Royal College of General Practitioners (2001) Public health in the New NHS Structure: The Primary Care Perspective. London: RCGP and FPHM.

9. Health Education Authority (1999) Meads, G et al. Mixing Oil and Water. London.

10. NHS Act 1999. London HMSO.

11. Department of Health (2000) Supporting Doctors, Protecting Patients. London: DOH

12. Department of Health (2002) Addressing Inequalities — Reaching Hard-to Reach Groups. London: DOH

13. Royal College of Nursing (2000) Evidence to the Commons Health Select Committee Inquiry into public Health. RCN.

14. Gardner, K. A Well Woman Clinic in an Inner-City General Practice. Journal of the Royal College of General Practitioners, 1983, 33, 711-714.

15. 15. Quinney, D (2003) Public Health and GPs: The Myths Exploded. Central Liverpool PCT.

Sarah McNulty was a registrar at Princes Park Health Centre in 2004 and is now director of public health in Knowsley (2019)

A radical practice in Liverpool: the rise, fall and rise of Princes Park Health Centre

References

Chapter 1

Berridge, V. 2003. 'The Black Report: Interpreting History', in *Health inequalities: proceedings of the meeting of the Health Equity Network*, ed. by A Oliver and M Exworthy (London: The Nuffield Trust), pp. 9-14

Cardew, B. 1959. *The Future of The Family Doctor* (London: Fabian society) <www.sochealth.co.uk/1959/06/12/future-family-doctor-2/>

Collings, J S. 1950. 'General practice in England today: a reconnaissance', *Lancet*, 255: 555-585.

Department of Health and Social Security. 1980. *Inequalities in Health: Report of a Research Working Group* [Black Report] (London: DHSS)

Downham, M. 1978. 'Medical Care in The Inner Cities', *British Medical Journal*, 2: 545-548

Gillam, S. 2017. 'The Family Doctor Charter: 50 years on', *British Journal of General Practice*, 67: 227-228

Gray, A M. 1982. 'Inequalities in health. The Black Report: a summary and comment', *International Journal of Health Services*, 12: 349-80

Hadfield, S J. 1953. 'A Field Survey of General Practice', *Br Medical J*, 2: 683-706

Hunt, J H. 1973. 'The foundation of a college. The conception, birth and early days of the College of General Practitioners', *Journal of the Royal College of General Practitioners*, 23: 5-20

Jarman, B. 1983. 'Identification of underprivileged areas', *Br Med J (Clin Res Ed)*, 286: 1705-1708

Merseyside Communist Party. 1982. *Liverpool's State of Health*, 1st edn (Liverpool: Merseyside Communist Party)

- 1985. *Liverpool's State of Health*, 2nd edn (Liverpool: Merseyside Communist Party)

Morrell, D. 1998. 'Introduction and Overview', in *General Practice under the NHS, 1948-1997*, ed. by I Loudon, J Horder and C Webster (Oxford: Clarendon Press), pp. 1-19

Pearse, I H and L H Crocker. 1947. *The Peckham Experiment: a study of the living structure of society* (London: George Allen and Unwin Ltd)

Pereira Gray, D. 1992. 'History of the Royal College of General Practitioners - the first 40 years', *Br J Gen Pract*. 42; 29-35

Petchey, R. 1995. 'Collings report on general practice in England in 1950: unrecognised, pioneering piece of British social research?', *Br Med J*, 311: 40-42 (p. 40)

Royal Commission on the NHS. 1979. 'Primary Care Services', in *Report of the Royal Commission on the NHS* [Merrison Report] (London: HMSO)

Sayle, A. 2010. *Stalin Ate My Homework* (London: Hodder and Stoughton)

Taylor, C. 1964. *Is your GP really necessary?* (London: Socialist Medical Association)

- 1974. 'What about the one-man band?', in *The Health Team in Action* (London: BBC Publications), pp. 109-111

- 1980. [Article, title unknown], *Socialism and Health* (Katy Gardner personal archive)

- 1986. [Quotation, source unavailable], in 'Dr Cyril Taylor 1921-2000, President of the SHA', 2000, Socialist Health Association <https://www.sochealth.co.uk/the-socialist-health-association/members/distinguished-members/dr-cyril-taylor-1921-2000-president-of-the-sha/>

Webster, C. 1998. 'The Politics of General Practice', in *History of General Practice*, ed. by Loudon, Horder and Webster, pp. 20-44

Additional resources:

Information on the history of Liverpool's first women's refuge is available at the Centre56 website: www.centre56.org.uk/our-history

Chapter 2

All Party Parliamentary Group on Health, Arts and Wellbeing. 2017. *Creative Health: The Arts for Health and Wellbeing. Inquiry Report* < https://www.culturehealthandwellbeing.org.uk/appg-inquiry/>

Ashton, J. 2020. *Practicing Public Health: An Eyewitness Account* (Oxford: Oxford University Press), pp. 68-70

Byrne, P S and B E L Long. 1976. *Doctors Talking To Patients* (London: HMSO)

Childs, R. 2007. *Catch me before I fall* (London: Virgin Books)

DOCTOR magazine. 1987. 'A kaleidoscope practice', March edition. Available at Cyril Taylor archive, Liverpool Central Library

Doll R and A B Hill. 1954. 'The mortality of doctors in relation to their smoking habits; a preliminary report', *Br Med J*, 1: 1451-1455

Frost D and R Phillips (eds). 2011. *Liverpool '81: Remembering the riots* (Liverpool: Liverpool University Press)

Graham-Jones, S. 1987. 'How user-friendly is your practice?', *Practitioner*, 231: 1041-5

Hart, J T. 1971. 'The Inverse Care Law', *Lancet*, 295: 405-412

Hikins, S. 1987. 'Consultation: an encounter between clinical and lay outlooks', *Practitioner*, 231: 1025-6

Munby, S. 2019. 'Social Cohesion, Public Services and Community Development', in *Shaping Diversity: Approaches to promoting Social Cohesion in European Cities*, ed. by N Alcaise and C Hocke C, eds (Berlin: Jovis), pp. 177-189

Parkinson, M. 1985. *Liverpool on the Brink* (Liverpool: Liverpool University Press)

Pietroni, P and D Chase. 1993. 'Patient Participation in General Practice: the Marylebone experiment', *Br J Gen Pract*, 43: 341-4

Taylor, C. 1974. 'What about the one-man band?', in *The Health Team in Action* (London: BBC Publications), pp. 109-111

-    1975. Speech from a Liverpool medical student conference (Katy Gardner personal archive)

-    1983. [Article, title unknown], *GP Magazine*. Available at Cyril Taylor archive, Liverpool Central Library

Prichard, P. 1981. *Patient Participation in General Practice. Occasional Paper 17* (London: RCGP)

Royal College of General Practitioners. 1972. *The Future General Practitioner: Learning and Teaching* (London: British Medical Association)

World Health Organisation. 1978. *Alma Ata Declaration* <www.who.int/publications/almaata_declaration_en.pdf>

Additional resources:

Spare Tyre theatre company website: www.sparetyre.org

Chapter 3

Ashton, J. 2020. 'Chapter 4: Promoting and improving health', in *Practicing Public Health: An Eyewitness Account* (Oxford: Oxford University Press), pp. 62-88 (p. 82)

Berger, J and J Mohr. 1967. *A Fortunate Man: The Story of a Country Doctor* (London: Allen Lane)

Burke, L and K Gardner K. 1979. *Why Suffer? Periods and their problems* (London: Virago)

Downham, M. 1978. 'Medical Care in The Inner Cities', *Br Med J*, 2: 545-548

Freeman, G, J Walker, D Heaney and J Howie. 2002. 'Personal continuity and the quality of GP consultations', *The European Journal of General Practice*, 8: 90-94

Gardner, K. 1983. 'A well woman clinic in an inner-city general practice', *J R Coll Gen Pract*, 33: 711-714

Howie, J G R, D J Heaney, M Maxwell, J J Walker, G K Freeman and H Rai. 1999. 'Quality at general practice consultations: cross sectional survey', *Br Med J, 319*: 738-43

Hudson, R. 1992. 'From Heartsink to Hope', *Health Matters*, 11

Livingstone, A and D Widgery. 1990. 'The new general practice: the changing philosophies of primary care', *Br Med J*, 301: 708-10

London Health Planning Consortium, Primary Health Care Study Group. 1981. *Primary health care in inner London* (London: DHSS)

McGuinness, B, I Stanley and C Dowrick. 2011. 'The University of Liverpool', in *Academic General Practice in the UK Medical Schools 1948-2000: A Short History*, ed. by J Howie and M Whitfield (Edinburgh: Edinburgh University Press), pp. 61-63

Medical Research Council Working Party. 1985. 'MRC trial of treatment of mild hypertension principal results'. *Br Med J (Clin Res Ed)*, 291: 97-104

Orbach, S. 1978. *Fat is a feminist issue: the anti-diet guide to permanent weight loss* (New York: Paddington Press)

Pulse. 1985. 'Let your patients help', *Pulse publications*, p. 48. Available at Katy Gardner archive, Liverpool Central Library

Robinson, R. 2001. 'Fi Frances: Obituary', *Guardian* <www.theguardian.com/news/2001/dec/21/guardianobituaries>

Royal College of Psychiatrists. 2020. *Position Statement 01/20: Services for people diagnosable with personality disorder* <https://www.rcpsych.ac.uk/docs/default-source/improving-care/better-mh-policy/position-statements/ps01_20.pdf?sfvrsn=85af7fbc_2>

Royal Commission on Medical Education. 1968. *Report of the Royal Commission on Medical Education* (London: HMSO)

Additional resources:

Sutton Trust website: www.suttontrust.com

Chapter 4

Balint, M. 1957. *The Doctor, His Patient and the Illness* (London, Churchill Livingstone)

Fisher, M. 2019. 'Looking back in anger and gratitude', *Simon Fisher Blog* <https://simonmfisher.blogspot.com/2019/06/looking-back-in-anger-and-gratitude.html>

Gask, L. 1992. 'Training general practitioners to detect and manage emotional disorders', *International Review of Psychiatry*, 3-4: 293-300

Hart, J T. 1988. *A New Kind of Doctor: the general practitioner's part in the health of the community* (London: Merlin Press) <http://www.sochealth.co.uk/2013/10/09/new-kind-doctor/>

Hudson, R. 1988a. 'A Brief Encounter with Distrust', *Health Matters*, 6. Available at Katy Gardner archive, Liverpool Central Library

-      1988b. [Article, title unknown], *7 Days*, July issue. Available at Katy Gardner archive, Liverpool Central Library

Marzillier, J and J Hall. 2009. 'The challenge of the Layard initiative', *The Psychologist*, 22: 396-399

Ross, M and M Scott. 1985. 'An evaluation of the effectiveness of individual and group cognitive therapy in the treatment of depressed patients in an inner city health centre', *J R Coll Gen Pract*, 274: 239-242

Chapter 5

Ashton, J. 1994. *The Changing Health of Mersey:1948-1994: Report of the Mersey Regional Director of Public Health* (Liverpool: Mersey Regional Health Authority Information Unit)

Belbin, R M. (1981). *Management teams: why they succeed or fail* (Oxford: Butterworth-Heinemann). Heinemann Belbin role inventory available at www.belbin.com

Bolden, K J. 1981. 'Inner cities', *J R Coll Gen Pract. Occasional Paper*, 19: 1-13

Delamothe, A. 1988. 'First UK Healthy Cities Conference, Liverpool', *Br Med J*, 296: 1117-1120

Hudson, M F. 1982. 'Computers in General Practice', *Newsletter of the Merseyside and North Wales Faculty of the Royal College of General Practitioners,* July edition

Hudson, R. 1988. 'Time for a parakeet', *7 Days (Communist Party of Great Britain),* November issue. Available at Katy Gardner archive, Liverpool Central Library
-      1989. [Article, title unknown], 7 Days (Communist Party of Great Britain), April issue. Available at Katy Gardner archive, Liverpool Central *Library*

Jarman, B. 1981. 'A survey of primary care in London', *J R Coll Gen Pract. Occasional Paper*, 16: 1-139

Liverpool City Council. 1989. *Quality of Life Survey* (Liverpool: Liverpool City Council)

Livingstone, A and D Widgery. 1990. 'The new general practice: the changing philosophies of primary care', *Br Med J*, 301: 708-10

Lorentzon, M, B Jarman and M Bajekal. 1994. 'Report of the Inner City Task Force of the Royal College of General Practitioners', J R Coll Gen Pract. Occasional Paper, 66: 1-53

Socialist Health Association. 2000. 'Dr Cyril Taylor 1921-2000 President of the SHA' <https://www.sochealth.co.uk/the-socialist-health-association/members/distinguished-members/dr-cyril-taylor-1921-2000-president-of-the-sha/>

Watt, G. 2019a. 'Building equity in the NHS: the role of general practice', *Br J Gen Pract*, 69: 374-375

Watt, G (ed.). 2019b. *The Exceptional Potential of General Practice: Making a Difference in Primary Care* (Boca Raton: CRC Press), pp. 16, 250

Chapter 6

BBC. 1982. *Mission of Mersey* (Open Space production)

Department of Health. 1989. *Working for patients* (London: HMSO) <https://navigator.health.org.uk/content/working-patients-1989>

Department of Health and Social Security. 1983. *NHS Management Inquiry. Report* [Griffiths Report] (London: DHSS)

Drury, M. 1998. 'The General Practitioner and Professional Organisations', in *General Practice under the NHS, 1948-1997*, ed. by I Loudon, J Horder and C Webster (Oxford: Clarendon Press), pp. 205-223

Gardner, K. 1998. 'If I wasn't a GP, I would be a community health worker', *Horizons magazine*. Available at Katy Gardner archive, Liverpool Central Library

Hudson, R. 1990. 'A very peculiar practice', *Health Matters*, 4

- 1992. 'Art for heartache', *Health Matters*, 12

Hutt, P. 2015. *Confronting an Ill Society* (Oxford: Radcliffe Press)

Liverpool Family Health Services Authority. 1992. [Untitled news article], *Liverpool Primary Care News*, 9

Office of Health Economics. 1995. *Compendium of Health Statistics* (London: OHE) <www.ohe.org/publications/compendium-health-statistics>

Pratt, J. 1995. *Practitioners and Practices: a conflict of values?* (Oxford: Radcliffe Medical Press)

Smith, C. 1997. Keynote speech to Annual Conference of National Association of Commissioning GPs (Katy Gardner personal archive)

Watt, A. 1987. 'Room for improvement? The community response to medical dominance', *Radical Community Medicine*, Spring: 40-45

Chapter 7

Abbott, S and L Davidson. 2000. 'Easing the burden on primary care in deprived urban areas: a service model', *Primary Health Care Research and Development*, 1: 201-206

Gaulton, L. 1994. 'Homeless but not helpless', *Nursing Times* 90: 53-55

- 1998. 'Equity in health: lightening the primary care load', *Primary Health Care*, 8: 26-29

Graham-Jones, S, S Reilly, E Gaulton-Berks and E Davidson. 2004. 'Tackling the needs of the homeless: a controlled trial of health advocacy', *Health and Social Care in the Community*, 12: 221-232

Reilly, S. 2000. 'Addressing the health problems of the (inner city) homeless: a systematic review and a controlled trial' (Doctoral thesis, Liverpool John Moores University)

Reilly, S, L Gaulton, S Graham-Jones and E Davidson. 1996. *Effective Health Care for Homeless People - an evaluation of the Family Health Project* (Susanna Graham-Jones personal archive)

- 2004. 'Can a health advocate for homeless families reduce workload for the primary care team? A controlled trial', *Health Soc. Care Community*, 12: 63-74

Williams S. 1995. *Review of Primary Care Projects for Homeless People. Final Report for Department of Health* (London: Department of Health)

Chapter 8

Al-Shehri, A, I Stanley and P Thomas. 1993. 'Continuing education for general practice. 2. Systematic learning from experience', *Br J Gen Pract*, 43: 249-253

Boyle, R. 2005. 'Cardiovascular Disease Mortality trends and Projections 1995-7 to 2009-11', presentation to Cheshire and Merseyside Cardiac Network (Katy Gardner personal archive)

Campion, P, I Stanley and M Haddleton. 1992. 'Audit in General Practice: students and practitioners learning together', *Quality in Health Care*, 1: 114-8

Coulter, A. 2009. *Engaging communities for health improvement* (London: The Health Foundation) <https://www.health.org.uk/publications/engaging-communities-for-health-improvement>

Gardner, K and A Chapple. 1999. 'Barriers to referral in patients with angina: qualitative study', *Br Med J*, 319: 418-22

Goldberg D P and V F Hillier. 1979. 'A scaled version of the general health questionnaire', *Psychological Medicine*, 9: 139-45

Jacoby, A, S Graham-Jones, G Baker, L Ratoff, L, J Heyes, M Dewey and D Chadwick. 1996. 'A general practice records audit of the process of care for people with epilepsy' *Br J Gen Pract*, 46: 595-599

Liverpool Health Authority. 1996. *Annual Report* (Liverpool: Liverpool Health Authority)

Stanley, I, A Al-Shehri and P Thomas. 1993. 'Continuing education for general practice. 1. Experience, competence and the media of self-directed learning for established general practitioners', *Br J Gen Pract*, 43: 210-214

Thomas, P. 2006. *Integrating Primary Health Care: Leading, Managing, Facilitating* (Oxford: Radcliffe Publishing)

-       2018. *Collaborating for Health* (Abingdon: Routledge)

Tod, A M, C Read, A Lacey and J Abbot. 2001. 'Barriers to uptake of services for coronary heart disease: qualitative study', *Br Med J*, 323: 214

Wilkinson, E. 2003. *The future of CHD in Central and South Liverpool: reducing the burden and closing the gaps* (Liverpool: Central Liverpool Primary Care Trust)

Chapter 9

Abba, K. 2001. *Black and Minority Ethnic Health Service provision in Liverpool Primary Care Trusts* (Liverpool: Liverpool John Moores University)

BMJ News. 1993. [Untitled news article], *Br Med J*: 307: 467

Central Liverpool Primary Care Trust. 2004. *Diversity Equality Report* (Liverpool: Central Liverpool Primary Care Trust). Available at Katy Gardner archive, Liverpool Central Library

Commission for Racial Equality. 1984. *Why keep ethnic records?* (London: CRE)

Department of Health. 1992. *The Health of the Nation: a strategy for Health in England* (London: HMSO)

Dowrick, C. 2009. *Beyond Depression: A New Approach to Understanding and Management,* 2nd edn (Oxford: Oxford University Press)

Gardner, K, S Salah, C Leavey and L Porcellato. 2010. 'The perfect size: perceptions of and influences on body image and body size in young Somali women living in Liverpool', *Diversity in Health and Care*, 7: 23-34

Ghebrehewet, S, M Regan, L Benons and J Knowles. 2000. 'Provision of services to asylum seekers. Are there lessons from the experience with Kosovan refugees?', *Journal of Epidemiology and Community Health*, 56: 223-6

Gifford, A, W Brown and R Bundley. 1989. *Loosen the Shackles: First Report of the Liverpool 8 Inquiry into Race Relations in Liverpool* (London: Karia Press)

Granby Toxteth Community Project. 1991. *Census 1991* (Liverpool: Granby Toxteth Community Project)

Heath, I. 1991. 'The role of ethnic monitoring in general practice', *Br J Gen Pract*, 41: 310-311

Horton, C. 1992. *Ethnic Monitoring Officer in Thames Regional Health Authorities* (Unpublished report)

Hull, S A, M Mathur, E Badrick, J Robson and K Boomla. 2011. 'Recording ethnicity in primary care - assessing the methods and impact', *Br J Gen Pract*, 61: e290-e294 <https://doi.org/10.3399/bjgp11X572544>

ICARUS. 2006. *MAAN final evaluation* (Liverpool: ICARUS). Available at Katy Gardner archive, Liverpool Central Library

Jones, B and K Gardner. 2003. 'Patient profiling in primary care', in *Ethnicity, Health and Primary Care*, ed. by J Kai (Oxford: Oxford University Press), pp. 41-49

Jones, M and J Kai. 2007. 'Capturing ethnicity data in primary care: challenges and feasibility in a diverse metropolitan population', *Diversity in Health and Social Care*, 4: 211-220

Lee, B, K Gardner, B Jones, M Bellis and T Qassim, T. 2000. *Ethnicity Profiling in Primary Care - The Princes Park Health Centre Model* (Liverpool: North West Public Health Observatory)

Liverpool Health Authority. 1998. *Improving Primary Health Care of Ethnic Minority Communities*. Available at Katy Gardner archive, Liverpool Central Library

Mathur, R. 2013. 'Completeness and usability of ethnicity data in UK-based primary care and hospital databases', *Journal of Public Health*, 36: 684-692

Health Trends. 1991. [Untitled news article], *Health Trends*, 23: 88 (Katy Gardner personal archive)

Roberts, K. 1980. *Survey of school leavers in Granby Ward* (Liverpool: University of Liverpool) (Susanna Graham-Jones archive on ethnic monitoring)

Robson, J, K Boomla and S A Hull. 2020. 'Progress in using the electronic record to improve primary care', *Br J Gen Pract*, 70: e215-e220 <https://doi.org/10.3399/bjgp20X708281>

Royal Liverpool Children's Hospital. 1991. *Health Needs of Somali Communities* (Liverpool: Royal Liverpool Children's Hospital). Available at Katy Gardner archive, Liverpool Central Library

Small, S and S Moore. 1992. *Report for University of Liverpool* (Susanna Graham-Jones archive on ethnic monitoring)

Torkington, N P K. 1983. *The Racial Politics of Health - a Liverpool Profile* (Liverpool: Merseyside Area Profile Group, University of Liverpool)

- 1991. *Black health - a political issue* (Liverpool: Catholic Association for Racial Justice, Liverpool Institute of Higher Education)

Wilson, A. 1978. *Finding a Voice: Asian Women in Britain* (London: Virago Press)

Additional resources:

Savera UK charity website: www.saverauk.co.uk

A Girl From Mogadishu: Film based on the testimony of global FGM activist Ifrah Ahmed. Trafficked to Ireland as a teenager from war-torn Somalia, the film recounts her traumatic journey and her recognition, once in Ireland, of her brutal experience of FGM as a child. It shows how she channeled this experience into action against FGM at the highest level. For more information about the film, see: https://www.agirlfrommogadishu-themovie.com/

Chapter 10

Acheson, D. 1998. *Report of the Independent Inquiry into Inequalities in Health* (London: HMSO) <www.gov.uk/government/publications/independent-inquiry-into-inequalities-in-health-report>

Gardner, K. 1996. 'Diary of a desperate doctor', *RCGP Connection*, December: 2-3

Liverpool Health Authority. 1997. *Annual Report* (Liverpool: Liverpool Health Authority)

Marmot, M G and M E McDowall. 1986. 'Mortality decline and widening social inequalities', *Lancet*, 2: 274-6

Princes Park Health Centre. 1997. *Princes Park Health Centre PCAP application* (Katy Gardner personal archive)

Wilkinson, R G. 1992. 'Income distribution and life expectancy', *Br Med J*, 304: 165-8

Chapter 11

Communities and Local Government. 2007. *The English indices of deprivation* (London: Communities and Local Government Publications) <www.gov.uk/government/collections/english-indices-of-deprivation>

Department of Health. 1999. *Saving Lives: Our Healthier Nation* [White paper] (London: HMSO) <www.gov.uk/government/publications/saving-lives-our-healthier-nation>

Gardner, K. 1999. 'Towards a salaried service?', *Socialism and Health* (Katy Gardner personal archive)

Parkinson, M. 2019. *Liverpool Beyond the Brink* (Liverpool: Liverpool University Press)

Parkinson, M et al. 2006. *State of the English Cities, Volume 1* (London: Office of the Deputy Prime Minister)

Princes Park Health Centre. 1997. *Princes Park Health Centre PCAP application* (Katy Gardner personal archive)

Singer, R. 2000. [Article, title unknown], *Medeconomics*, June (Katy Gardner personal archive)

Socialist Medical Association. 1964. 'The case for health centres' < https://www.sochealth.co.uk/socialist-health-association-policy/the-case-for-health-centres-1964/>

Woodward, S and C Devaney. 2010. 'The Liverpool City-region Health is Wealth Commission', *European Review*, 18: 35-46

Chapter 12

Aweis, D, B J Brabin, N J Beeching, J E Bunn, C Cooper, K Gardner, C Iriyagolle and C A Hart. 2001. 'Hepatitis B prevalence and risk factors for HBsAg carriage amongst Somali households in Liverpool', *Communicable Disease and Public Health*, 4: 247-52

Bunn, J, K Gardner, K Vithlani, M Mohamud, B Brabin, S Salah, I Kahin, J Dutton, B Durham and W Fraser. 2004. 'Vitamin D Deficiency in Liverpool Somalis: A Significant Problem', presented at North West Public Health Conference. Available at Katy Gardner archive, Liverpool Central Library

Doctors in Unite. 2020. *Public health and primary care. Policy statement*

Gardner, K. 2003. 'Public health and primary care: a new kind of doctor and a new kind of relationship?', *Mersey Faculty newsletter of the Royal College of General Practitioners*. Available at Katy Gardner archive, Liverpool Central Library

Hart, J T. 1988. *A New Kind of Doctor: the general practitioner's part in the health of the community* (London: Merlin Press) <http://www.sochealth.co.uk/2013/10/09/new-kind-doctor/>

Harvey, J, A Webb and H Mallinson. 2000. 'Chlamydia trachomatis screening in young people in Merseyside', *British Journal of Family Planning*, 26: 199-201

'Liverpool children developing bone disease rickets', *Liverpool Echo*, 3 March 2012 <www.liverpoolecho.co.uk/news/liverpool-news/liverpool-children-developing-bone-disease-3346346>

Marinker, M. 1998. ''What is Wrong' and 'How We Know It': Changing Concepts of General Practice', in *General Practice under the NHS, 1948-1997*, ed. by I Loudon, J Horder and C Webster (Oxford: Clarendon Press), pp. 65-91 (p. 85)

Maxwell, S M, S M Salah and J E G Bunn. 2006. 'Dietary habits of the Somali population in Liverpool with respect to foods containing calcium and Vitamin D: a cause for concern?', *Journal of Human Nutrition and Dietetics*, 19: 125-9

McNulty, S. 2004. *Princes Park Health Centre as a Public Health Organisation* (Liverpool: Central Liverpool Primary Care Trust), see APPENDIX, p.232

NICE. 2018. *Vitamin D deficiency in adults - treatment and prevention* <https://cks.nice.org.uk/topics/vitamin-d-deficiency-in-adults-treatment-prevention/>

Pan Mersey Area Prescribing Committee. 2018. *Treatment of Vitamin D deficiency in adults* <www.panmerseyapc.nhs.uk/document-store/vitamin-d-deficiency-treatment-in-adults>

Thomas, K, E Barry, S Watkins, J Czauderna and L N Allen. 2020. 'GP with an extended role in population health', *Br J Gen Pract*, 70: 378-379

Chapter 13

Gardner, K. 2012. 'Tendering out general practice is bad for doctors - and patients', *Br Med J*, 344: e2461 <https://doi.org/10.1136/bmj.e2461>

King's Fund. 2011. *Impact of Quality and Outcomes Framework on Health Inequalities* (London: King's Fund)

Socialist Health Association. 2006. 'Bring back Community Health Councils', Press release <https://www.sochealth.co.uk/national-health-service/democracy-involvement-and-accountability-in-health/bring-back-community-health-councils/>

Turner, D and T Powell. 2016. *NHS Commissioning Before 2013*, House of Commons briefing paper (London: House of Commons Library)

Williams, J, R Petchey, T Gosden, B Leese and B Sibbald. 2001. 'A profile of PMS salaried GP contracts and their impact on recruitment', *Family Practice*, 18: 283-7

Chapter 14

BMA. 2012. [Untitled news article], *BMA news* (Katy Gardner personal archive)

Care Quality Commission. 2014. *Princes Park Health Centre* <www.cqc.org.uk/location/1-850677967/reports>

-        2015. *Princes Park Health Centre* <www.cqc.org.uk/location/1-850677967/re-ports>. See also: www.cqc.org.uk/news/releases/cqc-rates-merseyside-gp-sur-gery-inadequate

Gardner, K. 2012. 'Tendering out general practice is bad for doctors - and patients', *Br Med J,* 344: e2461 <https://doi.org/10.1136/bmj.e2461>

Keep Our NHS Public. 2015. *Princes Park Health Centre - The destruction of community based GP services* (Liverpool: Keep Our NHS Public Merseyside) <www.labournet.net/other/1502/PPHC%20Report.pdf>

Kirkup, B. 2018. *Liverpool Community Health Trust Independent Review: NHS improvement* <www.england.nhs.uk/publication/report-of-the-liverpool-community-health-independent-review>

NHS England and Ipsos MORI. 2014. *GP Patient Survey 2013-14* <www.england.nhs.uk/statistics/2014/07/03/gp-patient-survey-2013-14>

Kyprianou, P (ed.). 2015. *Getting By? The lives of 30 working families on low incomes,* Report for Liverpool City Council (Liverpool: Praxis)

Taylor, J. 2015. 'Patients forced to queue in street for appointment at Princes Park Surgery in Toxteth', *Liverpool Echo*, 16 August <www.liverpoolecho.co.uk/news/liverpool-news/queues-princes-park-surgery-toxteth-9803921>

Chapter 15

Anderson J. 2019. Email to Labour Party members, March 2019

BBC. 2015. 'Winners announced for BBC Food and Farming Awards 2015', *Media Centre*, 30 April <www.bbc.co.uk/mediacentre/latestnews/2015/food-and-farming-awards-winners>

Liverpool City Council. 2017. *Princes Park ward profile* <https://liverpool.gov.uk/media/9961/princes-park.pdf>

Munby, S. 2019. 'Social Cohesion, Public Services and Community Development', in *Shaping Diversity: Approaches to promoting Social Cohesion in European Cities,* ed. by N Alcaise and C Hocke C, eds (Berlin: Jovis), pp. 177-189

Parkinson, M. 2019. *Liverpool Beyond the Brink* (Liverpool: Liverpool University Press), p. 113

Additional resources:

Granby 4 Streets website: www.granby4streetsclt.co.uk

Chapter 16

Doctors in Unite. 2019. *Towards a Future Socialist General Practice - a Vision*. Draft report from DiU conference, April 2019 (J Czauderna, pers. comm.)

Heath, I. 2018. 'Back to the future: aspects of the NHS that should never change', *Br Med J*, 362: k3187 https://doi.org/10.1136/bmj.k3187

Levene, L S, R Baker, J Bankart, N Walker and A Wilson. 2019. 'Socioeconomic deprivation scores as predictors of variations in NHS practice payments', *Br J Gen Pract*, 69: e546-e554 <https://doi.org/10.3399/bjgp19X704549>

Thomas, K, E Barry, S Watkins, J Czauderna and L N Allen. 2020. 'GP with an extended role in population health', *Br J Gen Pract*, 70: 378-379

Watt, G (ed.). 2019. *The Exceptional Potential of General Practice: Making a Difference in Primary Care* (Boca Raton: CRC Press)

Further Reading

General Practice under the NHS, 1948-1997,
ed. I Loudon, J Horder and C Webster (1988) Oxford: Clarendon Press
- an excellent source on development of primary care in the first 50 years of the NHS, including a chapter by Ian Tait and Susanna Graham-Jones : *General practice, its patients, and the public.*

From Cradle to Grave: The history of the NHS 1948-1987, and
From Cradle to Grave: The history of the NHS - 1988 onwards.
This is Geoffrey Rivett's invaluable history of the NHS. The second part (1988 – 2017) was published in print in 2017, and the updated online version can be accessed on the Nuffield Trust website:

www.nuffieldtrust.org.uk/health-and-social-care-explained/the-history-of-the-nhs

The Exceptional Potential of General Practice: Making a Difference in Primary Care
ed. G Watt (2019) Boca Raton: CRC Press
- an inspiring collection of essays on the potential of general practice, written by Deep End GPs seeking to provide high quality personalised care in challenging circumstances.

Darbishire: The story of Academic General Practice in Manchester
Carl R Whitehouse (2016) www.shortrunpress.co.uk
- this book describes the vicissitudes of another visionary health centre with its potential for medical education, educational research and clinical research.

Writing on the Wall has a selection of archival material and books on the history of Liverpool 8 and its communities, written by local authors: www.writingonthewall.org.uk/

Note on Archival Material

Material about Cyril Taylor, women's health and health of BAME communities, including copies of *VOICES* newspaper, is available in Liverpool Central Library archives, curated by librarian Helena Smart (see: https://liverpool.gov.uk/libraries/archives-family-history/). Digital copies of *Reminiscence* exhibition also available.

Photos

Most photos are from Katy Gardner's personal archive, photographers unknown. Some were previously published in the PPHC newspaper, *Prinny Post*.

1985 - Prizewinning leaflet photo taken for *Pulse* magazine by Michael Arron

1995 - Reopening of PPHC taken for the *Liverpool Daily Post* and *Echo*

2017 - Photos of 40th birthday, 7 Sefton Drive and Drs Faint and McKinnell by Katy Gardner

2019 - Photos of PPHC by Tracey Dunn

Band members in photos:

- Ceilidh band, 1983: Mike Hogan, Seamus Murphy, Ken Dunlop, Keith Price, Alan Bornat.
- The Rhythm Angels, 1992: Suzanne Taylor, Sarah Tobias, Iain Templeton, Reynold Parry with his son Nile Denvir-Parry, Claire Mathews, Julie Taylor, Jane.

Katy Gardner studied at Cambridge University and then at the London Hospital (now part of Barts NHS Trust). She changed course from Natural Sciences after meeting a group of left-wing medical students at Cambridge (Reds in Medicine) and realising that inner-city general practice was what she wanted to do. Katy's mum had moved to Liverpool, and after a childhood mostly spent in Scotland, Katy fell in love with the city. In the 1960s it was the place to be. After meeting Cyril Taylor as a medical student in 1973, she knew she wanted to work in Liverpool 8. She was involved in women's health from the early 1970s and ran self-help health groups in London while a student. She joined the Communist Party in 1976, and the Labour Party in 1989. She remained active in community health all her working life, retiring in 2018. After leaving Princes Park Health Centre she became involved with the Friends of Princes Park, Liverpool 8, working to make it a safer, greener, and more inclusive place.

Susanna Graham-Jones wanted to be a doctor from the age of 4. She read Physiology and Psychology at Somerville College, Oxford, did her clinical training at St Mary's Hospital, Paddington in 1972-5, joined Women in Medicine, and returned to Oxford to do her house jobs. She then trained in psychiatry and completed a neuroscience research degree. In 1981-2 she enjoyed a year as a GP trainee in Wantage, Oxon. She ran a Mother and Child Health project in Nepal with Save The Children Fund for the next 3 years, and arrived in Liverpool in 1985 with her partner and a one-year-old son. She worked at Liverpool University Medical School and Princes Park Health Centre for 8 years, then returned to Oxford in 1993 as a University Lecturer in General Practice. She became a partner at the Nuffield Health Centre in Witney, West Oxfordshire, retiring in 2015.

Congratulations to Katy Gardner and Susanna Graham-Jones on this superb and vital book, and to all those who work with and support The Princes Park Health Centre. We are very proud to be able to play our part in sharing the amazing work and important lessons for community health care that it pioneered.

Writing on the Wall is a dynamic, Liverpool-based community organisation that celebrates writing in all its forms. We hold an annual festival and a series of year-round projects. We work with a broad and inclusive definition of writing that embraces literature, creative writing, journalism and nonfiction, poetry, song-writing, and storytelling. We work with local, national and international writers whose work provokes controversy and debate, and with all of Liverpool's communities to promote and celebrate individual and collective creativity.

WoW creative writing projects support health, wellbeing and personal development. If you have a story to tell, or would like to take part in, or work with WoW to develop a writing project, please get in touch – we'd love to hear from you.

Mike Morris and Madeline Heneghan, Co-Directors

info@writingonthewall.org.uk

www.writingonthewall.org.uk

0151 703 0020

@wowfest